1995

THE BOOK OF SURPRISES

AN ANTHOLOGY OF THE UNUSUAL

The Book of Surprises

SELECTED AND EDITED BY *Rudolf Flesch*

HARPER & ROW, PUBLISHERS  NEW YORK

CREDITS AND COPYRIGHTS

Contents

Preface

Everybody loves surprises, and everybody loves to read about them. What I've done here is to pull together, from a lifetime of reading, forty-eight stories and articles that are surprising, unexpected, unusual, astonishing, extraordinary, or shocking.

I've used both fiction and nonfiction because a straight short-story anthology wouldn't have given me the range I was after. No fiction writer would dare use characters like that improbable President, Franklin Pierce, or the circus-giant-turned-archeologist Belzoni. No made-up story could match the plain recital of the effects of Müller's prayers or Coué's formula. No novelist could come up with as bizarre a plot as the origins of spiritualism or the events that led to Appomattox.

In contrast, when it came to fiction I had to content myself with the product of the sadly limited human imagination. Still, I don't think anyone could possibly guess the outcome of *Desirable Villa* or *The Human Element* or *A Queer Tale.* . . .

Have I whetted your appetite? Well, then I mustn't keep you from sampling the first item on the menu, which deals with the peculiar problem of a knife thrower. I guarantee that when you get to the last entry—the strange antics of O. O. McIntyre's dog—you'll have been shocked, amazed, astonished and surprised again and again.

R. F.

THE BOOK OF SURPRISES

GUY DE MAUPASSANT

The Artist

ह

Among the hundreds of stories written by the French master,
here's a very special item.

"Bah! monsieur," the old mountebank said to me; "it is a matter of
exercise and habit, that is all! Of course, one requires to be a little
gifted that way and not to be butter-fingered, but what is chiefly
necessary is patience and daily practice for long, long years."

His modesty surprised me all the more, because of all performers
who are generally infatuated with their own skill, he was the most
wonderfully clever one I had met. Certainly I had frequently seen
him, for everybody had seen him in some circus or other, or even
in traveling shows, performing the trick that consists of putting a
man or woman with extended arms against a wooden target, and in
throwing knives between their fingers and round their heads from a
distance. There is nothing very extraordinary in it, after all, when one
knows the tricks of the trade, and that the knives are not the least
sharp and stick into the wood at some distance from the flesh. It is the
rapidity of the throws, the glitter of the blades, and the curve which
the handles make toward their living object which give an air of
danger to an exhibition that has become commonplace and only requires very middling skill.

But here there was no trick and no deception, and no dust thrown
into the eyes. It was done in good earnest and in all sincerity. The
knives were as sharp as razors, and the old mountebank planted
them close to the flesh, exactly in the angle between the fingers. He
surrounded the head with a perfect halo of knives, and the neck with a
collar from which nobody could have extricated himself without

ह 1

cutting his carotid artery, while, to increase the difficulty, the old fellow went through the performance without seeing, his whole face being covered with a close mask of thick oilcloth.

Naturally, like other great artists, he was not understood by the crowd, who confounded him with vulgar tricksters, and his mask only appeared to them a trick the more, and a very common trick into the bargain.

"He must think us very stupid," they said. "How could he possibly aim without having his eyes open?"

And they thought there must be imperceptible holes in the oil-cloth, a sort of latticework concealed in the material. It was useless for him to allow the public to examine the mask for themselves before the exhibition began. It was all very well that they could not discover any trick, but they were only all the more convinced that they were being tricked. Did not the people know that they ought to be tricked?

I had recognized a great artist in the old mountebank, and I was quite sure that he was altogether incapable of any trickery. I told him so, while expressing my admiration to him; and he had been touched by my open admiration and above all by the justice I had done him. Thus we became good friends, and he explained to me, very modestly, the real trick which the crowd do not understand, the eternal trick contained in these simple words: "To be gifted by nature and to practice every day for long, long years."

He had been especially struck by the certainty which I expressed that any trickery must become impossible to him. "Yes," he said to me, "quite impossible! Impossible to a degree which you cannot imagine. If I were to tell you! But where would be the use?"

His face clouded over, and his eyes filled with tears. I did not venture to force myself into his confidence. My looks, however, were not so discreet as my silence, and begged him to speak; so he responded to their mute appeal.

"After all," he said, "why should I not tell you about it? You will understand me." And he added, with a look of sudden ferocity: "She understood it, at any rate!"

"Who?" I asked.

"My strumpet of a wife," he replied. "Ah! Monsieur, what an abominable creature she was—if you only knew! Yes, she understood it too well, too well, and that is why I hate her so; even more on that account than for having deceived me. For that is a natural fault, is it not, and may be pardoned? But the other thing was a crime, a horrible crime."

The woman, who stood against the wooden target every night with her arms stretched out and her fingers extended, and whom the old mountebank fitted with gloves and with a halo formed of his knives, which were as sharp as razors and which he planted close to her, was his wife. She might have been a woman of forty, and must have been fairly pretty, but with a perverse prettiness; she had an impudent mouth, a mouth that was at the same time sensual and bad, with the lower lip too thick for the thin, dry upper lip.

I had several times noticed that every time he planted a knife in the board, she uttered a laugh, so low as scarcely to be heard, but which was very significant when one heard it, for it was a hard and very mocking laugh. I had always attributed that sort of reply to an artifice which the occasion required. It was intended, I thought, to accentuate the danger she incurred and the contempt that she felt for it, thanks to the sureness of the thrower's hands, and so I was very much surprised when the mountebank said to me:

"Have you observed her laugh, I say? Her evil laugh which makes fun of me, and her cowardly laugh which defies me? Yes, cowardly, because she knows that nothing can happen to her, nothing, in spite of all she deserves, in spite of all that I ought to do to her, in spite of all that I *want* to do to her."

"What do you want to do?"

"Confound it! Cannot you guess? I want to kill her."

"To kill her, because she has—"

"Because she has deceived me? No, no, not that, I tell you again. I have forgiven her for that a long time ago, and I am too much accustomed to it! But the worst of it is that the first time I forgave her, when I told her that all the same I might some day have my revenge by cutting her throat, if I choose, without seeming to do it on purpose, as if it were an accident, mere awkwardness—"

"Oh! So you said that to her?"

"Of course I did, and I meant it. I thought I might be able to do it, for you see I had the perfect right to do so. It was so simple, so easy, so tempting! Just think! A mistake of less than half an inch, and her skin would be cut at the neck where the jugular vein is, and the jugular would be severed. My knives cut very well! And when once the jugular is cut—good-by. The blood would spurt out, and one, two, three red jets, and all would be over; she would be dead, and I should have had my revenge!"

"That is true, certainly, horribly true!"

"And without any risk to me, eh? An accident, that is all; bad luck, one of those mistakes which happen every day in our business. What could they accuse me of? Whoever would think of accusing me, even? Homicide through imprudence, that would be all! They would even pity me rather than accuse me. 'My wife! My poor wife!' I should say, sobbing. 'My wife, who is so necessary to me, who is half the breadwinner, who takes part in my performance!' You must acknowledge that I should be pitied!"

"Certainly; there is not the least doubt about that."

"And you must allow that such a revenge would be a very nice revenge, the best possible revenge which I could have with assured impunity."

"Evidently that is so."

"Very well! But when I told her so, as I have told you, and more forcibly still; threatening her, as I was mad with rage and ready to do the deed that I had dreamed of on the spot, what do you think she said?"

"That you were a good fellow, and would certainly not have the atrocious courage to—"

"Tut! tut! tut! I am not such a good fellow as you think. I am not frightened of blood, and that I have proved already, though it would be useless to tell you how and where. But I had no necessity to prove it to her, for she knows that I am capable of a good many things, even of crime, especially of one crime."

"And she was not frightened?"

"No. She merely replied that I could not do what I said; you understand. That I could not do it!"

"Why not?"

"Ah! Monsieur, so you do not understand? Why do you not? Have I not explained to you by what constant, long, daily practice I have learned to plant my knives without seeing what I am doing?"

"Yes, well, what then?"

"Well! Cannot you understand what she has understood with such terrible results, that now my hand would no longer obey me if I wished to make a mistake as I threw?"

"Is it possible?"

"Nothing is truer, I am sorry to say. For I really have wished to have the revenge which I have dreamed of, and which I thought so easy. Exasperated by that bad woman's insolence and confidence in her own safety, I have several times made up my mind to kill her, and have exerted all my energy and all my skill to make my knives fly aside when I threw them to make a border round her neck. I have tried with all my might to make them deviate half an inch, just enough to cut her throat. I wanted to, and I have never succeeded, never. And always the slut's horrible laugh makes fun of me, always, always."

And with a deluge of tears, with something like a roar of unsatiated and muzzled rage, he ground his teeth as he wound up: "She knows me, the jade; she is in the secret of my work, of my patience, of my trick, routine, whatever you may call it! She lives in my innermost being, and sees into it more closely than you do, or than I do myself. She knows what a faultless machine I have become, the machine of which she makes fun, the machine which is too well wound up, the machine which cannot get out of order— and she knows that I *cannot* make a mistake."

MARK TWAIN

At the Appetite Cure

⁊❧

This is one of Mark Twain's nonfiction pieces. Is it true? Or was it written with tongue in cheek? Decide for yourself.

This establishment's name is Hochberghaus. It is in Bohemia, a short day's journey from Vienna, and being in the Austrian empire is, of course, a health resort. The empire is made up of health resorts; it distributes health to the whole world. Its waters are all medicinal. They are bottled and sent throughout the earth; the natives themselves drink beer. This is self-sacrifice, apparently—but outlanders who have drunk Vienna beer have another idea about it. Particularly the Pilsener which one gets in a small cellar up an obscure back lane in the First Bezirk—the name has escaped me, but the place is easily found: You inquire for the Greek church; and when you get to it, go right along by—the next house is that little beer mill. It is remote from all traffic and all noise; it is always Sunday there. There are two small rooms, with low ceilings supported by massive arches; the arches and ceilings are whitewashed, otherwise the rooms would pass for cells in the dungeons of a bastille. The furniture is plain and cheap, there is no ornamentation anywhere; yet it is a heaven for the self-sacrificers, for the beer there is incomparable; there is nothing like it elsewhere in the world. In the first room you will find twelve or fifteen ladies and gentlemen of civilian quality; in the other one a dozen generals and ambassadors. One may live in Vienna many months and not hear of this place; but having once heard of it and sampled it the sampler will afterward infest it.

However, this is all incidental—a mere passing note of gratitude for blessings received—it has nothing to do with my subject. My subject is health resorts. All unhealthy people ought to domicile themselves in Vienna and use that as a base, making flights from time to time to the outlying resorts, according to need. A flight to Marienbad to get rid of fat; a flight to Carlsbad to get rid of rheumatism; a flight to Kaltenleutgeben to take the water cure and get rid of the rest of the diseases. It is all so handy. You can stand in Vienna and toss a biscuit into Kaltenleutgeben with a twelve-inch gun. You can run out thither at any time of the day; you go by the phenomenally slow trains, and yet inside of an hour you have exchanged the glare and swelter of the city for wooded hills, and shady forest paths, and soft cool airs, and the music of birds, and the repose and peace of paradise.

And there are plenty of other health resorts at your service and convenient to get at from Vienna—charming places, all of them. Vienna sits in the center of a beautiful world of mountains with now and then a lake and forests; in fact, no other city is so fortunately situated.

There are abundance of health resorts, as I have said. Among them this place—Hochberghaus. It stands solitary on the top of a densely wooded mountain and is a building of great size. It is called the Appetite Anstallt, and people who have lost their appetites come here to get them restored. When I arrived I was taken by Professor Haimberger to his consulting room and questioned:

"It is six o'clock. When did you eat last?"

"At noon."

"What did you eat?"

"Next to nothing."

"What was on the table?"

"The usual things."

"Chops, chickens, vegetables, and so on?"

"Yes; but don't mention them—I can't bear it."

"Are you tired of them?"

"Oh, utterly. I wish I might never hear of them again."

"The mere sight of food offends you, does it?"

"More, it revolts me."

The doctor considered awhile, then got out a long menu and ran his eye slowly down it.

"I think," said he, "that what you need to eat is—but here, choose for yourself."

I glanced at the list, and my stomach threw a handspring. Of all the barbarous layouts that were ever contrived, this was the most atrocious. At the top stood "tough, underdone, overdue tripe, garnished with garlic"; halfway down the bill stood "young cat; old cat; scrambled cat"; at the bottom stood "sailor boots, softened with tallow—served raw." The wide intervals of the bill were packed with dishes calculated to insult a cannibal. I said: "Doctor, it is not fair to joke over so serious a case as mine. I came here to get an appetite, not to throw away the remnant that's left."

He said gravely: "I am not joking, why should I joke?"

"But I can't eat these horrors."

"Why not?"

He said it with a naïveté that was admirable, whether it was real or assumed.

"Why not? Because—why, Doctor, for months I have seldom been able to endure anything more substantial than omelettes and custards. These unspeakable dishes of yours—"

"Oh, you will come to like them. They are very good. And you *must* eat them. It is the rule of the place, and is strict. I cannot permit any departure from it."

I said, smiling: "Well, then, Doctor, you will have to permit the departure of the patient. I am going."

He looked hurt, and said in a way which changed the aspect of things: "I am sure you would not do me that injustice. I accepted you in good faith—you will not shame that confidence. This appetite cure is my whole living. If you should go forth from it with the sort of appetite which you now have, it could become known, and you can see yourself that people would say my cure failed in your case and hence can fail in other cases. You will not go; you will not do me this hurt."

I apologized and said I would stay.

"That is right. I was sure you would not go; it would take the food from my family's mouths."

"Would they mind that? Do they eat these fiendish things?"

"They? My family?" His eyes were full of gentle wonder. "Of course not."

"Oh, they don't! Do you?"

"Certainly not."

"I see. It's another case of a physician who doesn't take his own medicine."

"I don't need it. It is six hours since you lunched. Will you have supper now—or later?"

"I am not hungry, but now is as good a time as any, and I would like to be done with it and have it off my mind. It is about my usual time, and regularity is commanded by all the authorities. Yes, I will try to nibble a little now—I wish a light horsewhipping would answer instead."

The professor handed me that odious menu.

"Choose—or will you have it later?"

"Oh, dear me, show me to my room; I forgot your hard rule."

"Wait just a moment before you finally decide. There is another rule. If you choose now, the order will be filled at once; but if you wait, you will have to await my pleasure. You cannot get a dish from that entire bill until I consent."

"All right. Show me to my room, and send the cook to bed; there is not going to be any hurry."

The professor took me up one flight of stairs and showed me into a most inviting and comfortable apartment consisting of parlor, bedchamber, and bathroom.

The front windows looked out over a far-reaching spread of green glades and valleys, and tumbled hills clothed with forests—a noble solitude unvexed by the fussy world. In the parlor were many shelves filled with books. The professor said he would now leave me to myself, and added: "Smoke and read as much as you please, drink all the water you like. When you get hungry, ring and give your order, and I will decide whether it shall be filled or not. Yours is a stubborn, bad case, and I think the first fourteen dishes in the bill are each and all too delicate for its needs. I ask you as a favor to restrain yourself and not call for them."

"Restrain myself, is it? Give yourself no uneasiness. You are going to save money by me. The idea of coaxing a sick man's appetite back with this buzzard fare is clear insanity."

I said it with bitterness, for I felt outraged by this calm, cold talk over these heartless new engines of assassination. The doctor looked grieved but not offended. He laid the bill of fare on the commode at my bed's head, "so that it would be handy," and said: "Yours is not the worst case I have encountered, by any means; still it is a bad one and requires robust treatment; therefore I shall be gratified if you will restrain yourself and skip down to No. 15 and begin with that."

Then he left me and I began to undress, for I was dog-tired and very sleepy. I slept fifteen hours and woke up finely refreshed at ten the next morning. Vienna coffee! It was the first thing I thought of —that unapproachable luxury—that sumptuous coffee-house coffee, compared with which all other European coffee and all American hotel coffee is mere fluid poverty. I rang and ordered it; also Vienna bread, that delicious invention. The servant spoke through the wicket in the door and said—but you know what he said. He referred me to the bill of fare. I allowed him to go—I had no further use for him.

After the bath I dressed and started for a walk, and got as far as the door. It was locked on the outside. I rang and the servant came and explained that it was another rule. The seclusion of the patient was required until after the first meal. I had not been particularly anxious to get out before, but it was different now. Being locked in makes a person wishful to get out. I soon began to find it difficult to put in the time. At two o'clock I had been twenty-six hours without food. I had been growing hungry for some time; I recognized that I was not only hungry now, but hungry with a strong adjective in front of it. Yet I was not hungry enough to face the bill of fare.

I must put in the time somehow. I would read and smoke. I did it, hour by hour. The books were all of one breed—shipwrecks; people lost in deserts; people shut up in caved-in mines; people starving in besieged cities. I read about all the revolting dishes that ever famishing men had stayed their hunger with. During the first hours these things nauseated me; hours followed in which they did not so affect me; still other hours followed in which I found myself smacking my lips over some tolerably infernal messes. When I had been without food forty-five hours I ran eagerly to the bell and ordered the second dish in the bill, which was a sort of dumplings containing a compost made of caviar and tar.

It was refused me. During the next fifteen hours I visited the bell every now and then and ordered a dish that was further down the list. Always a refusal. But I was conquering prejudice after prejudice right along; I was making sure progress; I was creeping up on No. 15 with deadly certainty, and my heart beat faster and faster, my hopes rose higher and higher.

At last when food had not passed my lips for sixty hours, victory was mine, and I ordered No. 15: "Soft-boiled spring chicken—in the egg; six dozen, hot and fragrant!"

In fifteen minutes it was there; and the doctor along with it, rubbing his hands with joy. He said with great excitement: "It's a cure, it's a cure! I knew I could do it. Dear sir, my grand system never fails—never. You've got your appetite back—you know you have; say it and make me happy."

"Bring on your carrion—I can eat anything in the bill!"

"Oh, this is noble, this is splendid—but I knew I could do it, the system never fails. How are the birds?"

"Never was anything so delicious in the world; and yet as a rule I don't care for game. But don't interrupt me, don't—I can't spare my mouth, I really can't."

Then the doctor said: "The cure is perfect. There is no more doubt nor danger. Let the poultry alone; I can trust you with a beefsteak now."

The beefsteak came—as much as a basketful of it—with potatoes, and Vienna bread and coffee; and I ate a meal then that was worth all the costly preparation I had made for it. And dripped tears of gratitude into the gravy all the time—gratitude to the doctor for putting a little plain common sense into me when I had been empty of it so many, many years.

Thirty years ago Haimberger went off on a long voyage in a sailing ship. There were fifteen passengers on board. The table fare was of the regulation pattern of the day: At 7 in the morning, a cup of bad coffee in bed; at 9, breakfast: bad coffee, with condensed milk; soggy rolls, crackers, salt fish; at 1 P.M., luncheon: cold tongue, cold ham, cold corned beef, soggy cold rolls, crackers; 5 P.M., dinner: thick pea soup, salt fish, hot corned beef and sauerkraut, boiled pork and beans, pudding; 9 till 11 P.M., supper: tea, with condensed milk. cold tongue, cold ham, pickles, sea biscuit, pickled oysters, pickled pig's feet, grilled bones, golden buck.

At the end of the first week eating had ceased, nibbling had taken its place. The passengers came to the table, but it was partly to put in the time, and partly because the wisdom of the ages commanded them to be regular in their meals. They were tired of the coarse and monotonous fare, and took no interest in it, had no appetite for it. All day and every day they roamed the ship half hungry, plagued by their gnawing stomachs, moody, untalkative, miserable. Among them were three confirmed dyspeptics. These became shadows in the course of three weeks. There was also a bedridden invalid; he lived on boiled rice; he could not look at the regular dishes.

Now came shipwreck and life in open boats, with the usual paucity of food. Provisions ran lower and lower. The appetites improved then. When nothing was left but raw ham and the ration of that was down to two ounces a day per person, the appetites were perfect. At the end of fifteen days the dyspeptics, the invalid, and the most delicate ladies in the party were chewing sailor boots in ecstasy, and only complaining because the supply of them was limited. Yet these were the same people who couldn't endure the ship's tedious corned beef and sauerkraut and other crudities. They were rescued by an English vessel. Within ten days the whole fifteen were in as good condition as they had been when the shipwreck occurred.

"They had suffered no damage by their adventure," said the professor. "Do you note that?"

"Yes."

"Do you note it well?"

"Yes—I think I do."

"But you don't. You hesitate. **You don't rise to the importance** if it. I will say it again—with emphasis—*not one of them suffered any damage."*

"Now I begin to see. Yes, it was indeed remarkable."

"Nothing of the kind. It was perfectly natural. There was no reason why they should suffer damage. They were undergoing nature's appetite cure, the best and wisest in the world."

"Is that where you got your idea?"

"That is where I got it."

"It taught those people a valuable lesson."

"What makes you think that?"

"Why shouldn't I? You seem to think it taught you one."

"That is nothing to the point. I am not a fool."

"I see. Were they fools?"

"They were human beings."

"Is it the same thing?"

"Why do you ask? You know it yourself. As regards his health—and the rest of the things—the average man is what his environment and his superstitions have made him; and their function is to make him an ass. He can't add up three or four new circumstances together and perceive what they mean; it is beyond him. He is not capable of observing for himself. He has to get everything at second hand. If what are miscalled the lower animals were as silly as man is, they would all perish from the earth in a year."

"Those passengers learned no lesson, then?"

"Not a sign of it. They went to their regular meals in the English ship, and pretty soon they were nibbling again—nibbling, appetiteless, disgusted with the food, moody, miserable, half hungry, their outraged stomachs cursing and swearing and whining and supplicating all day long. And in vain, for they were the stomachs of fools."

"Then as I understand it, your scheme is—"

"Quite simple. Don't eat till you are hungry. If the food fails to taste good, fails to satisfy you, rejoice you, comfort you, don't eat again until you are *very* hungry. Then it will rejoice you—and do you good, too."

"And I observe no regularity as to hours?"

"When you are conquering a bad appetite—no. After it is conquered, regularity is no harm, so long as the appetite remains good. As soon as the appetite wavers, apply the corrective again—which is starvation, long or short according to the needs of the case."

"The best diet, I suppose—I mean the wholesomest—"

"All diets are wholesome. Some are wholesomer than others, but all the ordinary diets are wholesome enough for the people who use them. Whether the food be fine or coarse, it will taste good and it will nourish if a watch be kept upon the appetite and a little starvation introduced every time it weakens. Nansen was used to fine fare, but when his meals were restricted to bear meat months at a time he suffered no damage and no discomfort, because his appetite was kept at par through the difficulty of getting his bear meat regularly."

"But doctors arrange carefully considered and delicate diets for invalids."

"They can't help it. The invalid is full of inherited superstitions and won't starve himself. He believes it would certainly kill him."

"It would weaken him, wouldn't it?"

"Nothing to hurt. Look at the invalids in our shipwreck. They lived fifteen days on pinches of raw ham, a suck at sailor boots, and general starvation. It weakened them, but it didn't hurt them. It put them in fine shape to eat heartily of hearty food and build themselves up to a condition of robust health. But they did not perceive that; they lost their opportunity; they remained invalids; it served them right. Do you know the tricks that the health-resort doctors play?"

"What is it?"

"My system disguised—covert starvation. Grape cure, bath cure, mud cure—it is all the same. The grape and the bath and the mud make a show and do a trifle of the work—the real work is done by the surreptitious starvation. The patient accustomed to four meals and late hours—at both ends of the day—now consider what he has to do at a health resort. He gets up at six in the morning. Eats one egg. Tramps up and down a promenade two hours with the other fools. Eats a butterfly. Slowly drinks a glass of filtered sewage that smells like a buzzard's breath. Promenades another two hours, but alone; if you speak to him he says anxiously, 'My water!—I am walking off my water!—please don't interrupt,' and goes stumping along again. Eats a candied rose leaf. Lies at rest in the silence and solitude of his room for hours; mustn't speak, mustn't read, mustn't smoke. The doctor comes and feels of his heart now, and his pulse, and thumps his breast and his back and his stomach, and listens for results through a penny flageolet; then orders the man's bath—half a degree, Réaumur, cooler than yesterday. After the bath, another egg. A glass of sewage at three or four in the afternoon, and promenade solemnly with the other freaks. Dinner at six—half a doughnut and a cup of tea. Walk again. Half past eight, supper—more butterfly; at nine, to bed. Six weeks of this regime—think of it. It starves a man out and puts him in splendid condition. It would have the same effect in London, New York, Jericho—anywhere."

"How long does it take to put a person in condition here?"

"It ought to take but a day or two; but in fact it takes from one to six weeks, according to the character and mentality of the patient."

"How is that?"

"Do you see that crowd of women playing football and boxing and jumping fences yonder? They have been here six or seven weeks. They were spectral poor weaklings when they came. They were accustomed to nibbling at dainties and delicacies at set hours four times a day, and they had no appetite for anything. I questioned them and then locked them into their rooms, the frailest ones to starve nine or ten hours, the others twelve or fifteen. Before long they began to beg; and indeed they suffered a good deal. They complained of nausea, headache, and so on. It was good to see them eat when the time was up. They could not remember when the devouring of a meal had afforded them such rapture—that was their word. Now, then, that ought to have ended their cure, but it didn't. They were free to go to any meals in the house, and they chose their accustomed four. Within a day or two I had to interfere. Their appetites were weakening. I made them knock out a meal. That set them up again. Then they resumed the four. I begged them to learn to knock out a meal themselves, without waiting for me. Up to a fortnight ago they couldn't; they really hadn't manhood enough; but they were gaining it, and now I think they are safe. They drop out a meal every now and then of their own accord. They are in fine condition now, and they might safely go home, I think, but their confidence is not quite perfect yet, so they are waiting awhile."

"Other cases are different?"

"Oh, yes. Sometimes a man learns the whole trick in a week. Learns to regulate his appetite and keep it in perfect order. Learns to drop out a meal with frequency and not mind it."

"But why drop the entire meal out? Why not a part of it?"

"It's a poor device, and inadequate. If the stomach doesn't call vigorously—with a shout, as you may say—it is better not to pester it but just give it a real rest. Some people can eat more meals than others and still thrive. There are all sorts of people and all sorts of appetites. I will show you a man presently who was accustomed to nibble at eight meals a day. It was beyond the proper gait of his appetite by two. I have got him down to six a day now, and he is all right and enjoys life. How many meals do you effect per day?"

"Formerly—for twenty-two years—a meal and a half; during the past two years, two and a half: coffee and a roll at nine, luncheon at one, dinner at seven-thirty or eight."

"Formerly a meal and a half—that is, coffee and a roll at nine, dinner in the evening, nothing between—is that it?"

"Yes."

"Why did you add a meal?"

"It was the family's idea. They were uneasy. They thought I was killing myself."

"You found a meal and a half per day enough, all through the twenty-two years?"

"Plenty."

"Your present poor condition is due to the extra meal. Drop it out. You are trying to eat oftener than your stomach demands. You don't gain, you lose. You eat less food now, in a day, on two and a half meals, than you formerly ate on one and a half."

"True—a good deal less; for in those old days my dinner was a very sizable thing."

"Put yourself on a single meal a day, now—dinner—for a few days, till you secure a good, sound, regular, trustworthy appetite, then take to your one and a half permanently, and don't listen to the family any more. When you have any ordinary ailment, particularly of a feverish sort, eat nothing at all during twenty-four hours. That will cure it. It will cure the stubbornest cold in the head, too. No cold in the head can survive twenty-four hours on modified starvation."

"I know it. I have proved it many a time."

NANCY MITFORD

A Bad Time

ร๛

Frankly, I put this in because of what the museum custodian said to Cherry Garrard when he delivered the eggs.

Apsley Cherry Garrard has said that "polar exploration is at once the cleanest and most isolated way of having a bad time that has yet been devised."* Nobody could deny that he and the twenty-four other members of Captain Scott's expedition to the South Pole had a bad time; in fact, all other bad times, embarked on by men of their own free will, pale before it. Theirs is the last of the great classic explorations; their equipment, though they lived in our century, curiously little different from that used by Captain Cook. Vitamin pills would probably have saved the lives of the polar party, so would a wireless transmitter; an electric torch have mitigated the misery of the winter journey. How many things which we take completely as a matter of course had not yet been invented, such a little time ago! Scott's *Terra Nova* had the advantage over Cook's

---

* Unless otherwise stated, the quotations in this essay are from *The Worst Journey in the World,* by Cherry Garrard.

Resolution of steam as well as sail. Even this was a mixed blessing, as it involved much hateful shoveling, while the coal occupied space which could have been put to better account in the little wooden barque (764 tons). Three motor sledges lashed to the deck seemed marvelously up to date and were the pride and joy of Captain Scott.

The *Terra Nova* sailed from London June 15, 1910, and from New Zealand November 26. She was fearfully overloaded; on deck, as well as the motor sledges in their huge crates, there were 30 tons of coal in sacks, 2½ tons of petrol in drums, 33 dogs, and 19 ponies. She rode out a bad storm by a miracle. "Bowers and Campbell were standing upon the bridge and the ship rolled sluggishly over until the lee combings of the main hatch were under the sea . . . as a rule, if a ship goes that far over she goes down." It took her thirty-eight day to get to McMurdo Sound, by which time the men were in poor shape. They had slept in their clothes, lucky if they got five hours a night, and had had no proper meals. As soon as they dropped anchor they began to unload the ship. This entailed dragging its cargo over ice floes which were in constant danger of being tipped up by killer whales, a very tricky business, especially when it came to moving ponies, motor sledges, and a pianola. Then they built the hut which was henceforward to be their home. Scott, tireless himself, always drove his men hard and these things were accomplished in a fortnight. The *Terra Nova* sailed away; she was to return the following summer, when it was hoped that the polar party would be back in time to be taken off before the freezing up of the sea forced her to leave again. if not, they would be obliged to spend a second winter on McMurdo Sound. Winter, of course, in those latitudes, happens during our summer months and is perpetual night, as the summer is perpetual day. The stunning beauty of the scenery affected the men deeply. When the sun shone the snow was never white but brilliant shades of pink, blue, and lilac; in winter the aurora australis flamed across the sky and the summit of Mount Erebus glowed.

The hut, unlike so much of Scott's equipment, was a total success. It was built on the shore, too near the sea, perhaps, for absolute security in the cruel winter storms, under the active volcano Mount

Erebus, called after the ship in which Ross discovered these regions in 1839. It was 50 feet by 25 and 9 feet high. The walls had double boarding inside and outside the frames, with layers of quilted seaweed between the boards. The roof had six layers of alternate wood, rubber, and seaweed. Though 109 degrees of frost was quite usual, the men never suffered from cold indoors; in fact, with twenty-five of them living there, the cooking range at full blast and a stove at the other end, they sometimes complained of stuffiness.

Life during the first winter was very pleasant. Before turning in for good they had done several grueling marches, laying stores in depots along the route of the polar journey; they felt they needed and had earned a rest. Their only complaint was that there were too many lectures; Scott insisted on at least three a week and they seem to have bored the others considerably—except for Ponting's magic-lantern slides of Japan. A gramophone and a pianola provided background music, and there was a constant flow of witticisms which one assumes to have been unprintable until one learns that Dr. Wilson would leave the company if a coarse word were spoken. In the hut they chiefly lived on flesh of seals, which they killed without difficulty, since these creatures are friendly and trustful by nature. "A sizzling on the fire and a smell of porridge and seal liver heralded breakfast which was at 8 A.M. in theory and a good deal later in practice." Supper was at 7. Most were in their bunks by 10 P. M., sometimes with a candle and a book; the acetylene was turned off at 10:30 to economize the fuel. Cherry Garrard tells us that the talk at meals was never dull. Most of these men were from the Royal Navy, and sailors are often droll, entertaining fellows possessing much out-of-the-way information. (Nobody who heard them can have forgotten the performances of Commander Campbell on the BBC—he was one of the greatest stars they ever had, in my view.) Heated arguments would break out on a diversity of subjects, to be settled by recourse to an encyclopedia or an atlas or sometimes a Latin dictionary. They wished they had also brought a *Who's Who*. One of their discussions, which often recurred, concerned "Why are we here? What is the force that drives us to undergo severe, sometimes ghastly hardships of our own free will?" The reply was the interest of science—it is important that man should know the features of the world he lives in, but this was not a complete answer. Once there was a discussion as to whether they would continue to like polar travel if, by the aid of modern inventions, it became quite easy and comfortable. They said no with one accord. It seems as if they really wanted to prove to themselves how much they could endure. Their rewards were a deep spiritual satisfaction and relationships between men who had become more than brothers.

Their loyalty to each other was fantastic—there was no jealousy, bickering, bullying, or unkindness. Reading between the lines of their diaries and records, it is impossible to guess whether anybody disliked anybody else. As for the Owner, as they called Scott, they all worshiped and blindly followed him. Cherry Garrard, the only one who could be called an intellectual and who took a fairly objective view of the others, gives an interesting account of Scott's character: subtle, he says, full of light and shade. No sense of humor—peevish by nature, high-strung, irritable, melancholy, and moody. However, such was his strength of mind that he overcame these faults, though he could not entirely conceal long periods of sadness. He was humane, so fond of animals that he refused to take dogs on long journeys, hauling the sledge himself rather than see them suffer. His idealism and intense patriotism shone through all he wrote. Of course he had the extraordinary charm without which no man can be a leader. In his diaries he appears as an affectionate person, but shyness or the necessary isolation of a sea captain prevented him from showing this side to the others. He was poor; he worried about provision for his family when it became obvious that he would never return to them. Indeed, he was always hampered by lack of money and never had enough to finance his voyages properly. Lady Kennet, his widow, once told me that Scott only took on Cherry Garrard because he subscribed £2,000 to the expedition. He thought him too young (twenty-three), too delicate, and too shortsighted, besides being quite inexperienced; he was the only amateur in the party. It is strange and disgraceful that Scott, who was already a world-famous explorer, should have had so little support from the government for this prestigious voyage.

These men had an enemy, not with them in the hut but ever present in their minds. His shadow fell across their path before they left New Zealand, when Captain Scott received a telegram dated from Madeira, with the laconic message AM GOING SOUTH. AMUNDSEN. Now, Amundsen was known to be preparing Nansen's old ship, the *Fram,* for a journey, having announced that he intended to do some further exploring in the arctic. Only when he was actually at sea did he tell his crew that he was on his way to try and reach the South Pole. There seemed something underhand and unfair about this. Scott's men were furious; they talked of finding the Amundsen party and having it out with them, but Scott put a good face on it and pretended not to mind at all. The two leaders could hardly have been more different. Amundsen was cleverer than Scott. "an explorer of a markedly intellectual type rather Jewish than Scandinavian." There was not much humanity or idealism about him, he was a tough, brave professional. He had a sense of humor and his description of flying over the North Pole in a dirigible with General Nobile is very funny indeed. Nobile was forever in tears and Amundsen on the verge of striking him, the climax coming when, over the pole, Nobile threw out armfuls of huge Italian flags which caught in the propeller and endangered their lives. All the same, Amundsen died going to the rescue of Nobile in 1928.

No doubt the knowledge that "the Norskies" were also on their way to the pole was a nagging worry to Scott all those long, dark, winter months, though he was very careful to hide his feelings and often remarked that Amundsen had a perfect right to go anywhere at any time. "The pole is not a race," he would say. He (Scott) was going in the interests of science and not in order to "get there first." But he knew that everybody else would look on it as a race; he was only human, he longed to win it.

The chief of Scott's scientific staff and his greatest friend was Dr. Wilson. He was to Scott what Sir Joseph Hooker had been to Ross. (Incredible as it seems, Hooker only died that very year, 1911. Scott knew him well.) Wilson was a doctor of St. George's Hospital and a zoologist specializing in vertebrates. He had published a book on whales, penguins, and seals and had prepared a report for the Royal

Commission on grouse disease. While he was doing this Cherry Garrard met him, at a shooting lodge in Scotland, and became fired with
a longing to go south. Wilson was an accomplished watercolorist.
Above all, he was an adorable person: "The finest character I ever
met," said Scott. Now Dr. Wilson wanted to bring home the egg of
an emperor penguin. He had studied these huge creatures when he
was with Scott on his first journey to the Antarctic and thought that
their embryos would be of paramount biological interest, possibly
proving to be the missing link between bird and fish. The emperors,
who weigh six and one half stone, look like sad little men and were
often taken by early explorers for human natives of the south polar
regions, are in a low state of evolution (and of spirits). They lay their
eggs in the terrible midwinter, because only thus can their chicks,
which develop with a slowness abnormal in birds, be ready to survive
the next winter. They never step on shore, even to breed; they live in
rookeries on sea ice. To incubate their eggs, they balance them on
their enormous feet and press them against a patch of bare skin
on the abdomen protected from the cold by a lappet of skin and
feathers. Paternity is the only joy known to these wretched birds and
a monstrous instinct for it is implanted in their breasts; male and
female hatch out the eggs and nurse the chicks, also on their feet, in-
discriminately. When a penguin has to go in the sea to catch his
dinner he leaves egg or chick on the ice; there is then a mad scuffle
as twenty childless birds rush to adopt it, quite often breaking or
killing it in the process. They will nurse a dead chick until it falls
to pieces and sit for months on an addled egg or even a stone. All
this happens in darkness and about a hundred degrees of frost. I often
think the R.S.P.C.A. ought to do something for the emperor
penguins.

Dr. Wilson had reason to suppose that there was a rookery of
emperors at Cape Crozier, about sixty miles along the coast. When
the ghastly winter weather had properly set in he asked for two
volunteers to go with him and collect some eggs. It was one of the
rules in the hut that everybody volunteered for everything, so Wilson
really chose his own companions: "Birdie" Bowers, considered by
Scott to be the hardiest traveler in the world, and Cherry Garrard.

The three of them left the light and warmth and good cheer of the hut to embark upon the most appalling nightmare possible to imagine. The darkness was profound and invariable. (They steered by Jupiter.) The temperature was generally in the region of 90 degrees of frost, unless there was a blizzard, when it would rise as high as 40 degrees of frost, producing other forms of discomfort and the impossibility of moving. The human body exudes a quantity of sweat and moisture, even in the lowest temperatures, so the men's clothes were soon frozen as stiff as boards and they were condemned to remain in the bending position in which they pulled their sleigh. It was as though they were dressed in lead. The surface of the snow was so bad that they had to divide their load and bring it along by relays. They could never take off their huge gloves for fear of losing their hands by frostbite; as it was, their fingers were covered with blisters in which the liquid was always frozen, so that their hands were like bunches of marbles. The difficulty of performing the simplest action with them may be imagined; it sometimes took over an hour to light a match and as much as nine hours to pitch their tent and do the work of the camp. Everything was slow, slow. When they had a discussion it lasted a week. If Cherry Garrard had written his book in a more uninhibited age he would no doubt have told us how they managed about what the Americans call going to the bathroom.* As it is, this interesting point remains mysterious. Dr. Wilson insisted on spending seven hours out of the twenty-four (day and night in that total blackness were quite arbitrary) in their sleeping bags. These were always frozen up, so that it took at least an hour to worm their way in and then they suffered the worst of all the tortures. Normally on such journeys the great comfort was sleep. Once in their warm dry sleeping bags the men went off as if they were drugged and nothing, neither pain nor worry, could keep them awake. But now the cold was too intense for Wilson and Cherry Garrard to close an eye. They lay shivering until they thought their backs would break, enviously listening to the regular snores of Birdie. They had got a spirit lamp—the only

* "They [the savages] go to the bathroom in the street." (Report from a member of the Peace Corps in the Congo.)

bearable moments they knew were when they had just swallowed a hot drink; for a little while it was like a hot-water bottle on their hearts; but the effect soon wore off. Their teeth froze and split to pieces. Their toenails came away. Cherry Garrard began to long for death. It never occurred to any of them to go back. The penguin's egg assumed such importance in their minds, as they groped and plodded their four or five miles a day, that the whole future of the human race might have depended on their finding one.

At last, in the bleakest and most dreadful place imaginable, they heard the emperors calling. To get to the rookery entailed a long, dangerous feat of mountaineering, since it was at the foot of an immense cliff. Dim twilight now glowed for an hour or two at mid-day, so they were able to see the birds, about a hundred of them, mournfully huddled together, trying to shuffle away from the intruders without losing the eggs from their feet and trumpeting with curious metallic voices. The men took some eggs, got lost on the cliff, were nearly killed several times by falling into crevasses, and broke all the eggs but two. That night there was a hurricane and their tent blew away, carried out to sea, no doubt. Now that they faced certain death, life suddenly seemed more attractive. They lay in their sleeping bags for two days waiting for the wind to abate and pretending to each other that they would manage somehow to get home without a tent, although they knew very well that they must perish. When it was possible to move again Bowers, by a miracle, found the tent. "We were so thankful we said nothing." They could hardly remember the journey home—it passed like a dreadful dream, and indeed they often slept while pulling their sleigh. When they arrived, moribund, at the hut, exactly one month after setting forth, the Owner said: "Look here, you know, this is the hardest journey that has ever been done."

I once recounted this story to a hypochondriac friend, who said, horrified, "But it must have been so *bad* for them." The extraordinary thing is that it did them no harm. They were quite recovered three months later, in time for the polar journey, from which, of course, Wilson and Bowers did not return, but which they endured longer than any except Scott himself. Cherry Garrard did most of the polar journey; he went through the 1914 war, in the trenches much of the time, and lived until 1959.

As for the penguins' eggs, when Cherry Garrard got back to London the first thing he did was to take them to the Natural History Museum. Alas, nobody was very much interested in them. The chief custodian, when he received Cherry Garrard after a good long delay, simply put them down on an inkstand and went on talking to a friend. Cherry Garrard asked if he could have a receipt for the eggs? "It's not necessary. It's all right. You needn't wait," he was told.

The winter journey was so appalling that the journey to the pole, which took place in daylight and in much higher temperatures, seemed almost banal by comparison; but it was terribly long (over seven hundred miles each way) and often very hard. Scott left the hut at 11 P.M. on November 1. He soon went back, for a book; was undecided what to take, but finally chose a volume of Browning. He was accompanied by a party of about twenty men with two motor sledges (the third had fallen into the sea while being landed), ponies, and dogs. Only four men were to go to the pole, but they were to be accompanied until the dreaded Beardmore glacier had been climbed. The men in charge of the motors turned back first, the motors having proved a failure. They delayed the party with continual breakdowns and only covered fifty miles. The dogs and their drivers went next. The ponies were shot at the foot of the glacier. The men minded this; they had become attached to the beasts, who had done their best, often in dreadful conditions. So far the journey had taken longer than it should have. The weather was bad for traveling, too warm, the snow too soft; there were constant blizzards. Now they were twelve men, without ponies or dogs, man-hauling the sledges. As they labored up the Beardmore, Scott was choosing the men who would go to the pole with him. Of course the disappointment of those who were sent home at this stage was acute; they had done most of the grueling journey and were not to share in the glory. On December 20 Cherry Garrard wrote: "This evening has been rather a shock. As I was getting my finesko on to the top of my ski Scott came up to me and said he had rather a blow for me. Of course, I knew what he was going to say, but could hardly grasp that I was going back—tomorrow night. . . . Wilson told me it was a toss-up whether Titus [Oates] or I should go on; that being so I think Titus will help him more than I can. I said all I could think of—he seemed so cut up about it, saying, 'I think somehow it is specially hard on you.' I said I hoped I had not disappointed him and he caught hold of me and said, 'No, no—no,' so if that is the case all is well."

There was still one more party left to be sent back after Cherry Garrard's. Scott said in his diary: "I dreaded this necessity of choosing, nothing could be more heartrending." He added: "We are struggling on, considering all things against odds. The weather is a constant anxiety." The weather was against them; the winter which succeeded this disappointing summer set in early and was the worst which hardened arctic travelers had ever experienced.

Scott had always intended to take a party of four to the pole. He now made the fatal decision to take five. Oates was the last-minute choice; it is thought that Scott felt the army ought to be represented. So they were: Scott, aged forty-three; Wilson, thirty-nine; Seaman Evans, thirty-seven; Bowers, twenty-eight; and Oates, thirty-two. The extra man was *de trop* in every way. There were only four pairs of skies; the tent was too small for five, so that one man was too near the outside and always cold; worst of all, there were now five people to eat rations meant for four. It was an amazing mistake, but it showed that Scott thought he was on a good wicket. The returning parties certainly thought so; it never occurred to them that he would have much difficulty, let alone that his life might be in danger. But they were all more exhausted than they knew, and the last two parties only got home by the skin of their teeth after hair-raising experiences on the Beardmore. Scott still had 150 miles to go.

On January 16, only a few miles from the pole, Bowers spied something in the snow—an abandoned sledge. Then they came upon dog tracks. Man Friday's footsteps on the sand were less dramatic. They knew that the enemy had won. "The Norwegians have forestalled us," wrote Scott, "and are first at the pole. . . . All the daydreams must go; it will be a wearisome return." And he wrote at the pole itself: "Great God! This is an awful place!"

Amundsen had left his base on October 20 with three other men, all on skis, and sixty underfed dogs to pull his sleighs. He went over the Axel Herberg glacier, an easier climb than the Beardmore, and reached the pole on December 16 with no more discomfort than on an ordinary antarctic journey. His return only took thirty-eight days, by which time he had eaten most of the dogs, beginning with his own favorite. When the whole story was known there was a good deal of feeling in England over these animals. At the Royal Geographical Society's dinner to Amundsen the president, Lord Curzon, infuriated his guest by ending his speech with the words, "I think we ought to give three cheers for the dogs."

And now for the long pull home. Evans was dying, of frostbite and concussion from a fall. He never complained, just staggered along, sometimes wandering in his mind. The relief when he died was tremendous, as Scott had been tormented by feeling that perhaps he ought to abandon him for the sake of the others. When planning the winter journey, Wilson had told Cherry Garrad that he was against taking seamen on the toughest ventures—he said they simply would not look after themselves. Indeed, Evans had concealed a wound on his hand which was the beginning of his troubles. A month later, the party was again delayed, by Oates's illness; he was in terrible pain from frostbitten feet. He bravely committed suicide, but too late to save the others. Scott wrote: "Oates's last thoughts were of his mother, but immediately before he took pride in thinking that his regiment would be pleased at the bold way in which he met his death. . . . He was a brave soul. He slept through the night, hoping not to wake; but he woke in the morning, yesterday. It was blowing a blizzard. He said 'I am just going outside and may be some time.'"

All, now, were ill. Their food was short and the petrol for their spirit lamp, left for them in the depots, had mostly evaporated. The horrible pemmican, with its low vitamin content, which was their staple diet was only bearable when made into a hot stew. Now they were eating it cold, keeping the little fuel they had to make hot cocoa. (This business of the petrol was very hard on the survivors. When on their way home, the returning parties had made use of it, carefully taking much less than they were told was their share. They always felt that Scott, who never realized that it had evaporated, must have blamed them in his heart for the shortage.) Now the weather changed. "They were in evil case but they would have been all right if the cold had not come down upon them; unexpected, unforetold and fatal. The cold in itself was not so tremendous until you realize that they had been out four months, that they had fought their way up the biggest glacier in the world, in feet of soft snow, that they had spent seven weeks under plateau conditions of rarefied air, big winds and low temperatures." They struggled on and might just have succeeded in getting home if they had had ordinary good luck. But, eleven miles from the depot which would have saved them, a blizzard blew up so that they could not move. It blew for a week, at the end of which there was no more hope. On March 29 Scott wrote:

MY DEAR MRS. WILSON.

If this reaches you, Bill and I will have gone out together. We are very near it now and I should like you to know how splendid he was at the end—everlastingly cheerful and ready to sacrifice himself for others, never a word of blame to me for leading him into this mess. He is suffering, luckily, only minor discomforts.

His eyes have a comfortable blue look of hope and his mind is peaceful with the satisfaction of his faith, in regarding himself as part of the great scheme of the Almighty. I can do no more to comfort you than to tell you that he died, as he lived, a brave, true man—the best of comrades and staunchest of friends. My whole heart goes out to you in pity.

Yours

R. SCOTT.

And to Sir James Barrie:

We are pegging out in a very comfortless spot . . . I am not at all afraid of the end but sad to miss many a humble pleasure which I had planned for the future on our long marches. . . . We have had four days of storm in our tent and nowhere's food or fuel. We did intend to finish ourselves when things proved like this but we have decided to die naturally in the track.

On March 19 Cherry Garrard and the others in the hut, none of them fit, began to be worried. The *Terra Nova* had duly come back, with longed-for mails and news of the outer world. They had to let her go again, taking those who were really ill. On March 27 Atkinson, the officer in charge, and a seaman went a little way to try and meet the polar party, but it was a hopeless quest, and they were a hundred miles from where Scott was already dead when they turned back. They now prepared for another winter in the hut, the sadness of which can be imagined. Long, long after they knew all hope was gone they used to think they heard their friends coming in, or saw shadowy forms that seemed to be theirs. They mourned them and missed their company. Scott, Wilson, and Bowers had been the most dynamic of them all, while "Titus" or "Farmer Hayseed" (Oates) was a dear, good-natured fellow whom everybody loved to tease. The weather was unimaginably awful. It seemed impossible that the hut could stand up to the tempests which raged outside for weeks on end and the men quite expected that it might collapse at any time. When at last the sun reappeared they set forth to see if they could discover traces of their friends. They hardly expected any results, as they were firmly convinced that the men must have fallen down a crevasse on the Beardmore, a fate they had all escaped by inches at one time or another. Terribly soon, however, they came upon what looked like a cairn; it was, in fact, Scott's tent covered with snow.

"We have found them. To say it has been a ghastly day cannot express it. Bowers and Wilson were sleeping in their bags. Scott had thrown the flaps of his bag open at the end. His left hand was stretched over Wilson, his lifelong friend." Everything was tidy, their papers and records in perfect order. Atkinson and Cherry Garrard read enough to find out what had happened and packed up the rest of the papers unopened. They built a cairn over the tent, which was left as they found it. Near the place where Oates disappeared they put up a cross with the inscription: "Hereabouts died a very gallant gentleman, Captain E. G. Oates of the Inniskilling Dragoons. In March 1912, returning from the pole, he walked willingly to his death in a blizzard to try and save his comrades, beset by hardship."

In due course Cherry Garrard and the others were taken off by the *Terra Nova*. When they arrived in New Zealand Atkinson went ashore to send cables to the dead men's wives. "The Harbor Master came out in the tug with him. 'Come down here a minute,' said Atkinson to me and 'It's made a tremendous impression. I had no idea it would make so much,' he said." Indeed it had. The present writer well remembers this impression, though only seven at the time.

Amundsen had won the race, but Scott had captured his fellow countrymen's imagination. It is one of our endearing qualities, perhaps unique, that we think no less of a man because he has failed —we even like him better for it. In any case, Amundsen complained that a year later a Norwegian boy at school in England was being taught that Captain Scott discovered the South Pole.

I don't quite know why I have felt the need to write down this well-known story, making myself cry twice: at the inscription on Oates's cross and when Atkinson said, "It has made a tremendous impression." Perhaps the bold, bald men who get, smiling, into cupboards, as if they were playing sardines, go a little way (about as far as from London to Manchester) into the air and come out of their cupboards again a few hours later, smiling more than ever, have put me in mind of other adventurers. It is fifty years to the day, as I write this, that Scott died. Most of the wonderful books which tell of his expedition are out of print now, but they can easily be got at second hand. I should like to feel that I may have induced somebody to read them again.*

* Books relating to the polar journey: *Scott's Last Expedition;* Cherry Garrard, *The Worst Journey in the World;* Priestly, *Antarctic Adventure;* E. R. Evans, *South with Scott;* Amundsen, *My Life as an Explorer.*

ELEANOR GRAHAM

Beatrix Potter

ଓ

I've always been fascinated by "successive double lives"—lives whose second half doesn't match the first half.

It is a strange story that lies behind the Beatrix Potter books—the story of a life begun in the chilliest, most cold-hearted, of Victorian households, all starch and pretentiousness bolstered up with nurses, governesses, butler, and coachmen with a lonely little girl living her orderly life in the forlorn isolation of a third-floor nursery in a Kensington house; and ending at Sawrey with a tough old lady going about her daily round in clogs with her skirts pinned back and a sack over her head, a successful farmer, and (though too late for any cluster of children) a happy wife.

Good things, we all know, have come out of lonely childhoods. Beatrix Potter certainly suffered, but the solitude intensified a naturally vivid imagination, and in the long spells of quiet she relived her experiences, both real and imaginary, drawing from the actual her own shrewd conclusions, and developing the sound sense of values which all her books evince.

Real life for her, even from an early age, was the hard, simple life of country folk as she saw it on farms and in cottages in Scotland during the three months of each year when her father took a house in the country and transferred to it his entire household—blissful holidays when she was free to live in all her members. There she saw and felt the meaning behind household drudgery with its endless scouring, washing and mending, cooking and baking, the contriving inspired by necessity and love. She recognized its dignity, and her own heart was touched by the warmth of that family life so different from her own. She seems almost to have studied it, learning its pattern phrase by phrase. In every period of her life, her love and admiration for the homely arts are evident, and it is this way of life which she expresses in nearly all her books.

She had the seeing eye and a memory which retained the feeling of a moment as well as the reflection of a scene. In London, with few books, hardly any toys, and no companions with whom to share the raptures of discovery, she had little to divert her, and the intensity of her experiences remained intact, so that she was able to return and enter into them again, expanding and developing them in the light of her imagination—following the mice and rabbits beyond the point at which they had, in reality, disappeared from sight. Her private world was undoubtedly one of many mansions.

She had some of the qualities which made Fabre great. She had the patience, the willingness to watch and wait, the powerful observation which many children have but so soon lose in the swarm of new activities which crowd in upon them in the ordinary course of everyday life. Even as a child she would lie still and watchful by the hour in the fields, learning the lives of the tiny creatures who moved about the tufty roots of meadow grass and wild flowers. She drew and painted—leaves, flowers, animals, skulls and bones, anything —but always earnestly, with a naturalist's care for accuracy of detail. At home she had a big natural history to refer to and when fresh specimens failed, she drew from its plates. Later she was permitted to go to the Natural History Museum at Kensington, alone and unchaperoned, and there she drew passionately.

This was only part of the vivid secret life which went on behind those wide, bright eyes of hers and the tight-shut mouth. Eager, lively, curious, she made a good listener even for those days when little girls were expected to be seen and not heard, and the stories of family history which she heard from her Grandmother Potter and others probably affected her whole life. They seemed to her, even then, so important that she devised a trick of writing very small so that she could put them down as they were told, without drawing attention to what she was doing.

Her father was a barrister, too wealthy to care about practicing; but Beatrix found to her pride that she came also from more interesting folk, "from generations of Lancashire yeomen and weavers, obstinate, hardheaded, matter-of-fact folk, Puritans, Nonjurors, Dissenters." They had been well known in the north and, in their own generations, as Unitarians, radicals, liberals: honest, thinking men, making their money in the mills and spending it on farms.

One of her grandmother's stories struck right home to the heart of the small girl who remembered it with special significance all her days. It described the grandmother as a little girl, driving with her father in a gig across Lancaster Sands under a rising moon, watching with great anxiety the incoming tide, for she carried a heavy bag of gold in her lap—gold with which to pay for another farm her father was buying.

"I hold that a strongly marked personality can influence descendants for generations," Beatrix Potter wrote very late in her life. She had become a great believer in heredity, in "breed," and put it to the test in her farming. As Mrs. Heelis of Sawrey, she proved also that *she* had bred true to type, for she became renowned throughout the county as, in the words with which she had proudly described her ancestors, an *obstinate, hardheaded, matter-of-fact* woman with whom it was difficult to associate the long row of pretty little nursery books.

The loneliness of childhood in Kensington had been relieved by the attentions of three good women, a nurse of character, a kind governess, and, finally, by a gay young governess who married early and remained at hand, near enough for at least regular if not frequent visits in one of the less important of the family carriages. That governess became Mrs. Moore and started a long family. To her children Beatrix Potter became something of a fairy godmother—and they were the means by which the spell of her dismal captivity was ultimately broken. For them she shaped into stories the fantasies with which she had lived so long, and drew the pictures which, in her books, have become as much a part of the inheritance of children everywhere as Hill Top Farm is of the whole nation.

The Tale of Peter Rabbit was first written in a letter with pictures in pen and ink for one of the Moore children during a long illness. It was not published until nine years later when Beatrix Potter was thirty-six, still cloistered in her nurseries and subject to her parents. She had become diffident, though quite untouched by bitterness or self-pity. She had given up some ambitions—notably to illustrate a serious work on fungi, for which she had filled albums at the Natural History Museum with exquisite, careful drawings. But she was no longer friendless. There was, for instance, Canon Rawnsley whom she had met during holidays (now mainly spent in the Lake District). He had encouraged her to make her little books, to try getting a publisher or, at worst, to print them herself. She did, in fact, print both *Peter Rabbit* and *The Tailor of Gloucester* privately before a publisher would have them.

Looked at in the light of her own circumstances, the published form of *Peter Rabbit* reveals itself as a great venture, anxiously undertaken. She was always confident of her ability to reach and please a child, but had no such faith to sustain her in facing the adult world; and she had now a publisher to satisfy and the buying public to attract. The careful simplicity of both text and drawings barely hides that tremulous anxiety to please. In her original letter to the sick child she had drawn the rabbit from one of her pets, a wild rabbit who had lived nine years in captivity and died just before she came to make the colored pictures for the book. She had to substitute a new and younger rabbit as model, and the difference in color and line worried her, as letters to her publisher show. Her background scenes were gathered from anywhere or nowhere—a tree from Keswick, Mr. McGregor from Scotland, the potting shed from her grandmother's house in Hertfordshire, the lily pond from Wales.

In her nursery she must often have watched the mice come out from behind the wainscot to play. She draws them with such felicity, and always as good little creatures with their own natural dignity. The mice in *The Tailor of Gloucester* are enchanting creatures, and all her own, though the rest of the tale was one she had heard in the West Country about a tailor, a waistcoat, and *No more Twist!* With the care and thoroughness which were so characteristic of her, she sketched the old streets of Gloucester which were its proper setting, searched the cottages for the hearths and home she wanted, found in Chelsea a tailor actually squatting on his bench in an old shop, just as she showed him in the book. She went to the Victoria and Albert Museum to copy the embroidery pattern from an old coat there. But for the mice she had only to set her fancy free, and this book is, indeed, a charming piece of self-expression, though actually written for a child, and she was, in fact, half afraid that it might appeal more to old ladies than children. In wartime editions it seemed to me that the street scenes had begun to fade a little, though the pretty, industrious, good-natured little mice and the pink-edged teacups are as fresh as when she first painted them.

She had, at last, a practical outlet for her mind, a stimulus for her ambition, and she was enjoying the satisfaction of accomplishing a set purpose. Her spirits rose and, with them, her courage, though her father was making himself exceedingly unpleasant over the whole business with his tantrums and scolding, detesting heartily anything which might promise her independence. The old obstinacy in the breed stood her in good stead now and, though for the sake of peace she had to beg her publishers to say no more for the present of another book, she must have gone on working at it, for *Squirrel Nutkin* came out in the same year as *The Tailor of Gloucester*. It sparkled with that brilliant inventiveness which had kept her spirit young and her mind alive throughout the long, drab years of her protracted childhood. She used an old repetitive pattern as the frame for this tale, and filled it with fun and gaiety: the enchanting ingenuity of the offerings made to Old Brown on each of the six days of the nutting, the impertinences of Nutkin, the cunning working in of old rhymes and riddles which all children of the day would know already—these show Beatrix Potter coming into her own. She had a particular feeling about bringing these old rhymes into her stories and expressed her thankfulness that the publishers did not want to cut them out.

Yet she was still not quite sure of herself, did not wholly trust her imagination, or believe how much more appreciated her own inventions would be than such borrowed notions as the squirrels' rafts.

The series was selling well. Even at a shilling a copy, they brought in a useful sum of money, and she suddenly realized that she could earn her own living.

Nevertheless, the two books she published in the following year gave little sign of that increased courage. One was a sequel to

Peter Rabbit, and when it was done she felt she had used every conceivable rabbit situation and prayed she might never draw one again. The other book, *The Tale of Two Bad Mice,* is very different from any of her others, as though she had lost her good feeling for everything in its proper place, as though the dolls and dolls' house had not been assimilated into her own personal fantasy—and indeed she had too little acquaintance with happy nursery life to be at home with them. Even the appearance of her two pets, Hunca Munca and Tom Thumb, does not put happiness into the tale: rather they introduce a tone of destructiveness which throws its own light on the conflict that was raging in the author's heart.

She was thinking of escape and freedom at that time, though her thoughts had as yet to be kept secret, and she knew she would have to fight every step of the way and to endure humiliating scenes with her parents.

She found herself on the one hand being drawn into an attachment to a member of her publishing house. At the same time, with her accumulating royalties, she had enough money to buy herself a haven—a farm to escape to.

By discussing the matter with her father as a form of investment not unusual in their family, she obtained his consent, and, in the following year, 1905, Hill Top Farm became hers. That she might have any thought of living there, or of running the farm herself, was too wildly preposterous in Mr. Potter's eyes for a moment's serious consideration. Throughout the rest of her life, however, there are signs in plenty of what a sense of fulfillment, of added strength and purpose, its mere possession gave her.

That summer, in spite of all her parents could say, she accepted Mr. Norman Warne's proposal of marriage. Before Christmas (before they could be married) he died. That was in her fortieth year—a strange year indeed—and what would she have done with the farm if she had married a London publisher?

The books of that remarkable year were the best she had yet done. A new vigor and self-confidence surged through them. She was happy; she was released. In *The Tale of Mrs. Tiggywinkle* she described a former pet, "the cleanest little creature" she had ever kept,

and delightfully transformed it into the conscientious little washer-
woman of the fells! The scene is not yet Sawrey, but on the other side
of Derwentwater, near Catbells; and for the first time she drew her
picture of that life to which she had given her heart when she was a
little girl. There is the cottage kitchen of her dreams, rag rug
before the gleaming range, the flagged floor, and the busy little
creature working industriously, and taking pride in all she does. The
promise of her own fulfillment is surely evident here.

In *The Pie and the Pattypan* appears Beatrix Potter's native brand
of humor, a dry humor, poking gentle fun at genteel folk, chuckling
over her own insight into the curious little ways of human nature,
good-humored, absolutely without sentimentality. Some at least
of the effects on her of Mr. Warne's death are to be seen in a
comparison of these with the books which came after them.

Three books were published in the next year: *The Tale of Mr.
Jeremy Fisher* has certainly less vitality, though again the germ
was ten years old, having appeared in another letter to the Moore
children. It has not the sparkle of later books, nor the cosy
warmth of *Mrs. Tiggywinkle,* nor anything of the humor in *The Pie
and the Pattypan.* The other two were the first in the smaller series,
The Fierce Bad Rabbit and *Miss Moppet,* the story being no more
than a caption to each picture and the drawings were bare, often with
no background scene at all. Both might have been potboilers (in
spite of an occasional dash of humor in the latter)—perhaps for extra
money for Hill Top? Or they may have been done merely to keep her
mind off heartbreak and disappointment. All three suggest a mind
much preoccupied with other things. The other two of the small
series came out several years later, in 1917 and 1922, and were a
good deal more lively both in words and pictures, consisting of
nursery rhymes, some traditional, some original. The best of all
pictures of Mrs. Tiggy appears in one of them, *Apply Dapply's
Nursery Rhymes.*

Beatrix certainly suffered deeply at this time, but the farm
remained to comfort her, and it brought about a new blooming
of spirit in her. She still was not free to go and live there, but at
this period her family usually took houses in the Lake District

for their long summer holiday, and from them she made her way determinedly to and fro every day to Sawrey, traveling by whatever means of transport were available—a slow, grueling journey as a rule.

Room by room she made the cottage her own. She planned and stocked the garden—the planning she could do, the year round, in London or anywhere else. Trusting to her own judgment—and wisely as it turned out—she put the former owner in as farm manager, and as she watched the development of her property in his capable hands, she began her own apprenticeship to the sort of life she had long loved and now most fervently desired to live.

She still found time to draw—indeed her books must have acquired new significance in her eyes—and what she drew was Sawrey and the farm. She drew Hill Top as it stands today, with the garden and farmyard and its typical interior. She felt no need to look beyond the immediate present for inspiration, neither back to former pets or abroad for quaint notions. All trace of conflict disappeared out of her work, though she was still fast under the thumb of her father. A sense of the duty she owed them had been ground into her by her parents to bitter purpose and she could not disregard it. Each autumn she had to leave her cherished land, to return with them to London. Her health suffered during these periods of banishment and her imagination wandered always back to Sawrey.

She can no longer have had any doubt of her ultimate escape. Hill Top would one day be her home though the present frustration, particularly at her age, was hard to bear. In the meantime, she put new friends into possession, Tabitha Twitchett and Tom Kitten, the Puddleducks, Sam Whiskers, Pigling Bland—yes, and even Messrs. Tod and Brock. It should, perhaps, be said here that she never did live at Hill Top. Her ultimate emancipation included marriage, and Hill Top seemed too small for two. Besides, by then she had bought another farm, an adjoining property with a larger house in which she and her husband were to spend thirty happy years together. But she never ceased to cherish Hill Top as the realization of a long dream. She never changed or let the house.

The cream of her work lies in the books that followed, and they were rich with full fertility of mind and imagination, sparkling with originality, the new elasticity of spirit, and her own dry humor. They reflected most surely her mounting confidence, not only in herself but in life. She knew with certainty that she had found her own niche and purpose in life and was glad that her lines had fallen in such pleasant places. Her whole being was resolutely moving toward fulfillment.

The first of these books was *Tom Kitten* in which fantasy is secondary altogether to the reality of the background scene, though the invention is rich and gay. Miss Potter painted into these pages (and those of the other "Sawrey" books) her own delight in her treasures. There in the frontispiece stands the little house itself, with gate, porch, and flower-bordered path up to the door. Through the later pages are pictures of the passage and the stairs, a deep window in one of the bedrooms, the farmyard and outhouses, the winding road disappearing over the hills. She peopled the house with cats, and, out of doors, introduced the Puddleducks, delicious, foolish neighbors, of whom more was to be heard in *Jemima Puddleduck,* a tale of the kind of everyday circumstances familiar to any country-bred child, with pictures which caught exactly the familiar expressions of farmyard creatures, the idiotic simplicity of ducks, the sagacity of sheepdogs—and, of course, the slyness of foxes. "It does not do to be sentimental on a farm," wrote Miss Potter, in connection with lambskin hearthrugs, and it is in this balance of mind that she finds the humor in commonplace things. She could even see the funny side of rats at Hill Top Farm, peculiarly destructive and pertinacious rats, which it took all her ingenuity and determination to outwit! She could laugh at the effrontery of Sam Whiskers (as she called the rat of Hill Top) sitting up in broad afternoon sunlight under the kitchen table to eat his dinner (certainly stolen from her larder), and he became as much a part of her life there as the mice behind the wainscot in the Kensington nurseries. So came *The Tale of Sam Whiskers,* also called *The Roly Poly Pudding,* with its delicious pictures of Sam stealing a pat of butter out of the dairy while his lean and anxious wife snatched a lump of dough out of the bread pan, set before the fire to rise.

Beatrix continued to give news of him for years afterward to the many children all over the world to whom she wrote.

It is strange that she followed these books with *The Flopsy Bunnies* which told another tale of the Peter Rabbit family and departed from the Sawrey scene. It was written and illustrated while she was with her parents in Wales, and the change of theme is suggestive. What was going on between her and the tyrants? Could she not bear to dream for the moment of her loved Hill Top? Or did she merely yield to pressure from readers for a sequel to an old favorite? It is idle, of course, to speculate—yet that was another fateful year for her. The books continued to sell widely and increasingly. She was always surprised to see how much money they yielded; and she was preparing to buy her second farm. Moreover, the negotiations for the sale brought her into contact with the man she married four years later, William Heelis, the solicitor who put the deal through for her. Could this evidence of her absorption in Sawrey and farming have roused her father to fresh storms of protest?

It is easily seen that her joy in Hill Top had been somehow dimmed, for though she returned to Sawrey for her next book (published in the same year as the *Flopsy Bunnies*) it was not about the farm nor the house, but the village shop—and a deliciously shrewd, good-humored picture of life on both sides of the counter it is in *Ginger and Pickles*. But in the next two books (and only one a year) she still avoids Hill Top, and goes down mouseholes again for *The Tale of Mrs. Tittlemouse,* while in *Timmy Tiptoes,* a tale about gray squirrels, she turns abroad for her chipmunk and the bear. Each of them has its moments, but neither can stand beside the Hill Top books for originality or inventiveness.

Through these years Beatrix Potter suffered a great deal from influenza and its familiar depression, and was kept for weeks in bed with an affected heart. She was on the far side of forty-five, and the future must often have looked dark to her as she lay there, at the mercy of her parents. However, the connection with William Heelis had "taken." It was he who kept her alive with news of Sawrey when she was ill. It was he who gave her the courage to take hold of life again. In 1912 she published *The Tale of Mr. Todd,* a much longer story than usual which begins: "I have made many books about well-behaved people. Now, for a change, I am going to make a story about two disagreeable people. . . . Nobody could call Mr. Todd nice. . . . He had half a dozen houses but he was seldom at home." The scene is round about Hill Top, though the farm does not appear; the spirit makes it plain that the author was recovering.

Beatrix had to face the same bitter opposition from her parents over her second offer of marriage. The Potters were "Bar and Bench" and Mr. Heelis only a country solicitor. Very reasonably she saw their objections but, as reasonably, made up her mind to accept the offer. She married William at St. Mary Abbots, Kensington, in 1913 and brought out, in the same year, the last and in some ways the best of the Sawrey tales, *The Tale of Pigling Bland.* She had had had it in mind all through these past years of depression for in 1910 she had written: "I think I shall put myself in my next book. It will be about pigs, and I shall put me walking about with my old sow, Goosie. She is such a pet!" And she did put herself into this "Tale of a Christmas Pig." It was the peak and climax of her literary work, cunningly bringing in old saws and rhymes about pigs, sparkling with delicious fun and rich with the country scene she loved so much. The characterization of the pigs is delicate and throughout there is an infectious welling-up of fun and gaiety. Pigs were an important feature of cottage economy at Hill Top. "The whole district is planted out with my pigs," she wrote, "but we still take an interest in them because if they grow well, we shall *get a name for pigs.* Such is fame!"

If the Pig book was the climax, the finale came six years later in *The Tale of Johnny Town Mouse,* the old fable re-dressed to suit the circumstances, for Beatrix could at last count herself settled and at peace, and through the mouth of the Country Mouse she makes her farewell speech. Other books were to come, but she did not want to write or paint any more. She had become Mrs. Heelis of Sawrey, the tough old lady successfully embarked on her late marriage and her late career as a farmer, going around her fields and byres in clogs, with her skirts pinned back and a sack over her head.

" 'What do you do when it rains?' the town mouse asked Timmy Willie.

" 'When it rains, I sit in my little sandy burrow and shell corn and seeds from my Autumn store. I peep out at the throstles and blackbirds on the lawn, and my friend Cock Robin. And when the sun comes out again, you should see my garden and the flowers —roses and pinks, and pansies—no noise except the birds and the bees, and the lambs in the meadows. . . .'

"One place suits one person, another place suits another person. For my part I prefer to live in the country, like Timmy Willie."

HENRY BESTON

Belzoni

ᔐ

Another "successive double life"—one of the most extraordinary careers in history.

A little over a hundred years ago the learned world of fashionable London was profoundly moved by the arrival of eventful news. After having been sealed to Europeans for some four thousand years, one of the great pyramids of Egypt had at length been opened, and torch in hand, a modern man had walked the untrodden dust of the oven-hot and silent galleries.

Now that all three pyramids stand open to the world, and tourists with green sun-goggles and parasols hesitate and giggle at the forbidding entrances, it is difficult to believe that the interiors should have been so recently a mystery. Save for a few measurements, however, the first years of the nineteenth century knew no more about the great pyramids than the Renaissance had known; all was tradition, legend, and conjecture. Of the familiar giants at Gizeh, only one, the Great Pyramid of Cheops, was open, and this but very partially so, for the famous well and the lower galleries were clogged with rubbish and debris. The second pyramid, that of Chephren, and the third, that of Mycerinus, were apparently solid mountains of limestone blocks with no sign whatsoever of an opening or a door.

It is scarce possible to exaggerate the hold which these locked giants had maintained on the imagination of mankind. The pilgrim of the Middle Ages thought them the granaries of Joseph, and stared at them with reverence; the conquering Arab called them the palaces of kings, sleeping enchanted in moated halls whose lamps were hollow emeralds.

All tales, however, agreed upon one point—that the pyramids concealed a treasure. The Arabic conquerors of Egypt had already sought it, and one of them, the tenth century caliph Al Mamun, baffled by the masonry of the third pyramid, had actually made a vain and lunatic attempt to destroy the entire edifice. So kings passed, and emperors and sultans and great ages of historic time, but the sunrise still rolled up the veiling mist from the great plain of Egypt, revealing the vast, solemn geometry of the masters of the Nile. What treasure, what strange secret lay within these stones? Who would be the first to enter them? What would he find?

In the year 1778, Jacopo Belzoni, a worthy barber of Padua, and Teresa his wife, were rejoicing at the arrival of a son. They had christened him Giovanni Battista, or "Gianbattista" for short. Had a soothsayer of ancient Egypt appeared by the cradle, and revealed the infant's destiny, the good *tonsore* would have surely opened his mouth and dropped his shears. For the soothsayer would have said something like this:

"This child will be a juggler at theaters and village fairs, a scholar, an author, and a traveler. For thirty-seven years, life will toss him about as a juggler tosses a ball in the air, but then his opportunity will come, he will win fame in a strange land and solve the most romantic of all mysteries."

The adventurous tale begins, strangely enough, in a monastery. The worthy Jacopo had fathered a brood of fourteen—something had to be found for each and every one of them, and in the distribution young Giovanni Battista was handed over to the church. He was to find a place in the world for himself as a monk. From the parental dwelling on a bystreet in Padua, the boy, still in his teens, walked the ancient highways of Umbria to the house of a monastic order in Rome. Somewhere in the old papal city, behind an encircling wall, his days of boyhood and youth began before the dawn with the clangor of a monastery bell, and ended with the echoing cave of a darkened church, the golden, pinpoint flames of altar lamps, and the solemn chanting of the offices.

Years pass, years of quiet and withdrawal from the world. Of a sudden comes alarming news, the pot of the Revolution has boiled over, the French are crossing the frontiers and invading Italy. Presently there are disorders in Rome and a descent of French troops upon the city; the bells are silenced, the monasteries closed or seized for barracks, and the monks harried out into the street.

Among the monks thus compelled to abandon the religious life was Gianbattista Belzoni. The Paduan novice had grown up into a giant, a colossus even, for he now stood six feet seven inches in height, and was broadly and solidly built in the same proportion. And not only did Gianbattista have a giant's strength, he had also the pride and the sense of decorum which accompany a giant stature. Those who are born of average height little know how huge is the influence of great stature on its possessor's conduct and character! He who is born a Titan must act the Titan; a frolicsome colossus is an outrage to nature. Gianbattista, moreover, though of Paduan birth, was of Roman stock, and Romans have to this day an eye for dignity. Brown-eyed, and black-brown of hair, with a giant's mildness, a giant's decorum, and an Italian's grace of address, young Gianbattista was a figure for Michelangelo.

Walking with a giant's disdain through the rabble of soldiers and revolutionists jeering by the monastery gate, the young monk passed forth into the world.

The homeless young Titan, he was only twenty-two, may well have wondered what was now to become of him. At the monastery school he had chanced to make a special study of the science of hydraulics, but that was hardly a knowledge to be peddled about in those uncertain times. Having no choice, therefore, he fell back on his physical strength, and set about earning his living as a juggler and a Hercules of village fairs. From Italy the showman monk made his way through Germany, and then through Holland to the various kingdoms of the British Isles. Finding life pleasant in England, he settled down there, and spent the Napoleonic years amusing his hosts and becoming something of an Englishman.

For the next ten years, his life is that of an Italian mountebank in England. The English knew the huge, serious, well-mannered foreigner as "Signor" Belzoni; they saw him in their pantomimes and at Bartholomew Fair. He had a booth at the fair, and amid the smell of black puddings sizzling on the fire, and the shouts and cries of barrow vendors and showmen, our Signor delighted the London rabble with feats of strength and dexterity. His favorite show was a spectacle called "Samson," an edifying Biblical affair in whose course Belzoni pulled down the pillars of a stage temple with the most bloodcurdling roars, crash, dust, and general uproar. At Sadlers Wells Theatre, to quote an old play bill, his performance consisted "in carrying from seven to ten men in a manner never attempted by any but himself. He clasps round him a belt to which are affixed ledges to support the men who cling about him. . . . When thus encumbered, he moves as easy and as graceful as if about to walk a minuet, and displays a flag in as flippant a manner as a dancer on the rope." Another visitor became poetic. "Signor Belzoni," he wrote, "moved about the stage under this enormous pressure with as much steadiness and stateliness as the elephant does when his howdah is full of Indian warriors."

Ellar the comedian knew him well, and saw him perform; the giant was getting two pounds a week, and Edmund Kean was watching delighted in the stalls.

In England came Romance: there Gianbattista found his Sarah. This resolute spouse was an Englishwoman of a stature almost as magnificent as her lord's, and with a character and a mind as British

as the dome of St. Paul's. Indomitable Sarah Belzoni! Writing of the
Turks, she set down in her journal, "Though I may be condemned
for my opinion, there is no religion would suit them so well as the
Protestant church of England." She called her husband "Mr. B.," and
accompanied him on his expeditions, never once losing her nerve
or her practical grasp of life. The gigantic pair now set about the
serious business of earning a living.

After exhibiting "Samson" through Portugal and Spain, the
Belzonis drifted to Malta, then a dependency of Egypt, and there
Belzoni attracted the friendly attention of the Mohammedan governor.
The adventurer's old interest in hydraulics was becoming practical;
he had devised certain irrigating machines intended for agricultural
use, and the governor advised him to go to Cairo and bring these
contrivances to the attention of Mehemet Ali, the quasi-independent
governor of Egypt.

It is the month of August in the year 1815; the heat in Egypt
is the heat of a dry oven; a little wind blows, but merely serves to
pour the heat upon the flesh. There is no sun in the cloudless sky,
only an inundation of tremendous light whose source is no more to be
looked at than a god. Circling higher and higher, vultures ride the
furnace of the air, eying the broad, low-lying plain, the winding
Nile, the shrunken marshes, the cornelian sands, and the broken
tops of the Memphian pyramids. At a landing in Cairo, three Europeans are disembarking from a Nile boat; they are Gianbattista and
Sarah Belzoni and James Curtain, their little Irish serving lad.

The monk whom destiny had turned into a bohemian was now
thirty-seven years old, and the many influences he had undergone
had molded an exceptional mind and character. On the one hand,
he was a strolling mountebank; on the other, an educated man with
churchly learning and a genuine respect for scholarship. He was an
Italian with an Italian's suppleness, ingenuity, and Latin sense of
making the best of what life affords; he was an Englishman as well,
with the English language on his lips, and ten years' experience of
life in the English way. He wrote English extraordinarily well; he
could draw passably, and from his years as a stroller he had gained
a knack of getting along with men of all conditions and kinds. A

stroller, a scholar, a Roman, an Englishman—was there ever such another Hercules? Through the streets of Cairo he rides, with a giant's aloof peaceableness and a giant's propriety.

He was weary now, it would seem, of Samson's roars and tuggings. He had accepted the cards which life had dealt him and done his best to play them well—what else was there to do? Here in this new land, the game should begin again, and the showman vanish into the vagrant engineer.

In the dark underworld of vanished deities, the animal-headed gods of Egypt, the cow Hathor, the cat Pasht, and the jackal Anubis stir in their ancient dreams, for the first of the awakeners of their civilization is setting foot beside the Nile.

Negotiations with Mehemet Ali and the building and the test of Belzoni's water-lifting wheel consumed the greater part of a year; it was wasted time, for the Pasha decided against the use of the device.

From the uncertainty which followed, the adventurer was rescued by his old friend, John Lewis Burckhardt, the traveler, who now persuaded the British consul general, Henry Salt, to send Belzoni on a special expedition up the Nile. A colossal head of "Memnon" (in reality a head of Ramses II) was lying in the sands at Thebes, and Salt wished to have it carried down the river and shipped off to the British Museum. Belzoni accepted the charge gladly, and going to Thebes, surmounted a thousand difficulties, and carried off the prize. It was anything but an easy task, for the giant head, or more properly the bust, measured some six by eight feet and weighed over seven tons. Belzoni handled it with homemade machinery. The engineer side of him was real; it is a quality often found just below the surface in Italians.

Mrs. Belzoni was with him, and shared with her "Mr. B." a hut built of stones in the portico of the Memnonium. All the long hot summer, the giant lady cooked her Titan's rice and mutton, and kept a practical eye on everything. The British matron was the terror of rival French explorers—"Madame Belzoni, *Amazone formidable*," they wrote in their accounts.

Other voyages followed which cannot here be set down in detail.

The first voyage saw the removal of the head and an exploring trip up the river to Abu Simbel and the cataracts. At Abu Simbel—it was "Ypsambul" to Belzoni—that greatest of rock temples was clogged with a vast fanslope of fallen stones and sand in which the colossi sat up to their necks. A second journey carried the explorer back to Thebes. The labyrinth of mountain tombs was still full of the ancient dead, some lying on the floors of their cave sepulchers, some standing, some on their heads—all surfaced with a very fine and choking dust.

Mrs. Belzoni having lingered in Cairo, the explorer now and then accepted the hospitality of natives dwelling in the outer tombs. "I was sure of a supper of milk served in a wooden bowl," he wrote, "but whenever they supposed I should stay all night they killed a couple of fowls for me which were baked in a small oven heated with pieces of mummy cases, and sometimes with the bones and rags of the mummies themselves." It is a far cry from the sun-helmeted professors, the great officials, and the electric lights of Tutankhamen's tomb.

On this second journey, the explorer began the clearing of Abu Simbel, and discovered the tomb of Seti I in the Valley of the Kings, still the most beautifully decorated sepulcher in Egypt. Old usage called it Belzoni's tomb; new days have forgotten the explorer. Then followed expeditions to Philæ, to the site of the Roman city of Berenike on the Red Sea, and a journey to the oasis of Elwah which Belzoni mistook for the historic oasis of Jupiter Ammon. The fever of exploration now descended on Mrs. B., and the intrepid lady, disguised as a man, went off by herself on a pilgrimage to Jerusalem—a feat of extraordinary fortitude and daring.

At the close of his second journey, Belzoni had cleared and opened Abu Simbel, discovered the tomb of Seti I, and explored Philæ, the Theban necropolis and the Valley of the Kings. He had shown himself venturesome, courageous, and resolute. He had a way of getting things done, not by shouts and the whip, but by a certain steadiness of pressure, as if he were putting his giant shoulders to a door and slowly forcing it inward from its frame. There are passages in his account of his work which seem to reveal a quality of suspicion in the giant's mind; he could see the hand of rival gatherers of antiquities in every check and delay. Twenty-five years ago the trait would have required a moral explanation; the wiser and more traveled present simply points to the thermometer.

By an ironic turn of the wheel of fate, it chanced that the rival collector to whom Belzoni attributed his vexations was himself an Italian. Bernardino Drouetti, agent of France and gatherer of antiquities for the Louvre, had been born in Leghorn. The competition between this Frenchman from Leghorn and this Briton from Padua had thus a certain raciness and emotional quality. Keen as it was, the amenities were outwardly preserved, and Drouetti even went so far as to present Belzoni with the "rights" to a sarcophagus it was impossible to extricate. At Philæ, however, the duel became a battle, for Drouetti's henchmen rushed Belzoni and his party as the giant was making off with an obelisk. If Drouetti's indignant lament is to be believed, Belzoni snatched a shrieking, jabbering "Arab" out of the mob swarming about him, swung him up by the ankles, and used him *à la Samson* on the heads and shoulders of his fellow countrymen. The novel weapon, it is said, won a headlong victory, and the giant carried off his obelisk in peace.

Returning to Cairo during the inundation, Belzoni paused by night at the pyramids. So vividly were the stars of the Egyptian sky mirrored in the flood, that there seemed to be two heavens, one above and below. Awesome, even a little terrible, the vast and ancient shapes of the pyramids rose seemingly from the starry water to the splendor overhead.

The pyramids. Mystery of ancient mystery! Belzoni resolved to match his knowledge and skill with this riddle of the years.

He went first to Gizeh, and wandered about the three pyramids, studying and observing.

From the sands of the Egyptian desert, which are carnelian in hue and strewn with colored pebbles much like fragments of ancient pottery, the pyramids rise as masses of old ivory stone suffused with a certain golden rust; the description is labored, but the effect is not to be given in a word. Belzoni, trudging the sand, watched the late afternoon light bring out the gray. The second great pyramid, the pyramid of Chephren, had taken his eye, and round it and about he went, now gazing up to the cap of reddish surfacing still in place about the peak, now pausing to study the huge confusion of sand and wreckage washed up about the base like a wave of shattered stone. Was there an opening, and if so, where? Or was the pyramid a solid hill of stone as the Egyptians had told Herodotus twenty-five hundred years before? The French scholars attached to Napoleon's expedition had sought an entrance in vain, and the Europeans resident in Cairo were meditating a scheme of collecting 20,000 pounds "at various European courts," and "forcing their way into the center of this pyramid by explosions."

"It seems little short of madness," wrote Belzoni, "to renew the enterprise." The giant had now grown a fine black beard and taken to wearing Eastern dress, huge white turban and all. It was the proper thing to do then when traveling in the East.

The entrance to the Great Pyramid being on the north, Belzoni studied with particular care the northern face of the second pyramid, and presently discovered there "three marks" which seemed to offer a clue. Just under the center of the north face of the pyramid, the bordering wave of debris was high, as if it might possibly lie piled atop some entrance way; the accumulation of stone at the mound seemed less compact than the mass to either side, and the debris had apparently gathered since the removal of the surfacing. There was the place, there would he begin.

Somewhat to his surprise, he got his permission to dig quite easily, the authorities merely insisting that he must not disturb "ploughed ground." The capital on which he hoped to accomplish his undertaking consisted of a scant two hundred pounds, some of it a gift from Burckhardt, some of it a profit from the sale of "antiquities."

Early in February 1818, the adventurer left Cairo quietly and took up his quarters in a tent by the second pyramid. Alone in his tent he sits, this huge bearded man who has lived so fantastic a life; it is night, and he smokes his long Turkish pipe, and watches the giant Egyptian moon cast the pointed shadow of his pyramid upon sands traced with the paths of naked feet. That monastery in Rome, the bells of other convents heard over the wall as one walked the garden in the cool of the afternoon, the rumble and galopade of a cardinal's coach over the stones—how far away and old it all is in that still splendor of the Egyptian night!

At the pyramid all begins well, eighty natives have been secured, and Belzoni has put forty to clearing the ground between the temple and the pyramid, and forty more to clearing the debris at the rise by the northern rim. The plates which accompany his text show the workmen to have worn the short, rolled white drawers and turbans of this earlier day, a costume far more picturesque than the long-skirted nightgown affair and red felt fez of modern Egypt. A nimble folk these brown Egyptians; they scramble about the pyramids today with the agility of boys in an easy tree; even so they must have scrambled and chattered for Belzoni. He paid them sixpence English a day, and hired boys and girls to carry away the earth.

The giant sagely explained to his corps that it would be to their advantage to find the entrance to the pyramid, for they would then have another marvel to show to visitors, and thus get more bakshish* than ever. The natives began with a will, but for several days their labors promised no indication of success. It was particularly difficult work. The fringe of wreckage had become solidly jammed, and the only tools to be had were spades meant for the cutting of soft ground. There were times when it seemed as if the workmen could scarcely proceed. At the end of a fortnight's digging, the party working on the ground between the temple and the pyramid had cut through some forty feet of rubbish to a broad pavement which seemed to encircle the pyramid; but the workmen at the north side had uncovered only deeper and deeper layers of debris.

After some sixteen days of this, the workmen began to weary of the task. "The Arabs," said Belzoni, "continued, but with less zeal. Still I observed that the stones on that spot were not so consolidated as those on the sides of them, and I determined to proceed till I should be persuaded that I was wrong in my conjecture."

On the morning of February 18 an overseer of the workmen came across the sand dunes with promising news. A workman of the

* Tip money.

northern party had perceived "a small chink" between two stones of the newly uncovered lower side of the pyramid. Belzoni returned with the messenger and found the workers gathered in a talkative group awaiting his coming. Yes, there was a small open slit between two of the great stones, into which the giant was able "to thrust a palm stick to the length of two yards." The workmen took heart; their night of foolish labor for this incomprehensible European infidel was seemingly ending in a dawn.

The loose stone, torn from its place, revealed a mystery—a passage some three feet wide choked with smaller stones and sand. Belzoni, in his turban and loose white Eastern dress, peered within, while his half-naked, dusky workers pushed and peeped and whispered behind that Titan back. Was the mystery of the ages about to be unveiled? Would they presently behold the legendary spirit of the pyramid—an old man with a censer? This attendant guardian was still to be seen at sundown, making the tour of his pyramid at about halfway up the sides—a solemn, priestly figure who swung his censer as he walked. Trickles of sand fell noiselessly from the roof of the opening; they heard the drop of little stones; about them the quiet of the desert seemed to have become intensified.

On being excavated, this passage proved to be wider within, and after five days of clearing, the excavators arrived at an open tunnel leading inward.

"Having made it wide enough," said Belzoni, "I took a candle in my hand, and looking in, perceived a spacious cavity . . . bending its course to the center. It is evidently a forced passage executed by a powerful hand, and appears intended to find a way to the center of the pyramid."

It was less a passage he had discovered than a wound. In ancient times some ruler of the land had attempted to force the pyramid, but the deed and the man had perished from the memory of the world, and the pyramid itself had hidden the deep wound within its side. To make the entrance, huge stones of the outer casing had been cut and sawed; then a ragged tunnel had been pierced directly into the heart of the masonry. The task had certainly taken toll of many lives. It was an awesome place, and exceedingly dangerous. Huge stones, which the piercing of the tunnel had left hanging by a thread, fell down, and every time that Belzoni crawled down its length of a hundred feet, he never knew but what a cry and a muffled crash might announce his living entombment in the dark of the edifice.

Europeans from Cairo now got wind of the giant's enterprise and came riding over the sands to see Belzoni at his task. The discovery of the forced passage seems to have impressed them as an interesting failure, an attitude which struck at the giant's dignity and pride. He paused to mull things over in his mind and gave the workmen a special holiday.

The false passage ended in a pocket of fallen stone. He would abandon his exploration of it, and continue his search for the real entrance.

Staff in hand, the huge figure now resumes its trudge about the pyramid. The workmen have gone, the wind over the desert lifts the dust out of the hollows of the dunes and brings no human sound; sand and ruin prevail. The adventurer wanders over the waste to the Great Pyramid.

It was then open, and somewhere in the hot, repellent heart of it, rank with the sour-foul odor of multitudes upon multitudes of bats, a typical European adventurer was working simply because the pyramids were his hobby. The name of this enthusiast was Caviglia, and he was the Italian master of a Mediterranean trading vessel flying the British flag. The good sailor had little education, and needed little, for his work was primarily a matter of removing rubbish and discovering what lay beneath. In later years Colonel Howard Vyse had dealings with him, and found him temperamental. Captain Caviglia, dear excitable Latin, rushed out of his pyramid one morning and hurled on the colonel's breakfast table a subsidy of forty pounds done up in an old sock. It appears that he considered the sum quite unworthy of his efforts. The colonel, however, was equal to the occasion, and after taking out the money, returned the sock with his "best compliments." Such was the dawn of archæology!

Belzoni returned from his visit to his neighbor and countryman with a new notion in his head. Prompted by certain indications, he had been digging away the rubbish gathered before the center of the northern face of the second pyramid, while the entrance into the Great Pyramid was not in line with the center of that edifice, for some thirty feet to the east of center, for the tomb chamber lay in the center, and the passage entered at the chamber's eastern end. He would abandon his excavation at the forced passage and begin again thirty feet to the east.

He went to the spot, and saw, or thought he saw, that the coating of rubbish was there not so thickly piled. Moreover, it appeared sunken as if an entrance below it might have fallen in. "This gave me no little delight," wrote the giant later, "and hope returned to cherish my pyramidical brains."

Again work began merrily, for the natives had grown to appreciate the giant's sixpence a day. But they thought their employer quite mad, and Belzoni heard them whispering it to each other. "*Magnoon*," they said as he passed, and again "*magnoon*,"—the madman! More days of sunlight and scurrying and digging of a tribe of black-brown fellahin. On February 28 a world of excitement and heart-quickening anticipation: something which looks like an entrance has been reached, for now appears a large granite stone set into the pyramid at the same angle as the passage into the Great Pyramid. The shovels flew that day. On the day following, they have uncovered three great blocks of granite, one on each side and one on top, all "lying in an inclined direction toward the center."

It was the entrance at last. By the second of March, the debris in front of the three stones having been cleared away, the long-sought opening was seen. It proved to be a passage, four feet high and three feet six inches wide, which descended at a steep incline into the pyramid. Its granite walls were undisturbed, but the passage itself was full of wreckage which had slid down the incline and piled up to form a barrier.

Provided with torches and candles, Belzoni and a few workmen now followed the passage for a hundred and four feet down into the dark. Whither was it leading them? The giant bulk of Belzoni nearly filled up the passage, as he came crouching almost double and holding a dripping candle light. Suddenly, to their great dismay, the passage came to a blind end at three solid granite walls.

Discouragement fell upon them as heavy as a pyramid. "At first sight," said Belzoni, "it seemed a fixed block of stone which stared me in the face and said *ne plus ultra,* putting an end to all my projects as I thought." Suddenly a discovery, a catch of the breath; the stone at the end of the passage is not fixed solidly in place; it is a portcullis which can be raised; the barrier stone is already eight inches above the true floor, and rests on surface rubbish. There followed a hurrying back and forth through the passage, a coming of workmen with levers, and a time of hard work in the tiny cubicle of the passageway. The portcullis stone was one foot three inches thick, and rose slowly because the low ceiling permitted only a little play of the levers. At the outer entrance the workmen had gathered in a chattering and excited crowd; they questioned those who came and went—what of wonders within, and how vast was the treasure?

When the aperture had grown wide enough for a man to pass through, a native squirmed under carrying a candle, and "returned saying that the place within was very fine." Belzoni, poor Titan, had to wait.

It had chanced that on the day before a fellow countryman of Belzoni's, the Chevalier Frediani, had come to visit Gizeh; he had proved a pleasant guest, and the giant had invited him to remain for the opening of the pyramid. This second Italian now joined the little group lifting the portcullis. It was now high enough for Belzoni to crawl under, and he did so, followed by the chevalier.

Over a thousand years, perhaps more, had passed since the tunnels into which they crawled had echoed to the sound of human voices. Belzoni led the way, carrying a light; Frediani, too, had a torch. The huge shadow of Belzoni followed along the walls; the granite twinkled in the first light of ten long centuries. At the end of the passage was an open pit which they descended along a rope, and at the depth of the pit were passages thick with dark and silence. Ghostlike arborizations of niter hung on these lower walls, some projecting in fantastic ropes. Belzoni went off on one trail, Frediani on another. Presently the giant arrived at the door of the chamber of the tomb.

"I walked slowly two or three paces, and then stood still to contemplate the place where I was. Whatever it might be, I certainly considered myself in the center of that pyramid which from time immemorial had been the subject of the obscure conjecture of many hundred travelers, ancient and modern. My torch, formed of a few wax candles, gave but a faint light."

He heard a sound of footsteps, and Frediani entered with his candles.

But the treasure of the pyramid? The sarcophagus of Khaf-ra, king of Egypt, was cut in the floor, the lid was awry, and the stone coffin "full of a great quantity of earth and stones." Who had violated it in the long course of history's four thousand years? No one knows. There is evidence that the caliph Al Mamun had forced the pyramid, but there is no evidence that he found the mummy in its place. There are old Arabic tales of kings encased in figures of gold, with magical golden snakes on their crowns which spread their hoods in anger, hissed, and struck at the intruders. All is legend and myth. The forced tunnel, however, had certainly once entered the original passages, but later on the violated masonry had fallen in and barred the way.

Europe of the Dark Ages had never known of the attempt; the East had forgotten. The musing mind sees Al Mamun at the pyramid, mounted on a nervous Arab horse which paws the ancient sand; his mounted attendants and bodyguard have reined up behind him— Arabs with thin dark faces fierce as desert hawks. Captives, Christians for the most part, are digging away at the side of the great mass— men of Byzantium, fair-haired Norman sailors blown on the African coast by a storm, little Spaniards from the mountain kingdoms which are so valiantly battling the Moors. And King Khaf-ra, whom the Greeks called Chephren, sleeps he within in "the dark house of the counting of the years"?

There were Arabic inscriptions on the walls, written with charcoal, but the characters were nearly imperceptible, and rubbed off into dust at the slightest touch. Belzoni thought he discerned an inscription which may be thus translated: "The Master Mohamed Ahmed has opened them, and the Master Othman attended this, and the King Ali Mohamed at first . . . to the closing up." Sir Richard Burton, however, perhaps the greatest of all Arabic scholars, will have it that the Arabic characters as Belzoni transcribed them are for the most part unintelligible. And there the matter rests.

The Belzonis spent two more years in Egypt, and returned to London in September 1819.

Oh, the Bight of Benin, the Bight of Benin
One comes out where three goes in.
        —*Old British Navy Song*

Green pleasant England again, the white cliffs of Dover, and the autumn fog drifting down on London and the ships. Belzoni's fame had gone before him to the capital. His popular title of "Signor," which both Italianized him and linked him with his mountebank past, now fell into disuse, and it was as "Mr." Belzoni that he faced a new life of dignity and prestige. Winter found the traveler and his Sarah living happily in London lodgings, visited and consulted by the learned and the great. Belzoni kept his head. With his usual common sense he was busily at work arranging an exhibition.

"Belzoni's Exhibition"—the words were magical a hundred years ago. All London came to the hall on Piccadilly when the doors opened in the spring of 1821. The old red-faced generals who had fought Napoleon came to stare at Pasht and Osiris, egad, the port-sipping gentlemen of substance, the fine ladies, and the sober citizens linking arms with their bonneted wives. To please them, Belzoni had reproduced two of the principal chambers in the tomb of Seti I— painting, sculptures, and all—and displayed "idols, coins, mummies, scarabœi, articles of dress and adornment, lachrymatories, and a splendid manuscript of papyrus." The tomb of Seti was "lit within by lamps," and made a tremendous impression. And there was a poem by Horace Smith, "Address to a Mummy in Belzoni's Exhibition" which all the world was reading. Now and then the giant moved towering through the throng, and mothers would bid their little flaxen-haired boys and girls to look at the man who had opened the pyramid.

A season in Paris followed the year in London, and then came the last great adventure.

The fever of exploring woke again within his veins, and he determined to cross the great African desert and make his way to the almost fabulous city of Timbuctoo. He would land in Morocco, go south through the Moroccan possessions, and then join a caravan bound for the fateful city. The plan seemed practical enough, and on an autumn morning in 1822, the roving Titan bade farewell to his faithful amazon, and followed his boxes and baggages aboard a vessel for Gibraltar.

In Fez, the Moroccan capital, they seem to have played with him for a while, for the emperor first gave him a permission to go through the country, and then withdrew consent. The failure may have been due to intrigue, as Belzoni imagined, or to the deep-rooted native distrust of Europeans; it was probably a combination of the two. Much chagrined, the explorer now returned to Gibraltar, and there determined on a course which did honor to his courage and perseverance. The way south to Timbuctoo being barred, he would make his way along the African coast to the city of Great Benin, and then struggle northward to his goal. It was a route to daunt any explorer, for it led into one of the darkest and most dangerous areas of unknown Africa.

Sailing in trading ships and little vessels of one sort or another, the adventurer slowly made his way south along the west African shore to the English station of Cape Castle on the Guinea coast. There Sir R. Mends, commanding the British naval squadron on the African west coast, befriended him and sent him to Benin in His Majesty's gunbrig *Swinger*. On October 20, 1823, the brig arrived off the bar of Benin River.

The brig *Providence* was lying off Obobi, and Belzoni boarded her at the invitation of her master, Captain John Hodgson. A month later, a "Fantee canoe" belonging to the ship is lowered overside; it contains Hodgson and Belzoni. The poor giant seemed "a little agitated," particularly when the crew, to each of whom he had made a present, gave him three loud cheers on his stepping out of his vessel. "God bless you, my fine fellows," cried the explorer, "and send you a happy sight of your country and friends." He was clad in his eastern dress and turban, and still wore his great black beard.

A few days later word comes to the sailors that the guest whom they had so cherished, loved, even, as a shipmate, is lying ill at Benin. Good Hodgson hurried inland, and found the giant dying of African dysentery in Benin city. In a palanquin they hurry him down the river to Gwato, hoping to get him to the coast and the sea air. But the end is at hand, an end calmly envisaged; the last of his strength he spends trying to write a letter to his wife; he entrusts Hodgson with a ring for her and a message full of the most touching affection, then yields the ghost. They buried him at Gwato under a great tree, and there he lies in the dark of Africa.

So ends the tale of the monk who passed from the peace of a monastery to an acrobat's stage in a village square. The young Italian had accepted his destiny calmly and made the best of it, yet never bowed his head. Thrust violently from the most retired of lives into the most bohemian, he had remained—*Belzoni*. There is something amusing, something rather fine as well, in the way that he sailed through life like a fine ship sent by the fates of the sea on dubious voyages. And what a sense of achievement and honest adventure he had won from it all; it had all been so well worth while.

History will remember him as the first of modern explorer-archæologists. "One of the most remarkable men in the whole history of Egyptology," says Mr. Howard Carter, who found the Tutankhamen tomb.

Belzoni the giant! What sounds run through his life—the snipping of a barber's shears, the ringing of convent bells, the talk and endless brooklike chatter of crowds at a fair, the songs of laborers along the Nile, the shuffle of camels in the sand, and the squeak and grind of levers raising the portcullis of Chephren's pyramid!

MAURICE DRUON

The Black Prince

ह़→

This comes from a book of short stories, but if you check the Encyclopaedia Britannica, *you'll find that it all really happened.*

He was small but splendidly compact, his legs were slender but well muscled, the feet delicate, the chest deep, the eyes of a velvet brown with long, black lashes, the nostrils short but well open, and there were nobility, pride and panache in his carriage. . . . In short, he had quality as a horse that most men lack as men.

She . . . But I'll tell you about her later.

The story opens in Paris in the spring of 1730, on the afternoon of Corpus Christi, in the Gobelins district.

By tradition, the famous tapestry makers held an exhibition on that day not only of their celebrated collection but of the products of the past year; the walls of the great courtyard were hung from top to bottom with the most sumptuous tapestries in the world. The exhibition was warmly recommended by *The Guide to Paris for Foreign Tourists,* though the author issued a warning: "I advise foreigners to be careful of their pockets, for owing to the great crowd one cannot tell next to whom one may be standing."

Mr. Coke, an English tourist, wearing a large wig and a little round hat, was returning from the exhibition. He was not particularly knowledgeable about tapestries; indeed, he knew a great deal more about race horses. His arms swinging and his stomach swelling under his waistcoat, Mr. Coke drifted with the crowd down the Rue Croulebarde which, lined with market-gardens, gave into the Faubourg Saint-Marcel. He gazed with appreciation at the pretty women in their striped dresses, which were still similar to those Monsieur Watteau, who had died only a few years before, used to paint. Neither the noise nor the crowd surprised him; his guidebook had warned him about them.

"One should take proper care in the streets of Paris. Besides the jostling crowd on foot, a great number of coaches and carts fills the streets till late at night and they frequently travel at a great pace. One should look carefully about one. In trying to avoid a foot passenger in front, one may well be jostled by another bearing down on one from behind, for it is impossible to hear anything due to the noise of the traffic."

And, indeed, Mr. Coke was not keeping his eyes sufficiently about him, for he was suddenly sent sprawling in the dust by a violent blow on the shoulder. A crowd immediately gathered round, but he got to his feet without much harm and saw the cart that had knocked him over. It was a heavy water cart. Its driver, an Auvergnat like most water sellers, jumped down and helped Mr. Coke dust off his clothes.

"I'm sorry, monsieur," said the water seller; "it's this brute of a horse. He gets the bit between his teeth and I can't hold him. One day he'll kill someone and get me jailed."

He pointed to the horse between the shafts of the water cart; it looked a wretched screw; it was filthily dirty and so thin its bones stood out. It was covered with galls; and the bit was too big and heavy for its mouth and was obviously hurting it.

"I made a bad bargain when I bought this damned brute," said the Auvergnat, raising his whip to relieve his anger.

But Mr. Coke caught him by the arm. He was looking at the horse, and the horse was looking at him.

To a man who knows and loves horses, the look in a horse's eye can be as expressive and revealing as that in a human's. And horses, too, can recognize a man who understands them. A horse chooses his master just as much as a man chooses his mount. The large dark eye, which looked at Mr. Coke with both pride and fear, was not that of a draft horse born to a servile condition.

"Let me have a look at that horse," said Mr. Coke. "Where does he come from? How did you buy him?"

The water seller recognized the tourist's accent and at once began to address him as "my lord."

"You can look at him as much as you like; he was a bad bargain. I bought him because he came from the king's stables, or so I was told. But what use he was to the king, since he can't even pull a water cart, I'm damned if I know."

"The king's stables?" said the Englishman, who had as much difficulty in understanding the Auvergnat's accent as the Auvergnat had in understanding him. "How very strange! I didn't know the king of France had Arab horses. What's this one called?"

"Sham! and it's no name for a Christian horse."

Mr. Coke bent down and felt the horse's dusty legs. Then, straightening up, he looked at the angle of the shoulder, the depth of the chest, and the set of the head.

"Will you sell him to me?"

"Sell him to you? On the spot, my lord!" cried the Auvergnat.

But he quickly had second thoughts. The horse had been a bad buy, of course; but he had paid a high price for him; and corn didn't cost nothing; besides, he'd have to find another, and prices were rising.

In the end, the Auvergnat mentioned a sum that seemed to him huge: seventy-five francs. Mr. Coke agreed to it without argument.

"What fools the English are!" the water seller thought that evening as he led Sham to the stables of the Hôtel d'Entragues, in the Rue de Tournon.

The grooms of this luxury hotel for rich foreigners turned up their noses at having to currycomb the thin, black nag that looked as if it had been sleeping on a manure heap for months.

The next day, Mr. Coke set about discovering Sham's history. The horse had already passed through several hands. Going from one owner to another, all small people who had used Sham in harness and had accidents with him, Mr. Coke eventually reached a groom at Versailles.

The Auvergnat had told the truth; Sham had indeed come from the royal stables. He had been part of a lot of eight Arab stallions sent as a present to Louis XV by the bey of Tunis, on the occasion of the signing of a commercial treaty two years before.

These small, strong horses, so difficult to ride if you did not know them, whose fine delicacy, far from being to the taste of the period, was considered a disadvantage, merely made the king shrug his shoulders. As it happened, he had never been able to find a horse to his liking; during the course of his life he had tried over two thousand of which none had apparently ever suited him.

Since the king had merely shrugged his shoulders, the Master of the Horse had followed suit, and so had his underlings. The Arab stallions had been relegated to a corner of the stables and eventually given as presents to members of the court, who had in turn disposed of them.

And so Sham, that desert prince, the descendant of an ancestor known as "Wings of the Wind," a present from a Mohammedan sovereign to King Louis, had ended up between the shafts of a water cart in the Rue Croulebarde.

At this time he was six years old. Though he had begun life in so high a position, had suffered so many vicissitudes and fallen so low, his true destiny was in fact only just beginning.

He had crossed the Mediterranean in a Barbary galley but he was to cross the Channel in a good round ship; he had known the sands of Africa and the cobbles of Paris but he was to tread the soft turf of England.

In London, Mr. Coke frequented St. James's Street Coffee House, which was the fashionable resort of gamblers and racing men. Its proprietor, Mr. Roger Williams, owned race horses himself.

Mr. Coke was rather embarrassed by his purchase. He had yielded to sudden impulse, to curiosity, and also perhaps to a desire to astonish. He had a good story to tell, but no idea what to do with the horse that had knocked him down. He sold Sham for twenty guineas to Mr. Roger Williams, who put the young stallion out to grass for some time.

The desert prince began to look like his real self. He filled out, and once again had a long flowing mane, a magnificent tail that fanned the ground, a big handsome croup, chiseled muscles and silky coat, which was of such an intense black that it looked almost blue in the sunlight.

Horse racing had already become very fashionable in England; indeed, had been so for some thirty years. The ideal horse at that time was still very similar to the medieval war horse; tall, heavy, strong enough to carry a great weight of armor, it made a noise like an avalanche when it galloped.

Mr. Williams of the St. James's Street Coffee House enjoyed a joke. "I'm going to run 'The Nigger,' " he said, for that was the name he had given Sham.

But Sham had a sense of humor too. Taken to the racecourse, he refused to start. Pressed a little too roughly with the spurs, he reared, bucked, threw his jockey, and shaking his long mane, galloped back to his stable.

Two or three more attempts were made, but in vain. The horse had no competitive spirit. In training, and when alone, he promised wonderfully well and moved over the grass gallops like a black arrow; but as soon as he was matched against those big competitors he seemed outraged and became a danger to anyone who went near him.

"A bad business," said Mr. Williams, as had said King Louis XV, the Master of the Horse, the Versailles grooms, the water-seller and Mr. Coke before him.

Mr. Williams was delighted to hand Sham over to one of his customers, Lord Godolphin, contenting himself with a small profit. The deal was made for twenty-five guineas.

To Lord Godolphin, formerly Keeper of the Privy Purse and Member of Parliament for Oxford, now a member of the House of Lords and son-in-law to the first Duke of Marlborough whose daughter, Lady Henrietta Churchill, he had married, twenty-five guineas was a mere trifle, as indeed were a hundred or a thousand when it was a question of a horse. This highly civilized man had two passions, chess and racing; the second was to ruin him. He kept a large racing stable in Cambridgeshire; Sham was merely an exotic fancy.

"I'll send The Nigger to Gog Magog," decided Lord Godolphin for it was on the Gog Magog hills that his stables stood.

It is in the nature of the female to have a taste for the strange and the unusual, to be attracted by the foreign. The arrival of this handsome Oriental created a certain stir among the mares at Gog Magog. Seeing his fillies raise their heads and spread their nostrils wide as Sham went by, Lord Godolphin gave orders that the horse should earn his corn as a teaser.

And for several months the horse, who was already known by the name of the Godolphin Arabian, that is Lord Godolphin's Arab, was employed in this way.

When nuptials had been decided on at Gog Magog, the desert prince was brought to the mare to flirt with her and put her in the mood for love. And when the mare, charmed by the little black horse, seemed sufficiently disposed, the master stallion, the king of the stud, the great Hobgoblin, was brought to her. Complacent, huge, important, strutting a little in his fat, he came forward to do his duty as a sire with the minimum of effort. And the Godolphin Arabian had to retire before this imposing grandee whose pleasure he had prepared for him.

So humiliating a retreat was intolerable to so lively a horse, whose blood was accustomed to conquest, and who had developed so great a sense of his own honor; but a rein, firmly held by Lord Godolphin's stable lads, forced him away to a respectful distance.

Things went on like this till the day, the most memorable in the whole history of racehorses, when a superb blonde, a golden chestnut, still very young but of opulent build, nervous and anxious at being taken to her first nuptials, appeared before the Godolphin Arabian. Her name was Roxana.

Though she came from the royal stud—Lord Godolphin had paid sixty guineas for her—it did not prevent her from immediately falling in love with the Oriental teaser. More intuitive no doubt than men, she had recognized royal blood in the Godolphin Arabian. And the desert prince from the very first moment showed a compelling and impetuous passion for the fair Roxana—a passion such as he had never shown before.

There began a quivering dance of love between the two horses, an exotic ballet of seduction such as only animals—bees flying through the sunlight to celebrate their union, dragonflies that gambol mirrored in water, birds parading their colors—know how to achieve.

At the very moment Roxana was tremblingly about to yield, the huge Hobgoblin was led up as usual. But the little black horse turned mad with rage and, rearing up, went for his rival, his hooves beating the air. The stable lads clung vainly to the rein; the Godolphin Arabian broke the leather and the battle began. The frightened lads dared not interfere, for it would have been at the risk of their lives.

The straw flew, the wooden partitions resounded to the drumming hooves, and a cloud of dust half concealed the fighting stallions. The great Hobgoblin was unaccustomed to such treatment and unprepared for such an attack. He reared up heavily; but he was too slow to meet the furious, whirlwind assault of his slender adversary.

With hooves and teeth the Godolphin Arabian killed the huge Hobgoblin within a few minutes.

The David of horses had destroyed the Goliath and, like David, he demanded the royal princess as his reward. No one dared stand in his way as he broke down the doors and galloped to freedom, taking with him the beautiful Roxana, whose love he had won forever by his victory. Their pounding hooves crashed across the yard as they fled together to the neighboring woods.

They were found that same night, happy and a little tired. They were quiet again now as they nuzzled each other, the fair Roxana's head against her conqueror's black chest.

The stable was far from proud of itself. How was Lord Godolphin to be told that his best stallion was dead and his most promising and valuable filly gone off to honeymoon in the woods with The Nigger?

But Lord Godolphin had not only a taste for the eccentric but a sense of honor too. The story of the fight delighted him and, in spite of the damage done, his Arab horse rose in his esteem.

"We shall just wait and see what this produces," he said.

And the product of this romantic mating was a horse called Lath, who was born in 1732 and, from his first appearance on a racecourse, carried all before him. Such speed and stamina had never been seen before. His heavy competitors struggled along twenty lengths behind him. The love-child was invincible. And with him that race of horses so oddly called "English Thoroughbred" was born.

The Godolphin Arabian was relieved of his role of teaser. Everyone feared he might commit another murder. And Roxana, for her part, refused any other mate; she would belong to the Godolphin Arabian alone.

The two horses seemed unhappy when they were apart; they turned sad and nervous and went off their feed. They had to be put in neighboring boxes, and since Roxana became restive at any other stallion's approach, a second mating was decided on. Roxana was undoubtedly the mate of a single horse.

They had but few children, since the splendid chestnut mare died, alas, ten days after producing her second foal, in 1734. But they had many grandchildren.

Their second son, Cade, was brought up on cow's milk after his mother's death and became the sire of the celebrated Matchem, who won eleven races out of thirteen; and their descendants, crossed with the progeny of two other Arab stallions, the Byerley Turk and the Darley Arabian—called after the names of their respective owners, Captain Byerley and Mr. Darley of Aldby Park—are the ancestors of all the horses who have been racing all over the world since that time.

After Roxana's death, the Godolphin Arabian had still nearly twenty years to live. He was a widower, not inconsolable perhaps, but melancholy. He had several wives, and each time was born a horse famous either because of its own triumphs or because of its line, such as Regulus, such as Siletta, his granddaughter, the dam of Flying Childers, who was unbeaten eighteen times, and of the famous Eclipse, who were the two prodigious horses of the eighteenth century.

The Godolphin Arabian, the Gog Magog stallion, had become famous throughout England. His master gave him a Moorish groom who had no other duty but to see to him. Nevertheless, the stallion was of a solitary disposition. He seemed to take no pleasure in any companion other than a little tabby cat, called Grimalkin, who lived in his box, slept between his legs, and, during the day, purred upon his back.

When the Godolphin Arabian began to grow old, he was taken to the course on racing days, splendidly harnessed in the Oriental manner and with his Moorish groom, wearing a turban, on his back, so that he might witness the triumphs of his descendants, though he had never raced himself. The horse that had cost only seventy-five francs had already won, through his descendants, tens of thousands of pounds. The punters saluted him; the children surrounded and acclaimed him. Tossing his fine little head and long mane, he pawed the ground and whisked his tail, pretending to impatience while allowing himself to be admired like an old king.

When he died, at over twenty-nine, an exceptional age for a horse, he was buried in the stables of Gog Magog, in the passage between the boxes, at the very place from which he had fled to the woods with the blonde Roxana.

On his tombstone his name was graven and chains were placed round it. Both the Moorish groom and the cat Grimalkin died in the following month.

Two centuries have gone by. There are no longer horses at Gog Magog, which now belongs to the Cambridge Preservation Society. Only an old, white-haired groom, the caretaker of the premises, still remembers the days when the stud farm resounded to the neighing of horses. From time to time he sweeps the Godolphin Arabian's tomb.

The arched doorway is still there by which the two frenzied lovers fled. I have walked in the wood that was the scene of their love.

A striped ginger cat with gold eyes lives in the stables, haunts the box in which the Godolphin Arabian lived, and walks delicately over the graven stone.

The Godolphin Arabian has had his biographers, his painters, and his legend. George Stubbs, the great animal painter, painted his portrait; Rosa Bonheur, in a picture called *The Duel,* painted his fight with Hobgoblin; Eugène Sue, socialist, racing man, and one of the founders, with My Lord l'Arsouille, of the Jockey Club in Paris, made him the hero of a novel. And, finally, the supreme honor, a page of the *Encyclopaedia Britannica* is devoted to the little desert prince and his descendants.

On every racecourse in the world, amid thronging crowds, run horses that are the objects of both pride and passion, on which thousands of pounds are staked and whose victories are headlined on the front pages of the newspapers; and there is not one horse among them that does not possess in his veins at least a drop of the blood of Godolphin Arabian, of that king's horse who dragged a water cart, of that humiliated lover who triumphed, and whom fate destined to be born on the shores of Carthage only to die at last on the hills near Cambridge.

DOROTHY CANFIELD FISHER

The Bradlock Chest

ॐ

Dorothy Canfield Fisher was known as the First Lady of Vermont. Here's one of her finest studies of the Vermont character.

In horse-and-buggy days, Gardner Hollow had been a favorite drive for summer people. They liked to picnic in the Peck sheep pasture, draped like a green velvet scarf over the shoulder of the mountain. But the steep road is too narrow for automobiles to pass safely and it is corrugated with the bumpy thank-you-ma'ams that knock the stuffing out of low-hung modern cars. Since the coming of automobiles to the world, people in Gardner Hollow had been left to themselves. You didn't see them hanging any crape on their well-painted front doors about this, either.

But of course accidents will happen. One did happen to Mrs. W. Atkins-Smythe, or rather to a guest of hers. The two middle-aged Garden Club ladies had been told there were wild azaleas in the Woodward lot above Ashford. They had gone exploring, scrambling up the rocky, water-worn path, had taken the wrong turning, and after some wanderings had come out on the wrong slope of the mountain. By that time, the other lady had turned her ankle and they were in a hurry to get home. Coming straight downhill, across what had been the Peck sheep pasture, they found themselves at the top of the Gardner Hollow Road. And when you were there, you were in Miss Philinda Peck's back yard. Living on nothing a year as old Miss Philinda did, she had no telephone, so Mrs. Atkins-Smythe (most local people called her Mrs. Smith) left her friend there in Miss Philinda's sitting room, her ankle soaking in a hospitable pail of hot water, while she hurried on down to the Merritts' at the lower end of the Hollow.

After she had telephoned to her chauffeur to come for them, she found that although her ankles were all right, the rest of her stoutish person was extremely tired. She decided to wait for the car where she was instead of plodding back on foot uphill all the way to Miss Peck's house. She did not know the Merritts but they knew her. Some ten years before, a niece of theirs, now a teacher in a New York City school, had earned her way through normal college by waiting on the Atkins-Smythes' table, summers. If the Merritts had cared to, they could have told the lady a thing or two about what went on in her house that would have surprised her a good deal. But they also knew that she paid bills promptly, gave fair wages, and that her treatment of her help was approximately civilized. Their sympathies were called forth by seeing how used-up and all-gone she looked, poor old thing (after a little walk they, any of them, could have done easily in half an hour). So they made her a cup of hot tea and put some raisin cookies on the saucer.

While she ate, Gramma Merritt, too old to work, sat down in a rocking chair to keep her company. She was too old to work but not at all too old to talk. Long before the Atkins-Smythe automobile came boiling up the hill, rebounding from the water bars, Mrs. Atkins-Smythe had heard the life history of most of the five Gardner Hollow families; indeed had heard some of them, like the story of Miss Philinda's lost savings, twice.

She thanked her hosts, did not offer to pay them (she was really a nice person if she did hyphenate her name), was hoisted up into the car by her chauffeur, and drove on to the Peck house. Miss Philinda was out back, leaning on her crutch and feeding the hens; the lady with the ankle was indoors, still steeping one foot in a steaming pail. The moment Mrs. Atkins-Smythe appeared, she pointed with vehemence to a large dark boxlike piece of furniture between the front windows. Drawing Mrs. Atkins-Smythe down, she whispered sibilantly to her, "See that? It's a *Bradlock chest*. Came straight down in her family. She's been telling me about it."

Mrs. Atkins-Smythe did not know much about old furniture, but she knew enough to know what a Bradlock chest is, although she had never seen one before, except in illustrations of books on antique furniture. She looked, she saw, she gave a little cry of astonishment. And then because through Gramma Merritt's chatter, she had just learned how desperate was old Miss Philinda's economic situation, she gave a second cry of excited pleasure. "Don't they sell for really a great deal of money?" she asked eagerly, running her fingers over the incised carving on the front of the old chest. To which her friend answered with assurance, "That's worth a thousand dollars if it's worth a penny."

In the meager, scrubbed poverty of that room the naming of such a sum was like the silent bursting of an invisible bomb. From it rose thick cloudlike swirls of richness, fragrant and familiar as incense-smoke in the nostrils of the two well-to-do ladies.

They were genuinely kind, especially the excellent Mrs. Atkins-Smythe. Her first thought, her first words, were of joy for the owner of the Bradlock chest, and of solicitude for her protection. "Oh, we must tell Miss Peck! It will mean *every*thing to her, just now, when she needs money so terribly. I've just been hearing about her. The bank she had her savings in—enough to pay her entrance to that nice old ladies' home in Ashford—went broke. She has *nothing,* they tell me, but what she gets off this run-down place. At seventy-six! And lame! Why, this will absolutely *save* her! If we hadn't chanced to come along, some sharper might have bought it from her for a song. You know what antique dealers are like!"

So they did tell her. They enjoyed, as though it were something good to eat, the chance to give a total surprise which, unlike most surprises, had nothing in it but joy.

All the way home they talked to each other about how the old woman took it, how for a moment she forgot her decorous traditions of self-control, flushed, paled, cried a little, had to sit down.

"Will you ever forget how she stroked the top of the chest! Her hand was trembling with joy. And no wonder. How much does it cost to get into the old ladies' home? Not so much as a thousand dollars, does it? Not more than seven hundred, seems to me. Well, she's safe then. Isn't it like a fairy story? How does your ankle feel, now?" They told and retold the fairy story at the dinner table that evening, and, till everybody in their circle had heard it, at all the dinner tables of the next few days. They could soon round it out with news that, sure enough, when they inquired how much entrance to the old ladies' home cost for somebody of Miss Philinda's age, it was only seven hundred dollars.

They were not the only ones to talk about it. Before she could sleep that night, Miss Philinda had hobbled down the road, stopping at the house of each neighbor. "A thousand dollars! Not a cent less, those ladies said. I wish Grandfather was here. He set such store by that chest—used to keep it so nice. He oiled it all over every spring, the way his grandfather showed him how to. He was born in 1791, Grandfather was, the year Vermont voted to join the United States.

It was his grandfather that bought it when he was to be married—in 1740 long before any settlers come up into Vermont at all. Grandfather used to show me where they broke one leg off, getting it all the way from Connecticut up here on an ox cart. His father mended it with an old piece of wood he got from an Indian. They didn't have any seasoned lumber at first, when white folks first settled up here. But he was bound he wouldn't mend it with green wood that'd warp. He always said 'twas an old Indian war club he used. But we never said too much about that. Great-grandfather had a good deal of Elmsworth in him, and the Elmsworths would say anything to make a good story. But anyhow that mended leg is as straight as the others, always has been. A thousand dollars! My! I do wish Mother could know. She wanted to trade it off once when I was a little girl, for a new sideboard, but I told her Grandfather had given it to me and she couldn't have it. I thought a great deal of my grandfather. I think about him every time I dust the chest. Well, I must be going on, I want to tell the Kents."

Her bubble had been quickly blown; as quickly did it burst. A fine long low-hung car made a foolhardy attempt to get up the road, dented a hub cap on a rock at the hairpin turn, lost traction on the greasy clay of the steepest slope, slid back, and let out its passengers to walk. There were two of them, both portly middle-aged men. But one was portly and ordinary, and the other wore spats and carried a cane. At the first house, they stopped to ask where Miss Philinda Peck lived. Instantly everybody knew who they were and what they wanted. A boy was dispatched the shortcut path through the sugar bush to Miss Philinda's to give her time to wash her hands and put on a clean apron. She was, they all knew, canning raspberries.

Presently the men went back. They trod heavily down the steep hill, silent, each with a cigar. Nothing was to be learned, not from the sharpest stare at their impassive faces.

But the boy soon came running in and he brought news enough, in all conscience. "They took it out on the front porch to git a good light on it. Miss Philinda went back into the kitchen and went right on pickin' over raspberries. No, I didn't hear what they said. She wouldn't let me hang around front and listen. Said 'twouldn't be manners. So, first thing we knew, we heard 'em luggin' it back into the settin' room. Then the common-looking one come to the door of the kitchen, and says, 'I'm sorry to have to inform you, madam, that your chest is a modern imitation, not more than twenty-five years old, and of no value.' And then he turned around and walked away."

"For heaven's *sakes!*" cried his audience in a unanimous passion of astonishment. When his mother had her breath back enough to speak, she cried, "What *did* Miss Philinda say?"

"Well, she didn't say anything for a minute. She looked as though you could ha' knocked her over with a feather. Then she got her breath and rose right up, raspberries and all, and said, 'What are you talkin' about! That belonged to my *grandfather,* and he was born in . . .' But the man was out front by that time. She run out to the front porch and saw 'em startin' down the hill and hollered, 'Wait a minute! Wait a minute! There's some mistake.' They stopped and turned around, and she told 'em, 'That chest can't be a new one. It belonged to my *grand*father, and he got it from his—' She was so flustered she didn't hardly know what she was sayin' and she broke out laughing at the idea it wa'n't more than twenty-five years old. 'Mercy to goodness, *I've* put things away in it for seventy years myself,' she told 'em."

"What did they say to that?"

"Oh, they just looked at each other kinda queer, and the one with the cane took off his hat, 'It's always very painful, madam,' he says, 'to make a discovery of this kind, as painful to the specialist who makes it as to the owner of the piece.' He talked book-talk like that. And he told her he had expected to buy it for the Westfield Museum, and that the other fellow knew all about old furniture, and could tell absolutely for sure when something was an imitation. And Miss Philinda cut in, 'But how *could* that chest be an imitation? I'm seventy-six years old and I've—' The other one said, you could see he was trying to let her down easy, 'Sometimes, madam, it is found that during an absence of the owner, a fine original has been taken away and a modern imitation put in its place, unknown to the—'"

The boy's mother interrupted him here, "Goodness gracious, what an idea! Miss Philinda hasn't been away from home in—"

"Yes," said the boy. "She told 'em that. They just shook their heads and sort of spread their hands out and went on along down the hill. I lit out the back way. I thought likely Miss Philinda wouldn't want anybody around."

A foaming spate of talk poured along the Gardner Hill Road, that afternoon. It was followed early the next morning by Miss Philinda herself, hobbling slowly but steadily past.

"No, thank you," she told them with dignity, "I can't stop. I've got to git to Moffat Corner by nine. To catch the bus. I got business to do in Ashford." Not another word out of her. She looked, so they all said compassionately, simply terrible, almost like a person that had "had a shock."

Well, of course, she had had a shock. What could be at the bottom of this funny business about that old chest of hers? Could it really be an imitation?

"Haven't you always seen it there, Mother, in her settin' room?"

"Well, yes, seems as though I had. I can't say I ever took any special notice of it. But *seems* as though I always had."

"Could you swear in a courtroom that it had been there every single time you went to the house?"

"Well, no. How could anybody be as sure as that?"

"But of course, to say that it was only twenty-five years old was ridiculous! There wasn't a stick of furniture in *any*body's house as new as that."

"Nobody needn't try to tell me she sold the old one and got her a new one. She couldn't have. And if she had, we'd all know about that!" After a pause, more cautiously, "*Seems* as though we would, anyhow."

The two kind-hearted ladies were talking about it in Ashford, too, shaking their heads sadly, grieved and disillusioned about all nice-looking countrywomen. How innocent she had looked! How surprising the whole thing was. How ever could she have gotten hold of such a good imitation, back there in the woods?

They put this question to Mr. Hillyard, the expert, who was staying on in Ashford a day longer to look around. He smiled kindly at their simplicity and explained that people who did not know the ins and outs of the antique-furniture business simply could not imagine the double-dyed tricks that were played in it. "There are all sorts of dodges. This is one we have all encountered. Probably someone who knew values stopped in there some five or ten years ago, by accident, as you did, saw the chest, told her he'd give her a nice new chest that looked like the old one and some money to boot. When you came in and said so much about it, she thought she could repeat that deal. You say she needs money just now for something special."

So that was the way of it! Human nature was certainly a deep, dark well, mostly filled with iniquity, thought the two kind-hearted ladies.

They were somewhat shaken in this conviction that afternoon when the owner of the chest rang the Smythe bell. Her eyes were burning as though she had not slept the night before, her face was ash-gray as though she had not eaten anything that day. They tried to make her come in to rest and for a cup of tea, but no, she would not so much as put a foot over their threshold. All she wanted of them was to tell her where that man lived that had come to look at her chest yesterday. "He said my grandfather's chest is an imitation! A new one. *He's got to take that back!*"

But when she found him, taking tea with his wealthy patron, it was not so easy. Not that he was rough with her. No, he was very polite. He was not at all surprised by her excitement. He resigned himself to listen with patience—well, with an imitation of patience, at least—while she told him the old stories about the chest, explained how this and that old mark came to be on it, while she brought out from her handbag a sheaf of yellowed letters dated more than a century ago, with mentions here and there of "Grandfather's Bradlock chest." When she stopped for breath, he pointed out to her delicately —reluctantly as it were—that she could bring no proof that those stories and letters referred to the particular piece of furniture he had seen in her living room, which was, much as he regretted to repeat it, simply a very modern imitation.

She started back as though she had stepped on a snake; she drew herself up to a height she had not had for fifty years, she looked piercingly into his eyes. "Are you trying to say that I'm not telling the *truth?*" she asked in a low, fierce tone. She turned around to look for the door. "Have I lived long enough," she asked herself with horror, "to have a *York* state man call me a liar?"

It was really a very uncomfortable profession, his was, Mr. Hillyard told Mrs. Atkins-Smythe. "I don't know why it should be so, but nothing makes people more furious than to be found out in a deception about the age of a piece of furniture. Well, of course there often is a large sum of money involved. As in this case."

"Isn't there any possibility that somehow she herself may not have known—she does seem so hurt and surprised!"

"Oh, they always act that way," said the experienced Mr. Hillyard. He added, "I tell you what we sometimes do to save people's faces. When they insist, we tell them probably sometime when the article was sent to be repaired, the repairer substituted some modern parts—perhaps all modern parts, before sending it home. That really has been known to happen. Men who repair antiques know their market value of course, usually better than the owners do. With the original right there as a model, it is possible to manufacture an imitation so good that the unsuspicious owner does not notice it. I won't say this is a frequent occurrence. As a matter of fact, I personally have never known it to happen. But it's a convenient formula to smooth down excited owners."

"Oh, *that's* what I'll tell her," cried Mrs. Atkins-Smythe. "If I ever see her again, that is."

She did see her the very next day and did tell her. She was cutting roses in her garden when Miss Philinda, who never left Gardner Hollow except to attend funerals, came hobbling up the front walk. "Do you know where a lawyer lives?" she asked. "I got to see a lawyer."

"Well, my husband is a lawyer," admitted Mrs. Atkins-Smythe, her eyes going to a massive bald gentleman in golf clothes practicing putting at the other end of the lawn. At that moment she was called into the house to a telephone call, and by the time she came out, the old woman had told Mr. Smythe her long story, and he, who of course knew it already, was saying warmly, "Well, it's a darned shame. If there was a single thing a lawyer could do about it, I'd be glad to. But there isn't."

"Oh, I could get proof!" cried Miss Philinda. "I could get any amount of proof. Everybody up there knows all about—"

Now was the time for Mrs. Atkins-Smythe to bring out the antique-expert's face-saving formula. So she did. Old Miss Philinda listened attentively. At the end, she laughed—not mirthfully—and said, "The person that made that up did pretty good. The only trouble with his idea is that the chest never *was* sent out to be repaired. Never! It's never been out of the house I live in. And my father before me. And his father before him." She pulled her shawl straight, and said, "Well, I won't need to bother you any more till I git some proofs," nodded, and hitched herself away.

"Good gosh, dear!" said Mr. Atkins-Smythe, wiping his bald head. "I wish you'd kept out of Gardner Hollow."

Mrs. Atkins-Smythe mourned over that as heartily as he. "To think I had to go out of my way to bring temptation to the poor old thing!"

"No, no, her home isn't worth mortgaging. It was to get into the old ladies' home, here. She had saved enough, had it in the bank, wouldn't touch it for anything in the world—and then the bank broke. You can't blame her for jumping at a chance to make up for that. Anybody would.

"My guess is that she believes her own story. If she were a witness in the stand, I'd have a hunch that she wasn't consciously making anything up. Maybe the sideboard *is* old. Maybe whatever-his-name-is, the expert, maybe he made a mistake. People do."

His distressed wife clutched at this. "Oh, *do* you think he might have?"

"I don't say I think it. I don't know anything about antiques! It's no more than a tulip craze anyhow. No sense to it! I just say it's possible that he was wrong. But how could you prove it? What evidence could be brought to *prove* that the old lady never sold the old chest and put an imitation in its place? There's no evidence that can prove a negative like that. Looks to me as though the age of an antique and a woman's reputation were in the same boat. One accusation against them turns the trick. There's no way of *proving,* you know, where a woman's been, every half hour of her life, once somebody tells a nasty story about her."

He had a professional interest in the nature of evidence, and how far it can go, and was for a while rather interested in the incident, speaking of it at dinner once or twice to a legal colleague. But before his vacation was over, his interest had become exasperation. It seemed to him he and his wife could not drive anywhere without seeing a feeble old figure hobbling through the summer dust. What could they do but offer her lifts. And she always accepted lifts with exhausted gratitude. "I'm on my way to Stony Brook Hollow," she would explain. "My mother had a first cousin lived there. I want to see what she remembers about the chest." Or, "One of the Merritts told me an old man over Winchester-way used to work for Father years ago, before I was born, and remembered something Father told him about the carving on the front of the drawer." She was writing it all down, she told them, in a book, which she carried with her in a green bag with a drawstring. Every time they saw her she was whiter, thinner, more stooped. Mr. Smythe always meant—when he was away from her—to keep on explaining the point to her, till he had pounded it into her head. "It'll do you no good to get a *million* witnesses, can't you see that, if you can't prove they're talking about the same chest that stands in your house." But when she sat, pale and spent, beside him in the car he could never bring himself to say this.

Instead, "See here," he said to his wife, one time after they had let her out and watched her begin feebly to trudge up a steep hill, "how much was it she needed? Seven hundred dollars? Oh, let's get up a benefit or a collection or something, and give it to her. She'll drop dead on the road some of these days."

They meant to. They really did mean to. But seven hundred dollars is a lot of money, all their friends had lost a good deal recently, they said. They had too. Like many well-to-do people, they were really very hard up. The project never got beyond words. Like most plans for good works which do not get beyond words, it stuck heavily in the crop of the people who had spoken the words. They were sensible people, and they kept telling each other that it was absolutely no responsibility of theirs; but they were decent people and they went on feeling that it was. And when, just before they were to start back to the city after the vacation that had been so clouded by this affair, they found Miss Philinda unconscious, lying beside a back road, her skeleton hands clutching at her green bag, they stopped trying to be sensible and became helplessly and wholly decent. "Something's got to be *done*," said Mr. Smythe resolutely after they had revived her and taken her home.

He was an experienced man, and well knew which springs of action can be counted on to stir a modern brain into creative thought. "Suppose she were rich," he put the hypothetical case to himself, "suppose a really rich woman from whom I could expect a big fee had consulted me about this. What would I have advised her to do?" When the question was put in that way, it answered itself. He would have advised her to call in another expert on antique furniture. A brilliant idea. But returning to reality from his hypothesis, he perceived that an expert would ask a large fee, and that his client was as a matter of hard fact not rich. The idea was not so brilliant.

But Mrs. Atkins-Smythe, her kind heart plowed and harrowed by the misery she had unwittingly caused, cried out that she herself would pay an expert for coming. "Give me that instead of a Christmas present! It'd be such a relief to *know*. If *he* said it was an imitation, then we could stop being sorry for her. And, oh, think what it would mean if he said it really *is* genuine and she could get into the *home!*" After a moment's thought she went on, "And I know who we can get. Anita Frank's son-in-law has a brother who's the old-American expert for the Elliott Cary Museum. He'd know. And I don't care *what* it costs to have him come. I'll take him as my Christmas present from you."

When they told Miss Philinda about this plan they looked at her very hard to see if she feared another exposure from an expert. There was nothing in her face except a relief as great as their own. And gratitude! She too had been plowed to the depths. For a moment she quite lost the bearings by which she usually steered a straight course between self-control and self-expression. Self-control went overboard. "I can't ever thank you enough!" she said, blowing her nose and choking. "I never heard of anybody that was so good to anybody."

They were rather abashed by her thanks, and rather alarmed by her relief. She took it so for granted that the verdict would be in her favor. Suppose it wasn't! By the time the expert had arrived in Ashford, Mrs. Atkins-Smythe had worked herself up to a state of panic at the thought of how awful that would be! When the car was brought around to take the expedition to Gardner Hollow Hill she cravenly stayed in her bedroom and sent her protesting husband up with the expert. "I can't," she told him, wringing her hands. "I'd simply *expire* if I had to be the one to tell her that she's got to give up hoping to get into the home."

So the two men, leaving their car at the bottom, walked up the long hill by themselves, unaware that they were observed from every window, and naïvely surprised when they reached the Peck house, to see that Miss Philinda, standing on the porch, a clean white apron over her full skirts, evidently expected them. Mr. Atkins-Smythe did not wring his hands, but he felt very ill at ease as he bade her good day. "This is going to be damned uncomfortable," he thought, "looking the thing over with her standing right there." But Miss Philinda knew better than that. "I'm sorry," she said, after taking them in to her sitting room, "but I've got to go git some clothes in off my line. So if you'll just excuse me—" She melted away.

"They haven't any what you could call manners, at all, these plain old mountain-farm people," thought Mr. Smythe, "but I wish I could be sure I had as good breeding as theirs."

He had thought his wife slightly silly for getting so wrought up about this little matter, but when the expert, after a few minutes' examination of the chest, tapped it lightly, and said, "It's quite genuine. A remarkably fine specimen. What made you think it wasn't?" Mr. Smythe found that for a moment he could not speak. He swallowed, wiped his forehead, drew on his cigar and waited before he said, "Well, I'm glad to hear it."

His second emotion was wrath. He thought of his spoiled vacation, his wife's distress, Miss Philinda's misery. "What in hell would make anybody say it wasn't?" he cried, and told the story with indignation.

The expert was not so indignant as all that. "Oh, anybody's likely to make a mistake, once in a while. The color may have thrown him off. You don't often see genuine ones of that color. I should say this had been oiled pretty steadily. And that mended leg probably made him think it had been sent away for repairs. Though any modern repairer that wanted to put over a trick on an owner would have taken more pains than that, of course, to make it match the other. See, it's not even the same wood. The chest is oak and that leg is yellow birch. It looks to me as though your man just gave a snap judgment. Well, he wouldn't have been the first one to do that."

"For God's sake!" said Mr. Smythe. "When he knew that the comfort of a poor old woman's last years depended on it, wouldn't you have thought he'd take the trouble to make sure?"

"Did you never hear of human nature?" asked the expert. "He had passed judgment on it in the hearing of a wealthy patron. He naturally wouldn't want to go back on that, would he?" He added, "Of course there *is* the possibility that he wasn't any too straight himself. Maybe he wanted to get it labeled an imitation and then, in a year or so, send somebody around to buy it for him, cheap."

Mr. Smythe was no novice in the ways of the world. He was a lawyer of many years' standing and had had ample opportunity to observe the uncountable variety of devices to make money crookedly. But this was a new one. He took the cigar out of his mouth again and stared. "D'you really mean that's ever done?" he exclaimed, shocked.

"There's nothing that isn't done in the antique furniture business," replied the other, philosophically.

Mr. Atkins-Smythe now realized with compunction that Miss Philinda herself did not yet know the good news. But before he called her in, he asked anxiously, "Look here, it *is* worth a good deal, isn't it? I don't want any more mistakes made about it. She's absolutely got to have seven hundred, my wife tells me."

"Oh, I'll pay twelve hundred for it, this minute," said the other, taking out his checkbook. "If the museum doesn't want it, I'll make money reselling it."

Light-footed and lighthearted as a boy, the stout Mr. Atkins-Smythe ran to the door. "Miss Philinda, do come in," he called.

His radiant face told her the verdict before his words. For a second time, an Atkins-Smythe had the privilege of exploding a joy-bomb in that room. For a second time the withered old face flushed deeply, paled, its composure all broken. Her knees and her hands shook so that he guided her to a chair. Her trembling lips framed over and over the whispered words, "I'm so *glad!* I'm so *glad.*"

He gave her a glass of water. After she had taken a drink from it, she was able to say, "I just can't thank you enough!"

He had not been so happy in years. He put his hand on her bony shoulder, with a gesture of tender gratitude for her having given him such a moment. He drank up what was left of the water in the glass, set it down with a triumphant bang, and said exultantly, "As a matter of fact, it'll bring you *more* than my wife's friend told you. This gentleman will give you twelve hundred dollars for it this minute. Like that!" He snapped his fingers festively.

The bony old shoulder under his hand stiffened. Miss Philinda sat up in her chair. She shook his hand off. She hauled herself to her feet. She was no longer trembling. With intense seeking seriousness, she looked at her benefactor and from him to the other visitor, his checkbook in his hand. Her face set hard. She looked back at Mr. Smythe, her eyes blazing. In a voice that brought the gooseflesh out on him, she asked, "Didn't you know I had been called a liar?"

She took a step toward him, gazing as if to look more deeply into the recesses of his heart, and horrified him beyond measure by suddenly thrusting her face close to his with an ugly gesture, shouting, "Did you think all this time that what I was after was just to get more *money?*"

She had horrified herself as well as her visitor. She drew back, ashamed. There was a moment of intimidating silence while she confronted a situation far beyond her powers to cope with. What could she do? She had never ordered anyone out of her house in all her life. What phrases, what actions were possible for her to use with self-respect? For she must not forget her manners again. Once was bad enough! No matter what the provocation, it would be beneath her to let it happen twice.

It came to her—what she could do.

Addressing the universe at large, she hobbled to the front door and threw it open. "I make a mistake," she said seriously, with the accent of one admitting a regretted error. "I make a great mistake ever to let a York state person into my house at all. And I guess I better not from now on."

The men moved silently toward the door.

"I don't say it's their fault," she conceded to the air over their heads. "I don't say but what it's mine. I always heard that I was born dumb, and I s'pose I git dumber as I git older." The men passed through the door. She reached for the latch and, her eyes fixed earnestly on the maple tree across the road, explained, "I know they *mean* all right, York state folks do—" The door was all but closed. "But somehow I just don't know how to git *along* with 'em," she concluded, and dropped the latch into place.

JEROME and BARBARA FRANK

The Case of Clifford D. Shephard

ह�

The late Judge Jerome Frank and his daughter Barbara collected a whole bookful of miscarriages of justice. This one struck me as the most outrageous of them all.

Until April 1935, forty-nine-year-old Clifford Shephard commuted daily from North Plainfield, New Jersey, to Philadelphia, where he was a partner in a prosperous fund-raising organization. A bachelor, he lived alone in a boardinghouse owned by a Mrs. Betty Lester, with whom he was on casual friendly terms. This mode of life abruptly ended for Shephard on April 18.

On that day, about five in the afternoon, Shephard, on his way to the boardinghouse after the day's work, stood on a street corner, waiting for the traffic light to change. A quiet evening loomed attractively ahead. Mrs. Lester, who had been marketing in town that afternoon, chanced to arrive at the same corner while Shephard still waited for the light. Chatting companionably about the evening meal ahead, Shephard and Mrs. Lester crossed the street when the light turned green, and headed for Shephard's car. They did not see the man who had followed them for a block or two until they reached the car. Peering into Shephard's face, the man shouted, "That's him! I'd know him anywhere!"

Before Shephard could reply, the man went on in the same excited voice, "That's the same woman, too. She was with him then."

Shephard decided that this outrageous man did not merit a reply. Taking Mrs. Lester's arm, again he started toward the car. Suddenly two more men appeared. Although dressed in business suits, their police shields introduced them to the startled pair. They offered no explanation of the arrest. Only in the prosecutor's office did Shephard and Mrs. Lester learn the reason.

The man who had followed them to Shephard's car explained. "Three months ago," he told the prosecutor, "they came into my store and cashed a check for thirty-five dollars. It wasn't any good. I'd know them anywhere."

Shephard said that there had been some mistake. He had never been in this man's store, nor had any check he had written ever bounced. The merchant and the prosecutor listened but they did not hear.

"They hooked a lot of us merchants," the man went on. "I can get you plenty of witnesses."

A few days later nine more merchants identified Shephard and Mrs. Lester as the culprits. The two were soon indicted for forgery. For seven months they remained in jail awaiting trial.

The trial opened in November 1935. The prosecution exhibited the forgeries and called the ten merchants who testified that the accused were the criminals.

Since the defendants had been impoverished by their months in jail, they could not pay a lawyer to defend them. They were represented by a court-appointed counsel, a recent law-school graduate. Despite his inexperience, no doubt this lawyer thought of calling a handwriting expert to testify, but, lacking funds, the defendants could not pay an expert's fee. The defense consisted of the testimony of a series of character witnesses, and of a mechanic who swore that Shephard had been in his garage, waiting for his car to be repaired, while one of the crimes was taking place.

The jury found Shephard and Betty Lester guilty. The judge sentenced them to nine-month prison terms.

The nine months passed and the prisoners were released. Just outside the prison they were rearrested for another series of forgeries.

The second trial was a nightmare repetition of the first. Another group of outraged merchants testified for the state, and the forgeries were put in evidence. The defendants, not able to obtain a handwriting analysis, offered the same pitiful defense. After the guilty verdict, which to the defendants must have seemed inevitable, the judge sentenced Mrs. Lester to a nine-month term, Shephard to one of eighteen months.

The second time Shephard emerged from prison he had aged beyond his years. Nor did the thought of freedom appear golden now, for he had had time in which to reflect on what a prison record meant. His most depressing fantasies were not shaken by reality.

Once a man of standing in the business world, Shephard now counted himself lucky when he found an odd job or two a day. He subsisted on what he earned from mowing lawns and washing dishes. These jobs stopped when, for the third time, he was arrested on a charge of forgery.

Again a group of merchants identified him. But the grand jury did not indict Shephard for these forgeries, since he could prove an alibi, having been in prison when the crimes took place. The case was never brought to trial.

The fourth conflict between Shephard and the state began in 1938. It was then that Shephard, now fully realizing the consequences of his prison record, determined to prove his innocence.

Borrowing money from a friend, he enlisted the services of the Burns Detective Agency to discover the actual forger. Digging in their files, the investigators found information about a criminal, Edward Sullivan, who resembled Shephard. The agency's handwriting experts, comparing the signatures on the checks allegedly written by Shephard and those actually forged by Sullivan, saw that they were the same in each detail.

With the first feeling of confidence he had known in the long years since his first arrest Shephard applied to the Board of Pardons for a full pardon on the basis of this new evidence. The board reviewed it and, without giving any reason, turned Shephard down. Under the state law he could not reapply for a period of two years.

During those two years Shephard supported himself peddling rugs from door to door. In that period, through the Burns Agency, Shephard had an interview with the forger, Sullivan. Seeing Sullivan, then in prison for another crime, Shephard saw how alike he and the forger looked.

Shephard appealed to Sullivan to help clear his name. The forger, more easily touched by Shephard's plight than was the state, signed a full confession admitting his commission of the crimes for which Shephard had served two full prison terms. Mrs. Sullivan signed a written statement that she had passed the checks forged by her husband.

In April 1940, Shephard applied for a pardon a second time, presenting the Sullivans' confessions. This time, he felt sure, he could not lose. However, a few days after he had presented it, his application was returned. Stamped across its face, in large red letters, was the word "rejected."

That afternoon Shephard got a job as a handy man in a bar and grill. There he became friendly with a customer, a newspaper reporter who, outraged by Shephard's treatment at the hands of the Board of Pardons, helped him with his next appeal. It, too, the board rejected. Every two years after that Shephard and the reporter presented a new appeal. Each time it was turned down.

In the fall of 1950, the newspaperman succeeded in bringing Shephard's case to the attention of Governor Driscoll, who ordered a full-scale investigation. The old board had been replaced and three new members carefully reviewed the case. In its report to the governor the board recommended an unconditional pardon for Shephard, which, on June 14, 1950, Governor Driscoll signed. (A year later, on May

15, 1951, Betty Lester, who had waited until she saw the outcome of Shephard's case, was similarly cleared.)

"I'm grateful that I'm no longer a criminal in the eyes of the law," sixty-four-year-old Shephard said, his fifteen-year ordeal finally at an end. "I know that a guy can get awfully bitter holding a grudge, so I'm not looking back. There are a lot of years left ahead for me. I want them to be good."

O. JOHN ROGGE

Confessions of the Innocent

ఠ★

Unbelievably, many people confess to crimes they didn't commit.

From the time of the witchcraft prosecutions onward, and even before, there were many other confessions of the innocent. Moreover, such confessions were free and voluntary. Whenever a particularly atrocious act was committed innocent people often came forward and on their own initiative confessed themselves to be the authors of it. Indeed the more heinous and sensational the offense, the greater were the number of innocent confessants. More than two hundred innocent people confessed to the kidnaping and murder of the Lindbergh baby. At least seventeen innocent persons confessed to the highly publicized sex murder of Elizabeth Short, who was known as the Black Dahlia because of the sheer black clothing she wore. Various innocent persons at various times claimed responsibility for the death of Joseph B. Elwell, the bridge expert, who was mysteriously slain in 1920 in his home in New York City. More than one innocent person claimed responsibility for the Wall Street explosion of the same year.

The centuries have recorded a string of similar confessions. Numbers of early Christians falsely claimed to have committed offenses against the state. Indeed, so many of them at Antioch willfully sought martyrdom by such claims as well as actually by outraging pagan temples or insulting the magistrates that the proconsul Antonius amazedly asked whether they had not ropes or precipices to kill themselves.

In November 1580 a man was convicted and executed on his own confession for the murder, near Paris, of a widow who was missing at the time. Two years later she returned to her home. In 1660 arose the case of the Perrys in England. John Perry gave a detailed confession how he, his brother Richard, and his mother Joan had murdered and robbed their master William Harrison. Richard, so John said, strangled Harrison while he and his mother stood by, took a bag of money out of his pocket, and threw it in their mother's lap. They were all three executed. Some years later Harrison returned, with a story of being kidnaped and sold to the Turks. One may not believe Harrison's story, but certainly John's was false. Six years later, the year of the great London fire, came Hubert's case. Hubert, a young Frenchman, gave a detailed account of how he and three others were hired in Paris to set London on fire and how he had done it. He related so many circumstances that he was tried and executed. The account, however, related the doubts of those who heard the story: "Yet neither the judges nor any present at the trial did believe him guilty, but that he was a poor distracted wretch weary of his life, and chose to part with it this way."

John Bunyan told of the case of old Tod, who was hanged with his wife at Hartford about the same time that Hubert was hanged in London. While the judge was on the bench at a summer assize at Hartford, old Tod came into court clothed in a green suit, with a leathern girdle in his hand, his bosom open, and all in a dung sweat as if he had run for his life, and confessed: "My lord, here is the veryest rogue that breathes upon the face of the earth; I have been a thief from a child; when I was but a little one I gave myself to rob orchards, and to do such other like wicked things, and I have continued a thief ever since. My lord, there has not been a robbery committed this many years, within so many miles of this place, but I have either been at it or privy to it." The judge thought him mad, but after conferring with some of his brother judges let him and his wife be indicted of several felonious actions. He heartily confessed to all the charges.

In September 1797 the crew of the *Hermione,* an English frigate, mutinied, murdered the captain (a harsh man by the name of Pigot) and a number of the officers under circumstances of extreme barbarity, and took the ship into an enemy port. One midshipman escaped. He later identified many of the offenders. This incident became the basis for the confessions of numerous innocent English sailors. An admiralty official later stated: "In my own experience I have known, on separate occasions, more than six sailors who voluntarily confessed to having struck the first blow at Captain Pigot. These men detailed all the horrid circumstances of the mutiny with extreme minuteness and perfect accuracy. Nevertheless, not one of them *had ever been in the ship* nor *had so much as seen Captain Pigot in their lives.* They had obtained by tradition, from their messmates, the particulars of the story. When long on a foreign station, hungering and thirsting for home, their minds became enfeebled; at length they actually believed themselves guilty of the crime over which they had so long brooded, and submitted with a gloomy pleasure to being sent to England in irons for judgment. At the Admiralty we were always able to detect and establish their innocence, in defiance of their own solemn asseverations."

Sir Samuel Romilly told of another such English sailor whose case did not end so happily. This one confessed: "At the time the mutiny took place, I was a boy in my fourteenth year. Drove by the torrent of mutiny, I took the oath administered to me on the occasion. The examples of death which were before my eyes drove me for shelter amongest the mutineers, dreading a similar fate with those that fell, if I sided with or showed the smallest inclination for mercy . . ." He was executed. But he was innocent. At the time of the mutiny and murders on the *Hermione* he was at Portsmouth on board the *Marlborough.*

A sensational murder was committed in Edinburgh, Scotland in 1806: a bank porter with four or five thousand pounds of banknotes was struck dead by a single stab and robbed. A number of innocent people charged themselves with the offense. Lord Henry Cockburn later commented: "According to a strange craze or ambition not unusual in such cases, several charged themselves with the crime who to an absolute certainty had nothing to do with it."

In 1819 there occurred in Manchester, Vermont, a much-discussed case in this country, that of the Boorns, Stephen and Jesse, brothers. Stephen and Jesse's sister Sarah was married to Russell Colvin. In May 1812 Russell disappeared. Some years went by. In 1819 a neighbor had a dream which set investigation afoot. A boy walking near the Boorns' hovels came across a hollow stump partly filled with bones. The tidings ran. Murder will find a tongue: Manchester found hundreds. Jesse was taken into custody. He said Stephen did it. Stephen was extradited from New York and confessed. They were tried, convicted, and sentenced to be executed. Then a reward was offered for the discovery of the missing man. He was located in New Jersey and returned home in time to prevent the executions. The bones were those of an animal. Years later, in 1860, Jesse Boorn was arrested in Cleveland, Ohio, for forgery. In custody he confessed that forty years before he was concerned in a murder and escaped by a false impersonation of the deceased. Both confessions were false.

In 1888-1889 the Jack the Ripper murders took place in Whitechapel: again and again the bodies of women, murdered and mutilated, were found in the East End of London. These murders produced a round of innocent confessants, and furnished the basis for this observation by a subsequent editor of Best's work on evidence: ". . . murders of a specially horrible kind—as, for instance, the Whitechapel murders of prostitutes in 1888 and 1889—are followed by a series of false confessions."

A man named Shellenberger confessed that he and another murdered a husband and wife near Omaha, Nebraska. The facts showed that he was innocent. Later he gave a detailed account how in June 1899 he murdered Julian Bahuaud. There was corroboration but the indications were that he was innocent of this murder as well. The Supreme Court of Nebraska pointed out: "There are numerous cases upon record where men have voluntarily confessed themselves to be guilty of atrocious crimes, where investigation has proved their innocence, and the confession could only be attributed to a defective or abnormal mentality. . . . Even in this state in recent years, unfounded confessions of murder have been made, and the confessing party acquitted when all the facts were disclosed."

In 1904 in Stepney, England, Emily Farmer was murdered. After the conviction of the real murderers, two in number, an innocent man came forward and made a full detailed confession of the crime. Frederick P. Wensley, who related the case in his book *Detective Days,* added: "He was just one of those half-wits who, for some queer reason, turn up not infrequently to confess to crimes that have attracted public attention." At another point in his book he stated: ". . . I thought it was one of the usual bogus confessions that are not uncommon in murder cases."

An interesting case, which reflected great credit on the prosecutor, involved the murder in 1924 of Father Hubert Dahme of the St. Joseph's Church of Bridgeport, Connecticut. Someone shot Father Dahme in the back of the head. An innocent person, Harold Israel, confessed to the murder. The prosecutor in the case was Homer S. Cummings, later attorney general of the United States under President Franklin D. Roosevelt. His investigation developed the man's innocence and the case was dropped.

In Essex, England, a village constable named Gutteridge was brutally murdered on night patrol in September 1927. Two shots were fired into his head at close range and after he fell a shot was fired at each eye. A false confession was soon forthcoming. The confessant had given himself up earlier in another sensational case, a trunk murder committed the same year. His confession, too, was false. J. F. Moylan, who narrated the case in his book *Scotland Yard,* commented: "Bogus confessions by notoriety hunters or persons of unbalanced mind are common in murder cases, and one was soon forthcoming in this."

A French girl, Adele Bernard, was accused of murdering her newborn child. She confessed. But in prison she gave birth to a child in less than three months after the alleged birth of the child to whose murder she confessed. There are other instances where women have accused themselves of the murder of infants whom they never bore or who died naturally. One such described the whole scene with touching minuteness, the wailing of the young child, its piteous look, its burial in a little grave at the foot of a pine tree. And none of it was true.

The Chicago newspapers headlined the brutal killing of a pregnant woman whose body was found in a snowbank. William Kiss, a factory worker, turned himself in. Feeling immediately ran high against him because of the nature of the crime. Fortunately for him, a nineteen-year-old sailor at the Great Lakes Naval Station also came forward and confessed. This confession turned out to be true.

In 1953 Francis R. Noble, a thirty-nine-year-old counterman, confessed that he had strangled his common-law wife, whose nude body was found dead in bed beside him. He told the police: "I loved her so much, I had to do it." Actually the woman died of a heart attack.

In 1958 a New York seaman, Leo Turck, told the police that he had killed Serge Rubinstein, the financier who got into many legal difficulties, criminal as well as civil. But the seaman was innocent.

There are many, many more examples. In fact, there have been such a steady stream of them that various authorities, judges, prosecutors, detectives, and legal scholars have commented at different times on the frequency of the confessions of the innocent. Some of these comments we have seen. There are others. Johann Heineccius, a German lawyer, wrote in the first part of the 1700's: "Confession is sometimes the voice of conscience. Experience, however, teaches us that it is frequently far otherwise. There sometimes lurks, under the shadow of an apparent tranquillity an insanity, which impels men readily to accuse themselves of all kinds of iniquity. Some, deluded by their imaginations, suspect themselves of crimes which they have never committed. A melancholy temperament, the tedium vitae, and an unaccountable propensity to their own destruction, urges some to the most false confessions."

Francis Wharton, an American scholar, in an excellent work for its time observed: "Delusion, a morbid desire to attract attention, a sort of epidemic which strikes down whole classes with a passionate impulse to insist upon some bloodstain on the conscience, something like hypochrondriac epidemic impulse which insists upon some personal abnormality, weariness of life, a propensity to self-destruction through a channel which from its very tortuousness possesses its own fascination, a Lara-like desire to appear mysterious and dark, though in this case the propensity exudes in vague intimations of participation in nameless deeds of guilt rather than in confession of specific offenses ... So the publication of a conspicuous homicide is apt to generate a series of pretenders to the deed." In a treatise on criminal law Wharton remarked: "There is a species of morbid vanity which sometimes leads innocent persons to declare themselves guilty of crimes to which public attention is particularly drawn."

STEPHEN VINCENT BENÉT

The Curfew Tolls*

ஞ

A great masterpiece of hypothetical history.

It is not enough to be the possessor of genius—the time and the man must conjoin. An Alexander the Great, born into an age of profound peace, might scarce have troubled the world—a Newton, grown up in a thieves' den, might have devised little but a new and ingenious picklock. . . .
—DIVERSIONS OF HISTORICAL THOUGHT
JOHN CLEVELAND COTTON.

St. Philippe-des-Bains, September 3d, 1788.
My Dear Sister: ... I could wish that my excellent Paris physician had selected some other spot for my convalescence. But he swears by the waters of St. Philip and I swear by him, so I must resign myself to a couple of yawning months ere my constitution mends. Nevertheless, you will get long letters from me, though I fear they may be dull ones.

* These extracts have been made from the letters of General Sir Charles William Geoffrey Estcourt, C.B., to his sister Harriet, Countess of Stokely, by permission of the Stokely family. Omissions are indicated by triple dots.

I cannot bring you the gossip of Baden or Aix—except for its baths. St. Philip is but one of a dozen small white towns on this agreeable coast. It has its good inn and its bad inn, its dusty, little square with its dusty, fleabitten beggar, its posting station and its promenade of scrubby lindens and palms. From the heights one may see Corsica on a clear day, and the Mediterranean is of an unexampled blue. To tell the truth, it is all agreeable enough, and an old Indian campaigner, like myself, should not complain. I am well treated at the Cheval Blanc—am I not an English milord?—and my excellent Gaston looks after me devotedly. But there is a bluebottle drowsiness about small watering places out of season, and our gallant enemies, the French, know how to bore themselves more exquisitely in their provinces than any nation on earth. Would you think that the daily arrival of the diligence from Toulon would be an excitement? Yet it is to me, I assure you, and to all St. Philip. I walk, I take the waters, I read Ossian, I play piquet with Gaston, and yet I seem to myself but half alive. . . .

. . . You will smile and say to me, "Dear brother, you have always plumed yourself on being a student of human nature. Is there no society, no character for you to study, even in St. Philippe-des-Bains?" My dear sister, I bend myself earnestly to that end, yet so far with little result. I have talked to my doctor—a good man but unpolished; I have talked to the curé—a good man but dull. I have even attempted the society of the baths, beginning with Monsieur le Marquis de la Percedragon, who has ninety-six quarterings, soiled wristbands, and a gloomy interest in my liver, and ending with Mrs. Macgregor Jenkins, a worthy and red-faced lady whose conversation positively cannonades with dukes and duchesses. But, frankly, I prefer my chair in the garden and my Ossian to any of them, even at the risk of being considered a bear. A witty scoundrel would be the veriest godsend to me, but do such exist in St. Philip? I trow not. As it is, in my weakened condition, I am positively agog when Gaston comes in every morning with his budget of village scandal. A pretty pass to come to, you will say, for a man who has served with Eyre Coote and but for the mutabilities of fortune, not to speak of a most damnable cabal . . . (A long passage dealing with General Estcourt's East Indian services and his personal and unfavorable opinion of Warren Hastings is here omitted from the manuscript.) . . . But, at fifty, a man is either a fool or a philosopher. Nevertheless, unless Gaston provides me with a character to try my wits on, shortly, I shall begin to believe that they too have deteriorated with Indian suns. . . .

September 21st, 1788.

My Dear Sister: . . . Believe me, there is little soundness in the views of your friend, Lord Martindale. The French monarchy is not to be compared with our own, but King Louis is an excellent and well-beloved prince, and the proposed summoning of the States-General cannot but have the most salutary effect. . . . (Three pages upon French politics and the possibility of cultivating sugarcane in southern France are here omitted.) . . . As for news of myself, I continue my yawning course, and feel a decided improvement from the waters. . . . So I shall continue them though the process is slow. . . .

You ask me, I fear a trifle mockingly, how my studies in human nature proceed?

No so ill, my dear sister. I have, at least, scraped acquaintance with one odd fish, and that, in St. Philip, is a triumph. For some time, from my chair in the promenade, I have observed a pursy little fellow, of my age or thereabouts, stalking up and down between the lindens. His company seems avoided by such notables of the place as Mrs. Macgregor Jenkins and at first I put him down as a retired actor, for there is something a little theatrical in his dress and walk. He wears a wide-brimmed hat of straw, loose nankeen trousers, and a quasi-military coat, and takes his waters with as much ceremony as Monsieur le Marquis, though not quite with the same *ton*. I should put him down as a Meridional, for he has the quick, dark eye, the sallow skin, the corpulence and the rodomontish airs that mark your true son of the Midi, once he has passed his lean and hungry youth.

And yet, there is some sort of unsuccessful oddity about him, which sets him off from your successful bourgeois. I cannot put my finger on it yet, but it interests me.

At any rate, I was sitting in my accustomed chair, reading Ossian, this morning, as he made his solitary rounds of the promenade. Doubtless I was more than usually absorbed in my author, for I must have pronounced some lines aloud as he passed. He gave me a quick glance at the time, but nothing more. But on his next round, as he was about to pass me, he hesitated for a moment, stopped, and then, removing his straw hat, saluted me very civilly.

"Monsieur will pardon me," he said, with a dumpy hauteur, "but surely monsieur is English? And surely the lines that monsieur just repeated are from the great poet, Ossian?"

I admitted both charges, with a smile, and he bowed again.

"Monsieur will excuse the interruption," he said, "but I myself have long admired the poetry of Ossian"—and with that he continued my quotation to the end of the passage, in very fair English, too, though with a strong accent. I complimented him, of course, effusively —after all, it is not every day that one runs across a fellow admirer of Ossian on the promenade of a small French watering place—and after that, he sat down in the chair beside me and we fell into talk. He seems, astonishingly for a Frenchman, to have an excellent acquaintance with our English poets—perhaps he has been a tutor in some English family. I did not press him with questions on this first encounter, though I noted that he spoke French with a slight accent also, which seems odd.

There is something a little rascally about him, to tell you the truth, though his conversation with me was both forceful and elevated. An ill man, too, and a disappointed one, or I miss my mark, yet his eyes, when he talks, are strangely animating. I fancy I would not care to meet him in a *guet-apens,* and yet, he may be the most harmless of broken pedagogues. We took a glass of waters together, to the great disgust of Mrs. Macgregor Jenkins, who ostentatiously drew her skirts aside. She let me know, afterward, in so many words, that my acquaintance was a noted bandit, though, when pressed, she could give no better reason than that he lives a little removed from the town, that "nobody knows where he comes from" and that his wife is "no better than she should be," whatever that portentous phrase entails. Well, one would hardly call him a gentleman, even by Mrs. Macgregor's somewhat easy standards, but he has given me better conversation than I have had in a month—and if he is a bandit, we might discuss thuggee together. But I hope for nothing so stimulating, though I must question Gaston about him. . . .

October 11th.

. . . But Gaston could tell me little, except that my acquaintance comes from Sardinia or some such island originally, has served in the French army and is popularly supposed to possess the evil eye. About Madame he hinted that he could tell me a great deal, but I did not labor the point. After all, if my friend has been c-ck-ld-d—do not blush, my dear sister!—that, too, is the portion of a philosopher, and I find his wide range of conversation much more palatable than Mrs. Macgregor Jenkins' rewarmed London gossip. Nor has he tried to borrow money from me yet, something which, I am frank to say, I expected and was prepared to refuse. . . .

November 20th.

. . . Triumph! My character is found—and a character of the first water, I assure you! I have dined with him in his house, and a very bad dinner it was. Madame is not a good housekeeper, whatever else she may be. And what she has been, one can see at a glance—she has all the little faded coquetries of the garrison coquette. Good-tempered, of course, as such women often are, and must have been pretty in her best days, though with shocking bad teeth. I suspect her of a touch of the tarbrush, though there I may be wrong. No doubt she caught my friend young—I have seen the same thing happen in India often enough—the experienced woman and the youngster fresh from England. Well, 'tis an old story—an old one with him, too—and no doubt Madame has her charms, though she is obviously one reason why he has not risen.

After dinner Madame departed, not very willingly, and he took me into his study for a chat. He had even procured a bottle of port, saying he knew the Englishman's taste for it, and while it was hardly the right Cockburn, I felt touched by the attention. The man is desperately lonely—one reads that in his big eyes. He is also desperately proud, with the quick, touchy sensitiveness of the failure, and I quite exerted myself to draw him out.

And indeed, the effort repaid me. His own story is simple enough. He is neither bandit nor pedagogue, but, like myself, a broken soldier—a major of the French Royal Artillery, retired on half pay for some years. I think it creditable of him to have reached so respectable a rank, for he is of foreign birth—Sardinian, I think I told you—and the French service is by no means as partial to foreigners as they were in the days of the first Irish Brigade. Moreover, one simply does not rise in that service, unless one is a gentleman of quarterings, and that he could hardly claim. But the passion of his life has been India, and that is what interests me. And, 'pon my honor, he was rather astonishing about it.

As soon as, by a lucky chance, I hit upon the subject, his eyes lit up and his sickness dropped away. Pretty soon he began to take maps from a cabinet in the wall and ply me with questions about my own small experiences. And very soon indeed, I am abashed to state, I found myself stumbling in my answers. It was all book knowledge on his part, of course, but where the devil he could have got some of it, I do not know. Indeed, he would even correct me, now and then, as cool as you please. "Eight twelve-pounders, I think, on the north wall of the old fortifications of Madras—" and the deuce of it is, he would be right. Finally I could contain myself no longer.

"But, Major, this is incredible," I said. "I have served twenty years with John Company and thought that I had some knowledge. But one would say you had fought over every inch of Bengal!"

He gave me a quick look, almost of anger, and began to roll up his maps.

"So I have, in my mind," he said shortly, "but, as my superiors have often informed me, my hobby is a tedious one."

"It is not tedious to me," I said boldly. "Indeed, I have often marveled at your government's neglect of their opportunities in India. True, the issue is settled now—"

"It is by no means settled,'" he said, interrupting me rudely. I stared at him.

"It was settled, I believe, by Baron Clive, at a spot named Plassey," I said frigidly. "And afterward, by my own old general, Eyre Coote, at another spot named Wandewash."

"Oh, yes—yes—yes," he said impatiently, "I grant you Clive— Clive was a genius and met the fate of geniuses. He steals an empire for you, and your virtuous English Parliament holds up its hands in horror because he steals a few lakhs of rupees for himself as well. So he blows out his brains in disgrace—you inexplicable English!— and you lose your genius. A great pity. I would not have treated Clive so. But then, if I had been Milord Clive, I would not have blown out my brains."

"And what would you have done had you been Clive?" I said, for the man's calm, staring conceit amused me.

His eyes were dangerous for a moment and I saw why the worthy Mrs. Macgregor Jenkins had called him a bandit.

"Oh," he said coolly, "I would have sent a file of grenadiers to your English Parliament and told it to hold its tongue. As Cromwell did. Now there was a man. But your Clive—faugh!—he had the ball at his feet and he refused to kick it. I withdraw the word genius. He was a nincompoop. At the least, he might have made himself a rajah."

This was a little too much, as you may imagine. "General Clive had his faults," I said icily, "but he was a true Briton and a patriot."

"He was a fool," said my puffy little major flatly, his lower lip stuck out. "As big a fool as Dupleix, and that is saying much. Oh, some military skill, some talent for organization, yes. But a genius would have brushed him into the sea! It was possible to hold Arcot, it was possible to win Plassey—look!" and with that he ripped another map from his cabinet and began to expound to me eagerly exactly what he would have done in command of the French forces in India, in 1757, when he must have been but a lad in his twenties. He thumped the paper, he strewed corks along the table for his troops—corks taken from a supply in a tin box, so it must be an old game with him. And, as I listened, my irritation faded, for the man's monomania was obvious. Nor was it, to tell the truth, an ill-designed plan of campaign, for corks on a map. Of course these things are different in the field.

I could say, with honesty, that his plan had features of novelty, and he gulped the words down hungrily—he has a great appetite for flattery.

"Yes, yes," he said. "That is how it should be done—the thickest skull can see it. And, ill as I am, with a fleet and ten thousand picked men—" He dreamed, obviously, the sweat of his exertions on his waxy face—it was absurd and yet touching to see him dream.

"You would find a certain amount of opposition," I said in an amused voice.

"Oh, yes, yes," he said quickly, "I do not underrate the English. Excellent horse, solid foot. But no true knowledge of cannon, and I am a gunner—"

I hated to bring him down to earth and yet I felt that I must.

"Of course, Major," I said, "you have had great experience in the field."

He looked at me for a moment, his arrogance quite unshaken.

"I have had very little," he said quietly, "but one knows how the thing should be done or one does not know. And that is enough."

He stared at me for an instant with his big eyes. A little mad, of course. And yet I found myself saying, "But surely, Major—what happened?"

"Why," he said, still quietly, "what happens to folk who have naught but their brains to sell? I staked my all on India when I was young—I thought that my star shone over it. I ate dirty puddings— *corpo di Baccho!*—to get there—I was no De Rohan or Soubise to win the king's favor! And I reached there indeed, in my youth, just in time to be included in the surrender of Pondicherry." He laughed, rather terribly, and sipped at his glass.

"You English were very courteous captors," he said. "But I was not released till the Seven Years War had ended—that was in '63. Who asks for the special exchange of an unknown artillery lieutenant? And then ten years odd of garrison duty at Mauritius. It was there that I met Madame—she is a Creole. A pleasant spot, Mauritius. We used to fire the cannon at the sea birds when we had enough ammunition for target practice," and he chuckled drearily. "By then I was thirty-seven. They had to make me a captain—they even brought me back to France. To garrison duty. I have been on garrison duty, at Toulon, at Brest, at—" He ticked off the names on his fingers but I did not like his voice.

"But surely," I said, "the American war, though a small affair—there were opportunities—"

"And who did they send?" he said quickly. "Lafayette—Rochambeau—De Grasse—the sprigs of the nobility. Oh, at Lafayette's age, I would have volunteered like Lafayette. But one should be successful in youth—after that, the spring is broken. And when one is over forty, one has responsibilities. I have a large family, you see, though not of my own begetting," and he chuckled as if at a secret joke. "Oh, I wrote the Continental Congress," he said reflectively, "but they preferred a dolt like Von Steuben. A good dolt, an honest dolt, but there you have it. I also wrote your British War Office," he said in an even voice. "I must show you that plan of campaign—sometime —they could have crushed General Washington with it in three weeks."

I stared at him, a little appalled.

"For an officer who has taken his king's shilling to send to an enemy nation a plan for crushing his own country's ally," I said, stiffly, "well, in England, we would call that treason."

"And what is treason?" he said lightly. "If we call it unsuccessful ambition we shall be nearer the truth." He looked at me keenly. "You are shocked, General Estcourt," he said. "I am sorry for that. But have you never known the curse"—and his voice vibrated—"the curse of not being employed when you should be employed? The curse of being a hammer with no nail to drive? The curse—the curse of sitting in a dusty garrison town with dreams that would split the brain of a Caesar, and no room on earth for those dreams?"

"Yes," I said, unwillingly, for there was something in him that demanded the truth, "I have known that."

"Then you know hells undreamed of by the Christian," he said with a sigh, "and if I committed treason—well, I have been punished for it. I might have been a brigadier, otherwise—I had Choiseul's ear for a few weeks, after great labor. As it is, I am here on half pay, and there will not be another war in my time. Moreover, M. de Ségur has proclaimed that all officers now must show sixteen quarterings. Well, I wish them joy of those officers, in the next conflict. Meanwhile, I have my corks, my maps, and my family ailment." He smiled and tapped his side. "It killed my father at thirty-nine—it has not treated me quite so ill, but it will come for me soon enough."

And indeed, when I looked at him, I could well believe it, for the light had gone from his eyes and his cheeks were flabby. We chatted a little on indifferent subjects after that, then I left him, wondering whether to pursue the acquaintance. He is indubitably a character, but some of his speeches leave a taste in my mouth. Yet he can be greatly attractive—even now, with his mountainous failure like a cloak upon him. And yet why should I call it mountainous? His conceit is mountainous enough, but what else could he have expected of his career? Yet I wish I could forget his eyes. . . . To tell the truth, he puzzles me and I mean to get to the bottom of him. . . .

February 12th, 1789.

. . . I have another sidelight on the character of my friend, the major. As I told you, I was half of a mind to break off the acquaintance entirely, but he came up to me so civilly, the following day, that I could find no excuse. And since then, he has made me no embarrassingly treasonable confidences, though whenever we discuss the art of war, his arrogance is unbelievable. He even informed me, the other day, that while Frederick of Prussia was a fair general, his tactics might have been improved upon. I merely laughed and turned the question. Now and then I play a war game with him, with his corks and maps, and when I let him win, he is as pleased as a child. . . . His illness increases visibly, despite the waters, and he shows an eagerness for my company which I cannot but find touching. . . . After all, he is a man of intelligence, and the company he has had to keep must have galled him at times. . . .

Now and then I amuse myself by speculating what might have happened to him, had he chosen some other profession than that of arms. He has, as I have told you, certain gifts of the actor, yet his stature and figure must have debarred him from tragic parts, while he certainly does not possess the humors of the comedian. Perhaps his best choice would have been the Romish church, for there the veriest fisherman may hope, at least, to succeed to the keys of St. Peter. . . . And yet, heaven knows, he would have made a very bad priest! . . .

But, to my tale. I had missed him from our accustomed walks for some days and went to his house—St. Helen's it is called; we live in a pother of saints' names hereabouts—one evening to inquire. I did not hear the quarreling voices till the tousle-haired servant had admitted me and then it was too late to retreat. Then my friend bounced down the corridor, his sallow face bored and angry.

"Ah, General Estcourt!" he said, with a complete change of expression as soon as he saw me. "What fortune! I was hoping you would pay us a call—I wish to introduce you to my family!"

He had told me previously of his pair of stepchildren by Madame's first marriage, and I must confess I felt curious to see them. But it was not of them he spoke, as I soon gathered.

"Yes," he said. "My brothers and sisters, or most of them, are here for a family council. You come in the nick of time!" He pinched my arm and his face glowed with the malicious naïveté of a child. "They do not believe that I really know an English general—it will be a great blow to them!" he whispered as we passed down the corridor. "Ah, if you had only worn your uniform and your Garters! But one cannot have everything in life!"

Well, my dear sister, what a group, when we entered the salon! It is a small room, tawdrily furnished in the worst French taste, with a jumble of Madame's femininities and souvenirs from the Island of Mauritius, and they were all sitting about in the French after-dinner fashion, drinking tisane and quarreling. And, indeed, had the room been as long as the nave of St. Peter's, it would yet have seemed too small for such a crew! An old mother, straight as a ramrod and as forbidding, with the burning eyes and the bitter dignity one sees on the faces of certain Italian peasants—you could see that they were all a little afraid of her except my friend, and he, I must say, treated here with a filial courtesy that was greatly to his credit. Two sisters, one fattish, swarthy and spiteful, the other with the wreck of great beauty and the evident marks of a certain profession on her shabby-fine *toilette* and her pinkened cheeks. An innkeeper brother-in-law called Buras or Durat, with a jowlish, heavily handsome face and the manners of a cavalry sergeant—he is married to the spiteful sister. And two brothers, one sheeplike, one foxlike, yet both bearing a certain resemblance to my friend.

The sheeplike brother is at least respectable, I gathered—a provincial lawyer in a small way of business whose great pride is that he has actually appeared before the Court of Appeals at Marseilles. The other, the foxlike one, makes his living more dubiously—he seems the sort of fellow who orates windily in taprooms about the rights of man and other nonsense of M. Rousseau's. I would certainly not trust him with my watch, though he is trying to get himself elected to the States-General. And, as regards family concord, it was obvious at first glance that not one of them trusted the others. And yet, that is not all of the tribe. There are, if you will believe me, two other brothers living, and this family council was called to deal with the affairs of the next-to-youngest, who seems, even in this mélange, to be a black sheep.

I can assure you, my head swam, and when my friend introduced me, proudly, as a Knight of the Garters, I did not even bother to contradict him. For they admitted me to their intimate circle at once —there was no doubt about that. Only the old lady remained aloof, saying little and sipping her camomile tea as if it were the blood of her enemies. But, one by one, the others related to me, with an un-asked-for frankness, the most intimate and scandalous details of their brothers' and sisters' lives. They seemed united only on two points: jealousy of my friend, the major, because he is his mother's favorite, and dislike of Madame Josephine because she gives herself airs. Except for the haggard beauty—I must say, that, while her remarks anent her sister-in-law were not such as I would care to repeat, she seemed genuinely fond of her brother, the major, and expounded his virtues to me through an overpowering cloud of scent.

It was like being in a nest of Italian smugglers, or a den of quarrel-some foxes, for they all talked, or rather barked, at once, even the brother-in-law, and only Madame Mère could bring silence among them. And yet my friend enjoyed it. It was obvious he showed them off before me as he might have displayed the tricks of a set of per-forming animals. And yet with a certain fondness, too—that is the inexplicable part of it. I do not know which sentiment was upmost in my mind—respect for this family feeling or pity for his being burdened with such a clan.

For though not the eldest, he is the strongest among them, and they know it. They rebel, but he rules their family conclaves like a petty despot. I could have laughed at the farce of it, and yet, it was nearer tears. For here, at least, my friend was a personage.

I got away as soon as I could, despite some pressing looks from the haggard beauty. My friend accompanied me to the door.

"Well, well," he said, chuckling and rubbing his hands, "I am infinitely obliged to you, General. They will not forget this in a hurry. Before you entered, Joseph"—Joseph is the sheeplike one—"was boasting about his acquaintance with a *sous-intendant*, but an English general, bah! Joseph will have green eyes for a fortnight!" And he rubbed his hands again in a perfect paroxysm of delight.

It was too childlike to make me angry. "I am glad, of course, to have been of any service," I said.

"Oh, you have been a great service," he said. "They will not plague my poor Josie for at least half and hour. Ah, this is a bad business of Louis'—a bad business!"—Louis is the black sheep—"but we will patch it up somehow. Hortense is worth three of him—he must go back to Hortense!"

"You have a numerous family, Major," I said, for want of something better to say.

"Oh, yes," he said, cheerfully. "Pretty numerous—I am sorry you could not meet the others. Though Louis is a fool—I pampered him in his youth. Well! He was a baby—and Jerome a mule. Still, we haven't done so badly for ourselves; not badly. Joseph makes a go of his law practice—there are fools enough in the world to be impressed by Joseph—and if Lucien gets to the States-General, you may trust Lucien to feather his nest! And there are the grandchildren, and a little money—not much," he said, quickly. "They mustn't expect that from me. But it's a step up from where we started—if Papa had lived, he wouldn't have been so ill-pleased. Poor Elisa's gone, but the rest of us have stuck together, and, while we may seem a little rough, to strangers, our hearts are in the right place. When I was a boy"—and he chuckled again—"I had other ambitions for them. I thought, with luck on my side, I could make them all kings and queens. Funny, isn't it, to think of a numskull like Joseph as a king! Well, that was the boy of it. But, even so, they'd all be eating chestnuts back on the island without me, and that's something."

He said it rather defiantly, and I did not know which to marvel at most—his preposterous pride in the group or his cool contempt of them. So I said nothing but shook his hand instead. I could not help doing the latter. For surely, if anyone started in life with a millstone about his neck . . . and yet they are none of them ordinary people. . . .

March 13th, 1789.

. . . My friend's complaint has taken a turn for the worse and it is I who pay him visits now. It is the act of a Christian to do so and, to tell the truth, I have become oddly attached to him, though I can give no just reason for the attachment. He makes a bad patient, by the way, and is often abominably rude to both myself and Madame, who nurses him devotedly though unskillfully. I told him yesterday that I could have no more of it and he looked at me with his strangely luminous eyes. "So," he said, "even the English desert the dying." . . . Well, I stayed; after that, what else might a gentleman do? . . . Yet I cannot feel that he bears me any real affection—he exerts himself to charm, on occasion, but one feels he is playing a game . . . yes, even upon his deathbed, he plays a game . . . a complex character. . . .

April 28th, 1789.

. . . My friend the major's malady approaches its term—the last few days find him fearfully enfeebled. He knows that the end draws nigh; indeed he speaks of it often, with remarkable calmness. I had thought it might turn his mind toward religion, but while he has accepted the ministrations of his church, I fear it is without the sincere repentance of a Christian. When the priest had left him, yesterday, he summoned me, remarking, "Well, all that is over with," rather more in the tone of a man who has just reserved a place in a coach than one who will shortly stand before his Maker.

"It does no harm," he said reflectively. "And, after all, it might be true. Why not?" and he chuckled in a way that repelled me. Then he asked me to read to him—not the Bible, as I had expected, but some verses of the poet Gray. He listened attentively, and when I came to the passage, "Hands, that the rod of empire might have swayed," and its successor, "Some mute inglorious Milton here may rest," he asked me to repeat them. When I had done so, he said, "Yes, yes. That is true, very true. I did not think so in boyhood—I thought genius must force its own way. But your poet is right about it."

I found this painful, for I had hoped that his illness had brought him to a juster, if less arrogant, estimate of his own abilities.

"Come, Major," I said, soothingly, "we cannot all be great men, you know. And you have no need to repine. After all, as you say, you have risen in the world——"

"Risen?" he said, and his eyes flashed. "Risen? Oh, God, that I should die alone with my one companion an Englishman with a soul of suet! Fool, if I had had Alexander's chance, I would have bettered Alexander! And it will come, too, that is the worst of it. Already Europe is shaking with a new birth. If I had been born under the Sun King, I would be a marshal of France; if I had been born twenty years ago, I would mold a new Europe with my fists in the next half-dozen years. Why did they put my soul in my body at this infernal time? Do you not understand, imbecile? Is there no one who understands?"

I called Madame at this, as he was obviously delirious, and, after some trouble, we got him quieted.

> May 8th, 1789.

. . . My poor friend is gone, and peacefully enough at the last. His death, oddly enough, coincided with the date of the opening of the States-General at Versailles. The last moments of life are always painful for the observer, but his end was as relatively serene as might be hoped for, considering his character. I was watching at one side of the bed and a thunderstorm was raging at the time. No doubt, to his expiring consciousness, the cracks of the thunder sounded like artillery, for, while we were waiting the death struggle, he suddenly raised himself in the bed and listened intently. His eyes glowed, a beatific expression passed over his features. "The army! Head of the army!" he whispered ecstatically, and, when we caught him, he was lifeless . . . I must say that, while it may not be very Christian, I am glad that death brought him what life could not, and that, in the very article of it, he saw himself at the head of victorious troops. Ah, fame—delusive specter . . . (A page of disquisition by General Estcourt on the vanities of human ambition is here omitted.) . . . The face, after death, was composed, with a certain majesty, even . . . one could see that he might have been handsome as a youth. . . .

May 26th, 1789.

. . . I shall return to Paris by easy stages and reach Stokely sometime in June. My health is quite restored and all that has kept me here this long has been the difficulty I have met with in attempting to settle my poor friend, the major's, affairs. For one thing, he appears to have been originally a native of Corsica, not of Sardinia as I had thought, and while that explains much in his character, it has also given occupation to the lawyers. I have met his rapacious family, individually and in conclave, and, if there are further gray hairs on my head, you may put it down to them. . . . However, I have finally assured the major's relict of her legitimate rights in his estate, and that is something—my one ray of comfort in the matter being the behavior of her son by the former marriage, who seems an excellent and virtuous, young man. . . .

. . . You will think me a very soft fellow, no doubt, for wasting so much time upon a chance acquaintance who was neither, in our English sense, a gentleman nor a man whose Christian virtues counterbalanced his lack of true breeding. Yet there was a tragedy about him beyond his station, and that verse of Gray's rings in my head. I wish I could forget the expression on his face when he spoke of it. Suppose a genius born in circumstances that made the development of that genius impossible—well, all this is the merest moonshine. . . .

. . . To revert to more practical matters, I discover that the major has left me his military memoirs, papers, and commentaries, including his maps. Heaven knows what I shall do with them! I cannot, in courtesy, burn them *sur-le-champ,* and yet they fill two huge packing cases and the cost of transporting them to Stokely will be considerable. Perhaps I will take them to Paris and quietly dispose of them there to some wastepaper merchant. . . . In return for this unsought legacy,

Madame has consulted me in regard to a stone and epitaph for her late husband, and, knowing that otherwise the family would squabble over the affair for weeks, I have drawn up a design which I hope meets with their approval. It appears that he particularly desired that the epitaph should be writ in English, saying that France had had enough of him, living—a freak of dying vanity for which one must pardon him. However, I have produced the following, which I hope will answer.

Here lies
NAPOLEONE BUONAPARTE
Major of the Royal Artillery
of France.
Born August 15th, 1737
at Ajaccio, Corsica.
Died May 5th, 1789
at St. Philippe-des-Bains

"Rest, perturbed spirit . . ."

. . . I had thought, for some hours, of excerpting the lines of Gray's —the ones that still ring in my head. But, on reflection, though they suit well enough, they yet seem too cruel to the dust.

THOMAS BURKE

Desirable Villa

ಲ

Of all the surprise stories I've ever read, this is perhaps the most surprising. Don't, don't peek!

I do not for a moment (said old Quong) doubt it. You say the young lady claims to be psychic. She certainly is. She was filled all day, you tell me, with a sense of impending disaster and doom, of earthquakes and pestilence and the end of the world, and although you smile when you tell me that that very evening her lipstick gave out at a critical moment of the dance, I see no cause for the smile. She had received her warning, and it was fulfilled. (With this pawn I now retrieve my queen.)

No; I have never doubted that coming events cast their shadows before, particularly those of an unpleasant nature. This is not entirely because these events take pleasure in obscuring our view of the sun, but because events, being static, are perceived by us before we reach them, and we perceive more particularly the unpleasant because in the dim light of the not-yet-reached the unpleasant looms far more heavily than the pleasant. But dim light is deceptive; it holds the essence of the event, but gives it vague or fanciful form; a first draft of what the thing is going to be—and we all know what poets do with their first drafts when they begin work upon them. In such a light twisted trees take the form of wounded soldiers, little hills take the form of fighting galleons; and, to the mental sight, exhausted lipsticks take the form of earthquakes, and ill-made coffee takes the form of pestilence. That light is never to be trusted, because by the time we actually reach the event it is quite likely that the event will have changed its mind.

Take the case of that suburban villa, the story of which was related to me by a young schoolmaster of these parts. (Your move, I think.)

I made my move, and the game of chess, which had been begun that afternoon, went on and on into the long night, like the Vanderbilt family or the Fulham Road. Between moves he told me the story of the desirable villa.

All through one gray-skied afternoon of autumn the young schoolmaster, whose name was Shafe, had been wandering round the northern rim of that cup which holds London, and he had come at twilight into the bleak and chilblain country of the northeast. He was then beyond Walthamstow and beyond that chain of reservoirs which makes the sudden bulge in the course of the river Lea. On what speck of the map he was he didn't know, but he was in a land that some dark corner of his soul told him was very much like hell. It was neither town nor country nor suburb, but something that blasphemed all three. There were bits of field and wood, and bits of paved street, and bits of marshy land. Here and there were some nakedly new shops, and a few houses that were occupied but were not yet blessed with the gracious air that belongs to a house that is lived in. There were a hundred half-finished houses. The grass of the fields was sore with eruptions of brick and pole and toolshed. The unweathered hue of the bricks made them red-hot to the eye. The unmade roads clutched at the feet like satanic hands.

At all points of the outer circle you may come upon these spots of horror. They are not of the stuff or the spirit of horror—merely a part of the necessary business of "developing" a residential estate; yet, though we all live in houses, the sight of this business of making houses affects most of us as an hour in a slaughterhouse would affect a lover of pork. This place, the young man could see, was to be the estate agent's realization of the ideal home for people of small means—the unplaced people just above the self-sufficient dignity of the laboring class. There would be rows and rows of uniform six-room houses, with scullery, bathroom, and electric light. Newly married couples of that unplaced class would furnish their first little homes there. They would found their obscure families, and make pretty gardens, and live out their ignobly decent days in unwondering content. It stood for all that is simple and domestic and petty. His reason and observation told him this. But as that cadaverous light fell upon its litter, his reason was, he says, frozen, and his spirits were pressed into vapor. He could not see it as Kettering Park, N.E. He could only see it as a grouping of horror waiting upon horror.

And then, he says, as though his mind had launched horror into it, horror was born in it and took shape and substance to his eyes.

The workmen were just knocking off when he arrived, dropping their tool bags in the night watchman's shed, and slouching in twos and threes toward the station. But the little caravan "office" of the estate was still open, and potential tenants of the houses were still moving about the estate and asking questions of the two clerks who were there to answer them. They went in and out of the shells of houses, peering and probing, and Shafe watched them with sympathy.

A small river bordered one side of the estate, and to get to the main road leading back to London he had to cross this river by a stone bridge some two hundred yards north of the estate. He crossed it, and turned southward again, on an uphill road, and had a clear view of the houses on the far side. It was then that he noticed— not because they were noticeable, but because they were there—a man and a woman coming toward a house on the limits of the property. They came awkwardly through the wet clay, and their trim town clothes and urban deportment made a queer vibration against the welter of country mire and the shrill newness of the houses. The man carried an umbrella, tightly rolled, and a newspaper. He had small features and a yellow mustache out of proportion to them. His overcoat, trousers, and bowler hat were neither fresh nor shabby; just adequate. A clerk or accountant, Shafe thought, who had succeeded no farther than the point of making ends meet. The woman's face, what he could see of it, was the face of a woman of forty, and the droop of her mouth and her movements in walking suggested that this was a woman who felt that life owed her something. There are thousands of her in her rank of life.

Eminently respectable, both of them; eminently typical of the future residents of the estate; eminently negative.

The steep ascent of his path compelled him to walk slowly, and he had them in view until they entered the half-finished house at the end of the road-that-was-to-be. At this point his path turned inward to the river, and brought him closer to the house by sight, though the distance he had walked from the bridge had put it—because of the river—so much the farther from him. He could see into it, but he could not reach it.

He was at the nearest possible line to it when he heard the man's voice. It called: "Where are you?" The woman answered: "Upstairs. Back room." He could hear the man's boots on the uncovered stairs— he says he can hear quite sharply that gritty clumping now—and then, through the unglazed windows of the upper back room, he saw them together. At that moment his throat surprised him by making a queer noise. It was an unsuccessful cry; unsuccessful because it came from the physical without direction from the mental. It was a muscular explosion, and the detonator was the simple fact that this eminently negative couple had become in that moment eminently positive.

The woman was standing near the window. The man was approaching her from behind. It all happened swiftly, in a group of seconds, but it was in the fraction of the second in which Shafe realized the man's intention and the woman's danger that he delivered that abortive cry. Before that second had passed into time the man's hands were around her throat, and he was dragging her backwards from the window and downward. Shafe cried then, he says, with intent and clearly, but if the man heard him he did not let the cry disturb the business. From his point on the crest of the hill Shafe had to see the completed dreadfulness of the affair. He was an eyewitness and a possible savior, and he was as useful as if he had been at Tilbury. It was not a matter of distance, but of time, and between him and them was the time needed to flounder through six yards of running river. He saw him drag her back and down. He could see the knuckles tightening. Her hat fell off, and her hands made aimless pawings at the air. The man's hands pressed into her throat, and forced the neck back, and worried it from side to side. He was like a dog with a rat, and the great yellow mustache gave him an air of insipid geniality that was as dreadful as the business he was doing. The thing was accomplished in silence. The woman made no cry, and the man's movements were small and tense. A few more wrenches to right and left, and then the body jerked three times and was still. The man got up. He smoothed his clothes and eased his collar. His attitude and expression were as casual as if he really had killed nothing more than a rat. He looked down at the floor and around the bare room as one looks before locking up for a holiday. Then he picked up his newpaper and umbrella from the floor, made a movement of dusting his hands, and turned to go.

By these commonplace gestures Shafe's tension was so suddenly eased that he let out a series of large directed cries toward the office of the estate, and began to run back to the bridge. He hoped to get to the office in time to stop the man from getting off the property, but, though he cried as he ran, his cries created no answer nor movement anywhere. Once or twice in his run he looked back to note the path the man was taking, but he could see nothing of him. He guessed that he was making a sly course through the scattered houses and trying to reach the road by some other way than the main entrance to the estate; and he made a spurt for it. He tore across the bridge, and reached it in a time that surprised himself. He caught one of the clerks, but his want of practice in running found him breathless, and some moments were wasted before he could get the story out. His first effort was almost a coded telegram: "That end house. Down there. Something happened. Send someone—stop man—brown overcoat."

The clerk looked at him with a sort of alert stupidity. Shafe saw that he understood nothing. "Something happened? Where? *What's* happened?"

"Comansee. But send someone stop brown overcoat."

The clerk walked a pace or two with him, a little moved by his vigor, but still withholding attention. When Shafe had achieved coherence he was still without interest. "A man and a woman went into that end house. About three minutes ago. A man in a bowler hat and a brown overcoat. Carrying a rolled umbrella and a newspaper. About five foot nine. Woman about the same height wearing a gray coat. He attacked her in there. Didn't you hear me yell?" The clerk stopped and looked at him with what used to be called a quiz. "Look here—what's all this? I don't know what you're talking about at all. Nobody's been down to that house. I been here all the time. There *was* a man and woman like you say went to look at it, but they went out past my office half an hour ago. At five."

"Then they must have come back another way. Because I *saw* them. Saw them and heard them in the house. I saw him do it. Anyway, come and see. But do something about the man first."

The clerk was clearly annoyed, and Shafe could see that he had eight or nine different and confused ideas about his visitor. But he called to his fellow, who stood by one of the brick dumps, and went over to him, and muttered and jerked his head backward to Shafe. They grinned. Then the other went perfunctorily through scaffold poles and granite curbs toward the path that the man might have taken, and Shafe's young man came back to him. He came strolling, hands in trousers pockets, whistling. "Which house you say—the end one? I'll just come and have a look at it. But you can take it from me those parties left here at five o'clock. And they couldn't a-come back without my seeing 'em."

"Well, they did come back. You'll see when you get there. He brought her back and murdered her."

"Eh?" The clerk looked at him sideways and even more insolently. He was either a lunatic or drunk—a nuisance in any case, and possibly a dangerous nuisance. He called across to his fellow. "Don't go too far, Morton." Shafe could see Morton from where they stood, and he had had the house in full view while telling his story. Despite the quivering approach of the dusk, the light was still sharp and cold, and he was certain that nobody had come from the house since he reached the bridge, and it was certain that nobody had passed Morton. They went to it without secrecy, and walked straight to the front entrance. "Listen, now. If he hasn't got right away he's probably still in the house. So be careful."

Inside the house the light was not so good, but as the rooms were bare, only a glance here and there was necessary. He was not on the ground floor. "Now, then. Upstairs. It was the back room. You'll see something *there;* and you may see him in one of the others. Carefully." They went up, and Shafe looked first into the front rooms and the bathroom. Nothing there. Then he pointed to the back room. Despite the horror and pathos of the occasion, he says that he was aware of a detached interest in the prospect of seeing his cocksure clerk jump. He was guilty of the what-did-I-tell-you posture. "Now look in there." The clerk went in. Shafe gave him a few seconds to himself; then followed him. He looked round at Shafe with "Well?"

The room was empty.

If you have ever pulled a fire alarm and then found that the "fire" was a private bonfire, or tried to save a drowning man and found that he was a professor of swimming, giving an exhibition, you will understand how Shafe felt. The room was empty. All the rooms were empty. There was no corpse and no murderer. The clerk looked at him without any concealment of his grin. "Haven't made a mistake in the house. I suppose? Perhaps we'd better look over all off 'em."

"Perhaps you had. He might have carried it away while I was running. But this was the house. I was standing there—on the road just across the river. *I saw it in this house.*"

"Well, well, well. All I can say is, I've had a clear view of this house all the afternoon. Nobody's been in it except the two people you mentioned. And they went at five o'clock. And nothing's been near that house or come out of it in the last half-hour. Nothing *could* have come out without me seeing it—not out of any point of it—'cos it's in a corner. Certainly not a man carrying a bundle. No, sir. If you'll excuse me, I've got some things to clear up at the office." He turned toward the office with an air of conducting Shafe off the estate; and as there seemed nothing else to do Shafe went with him. On the way he made three firm attempts at stating that he had definitely seen the thing; then his voice refused to back him, and he gave it up. He made apologies for putting the clerk to purposeless trouble and walked away, he says, with what air of normal behavior he could summon. As he moved away he heard a grinning mutter, "Up the loop, I reckon."

He came away disgusted and distressed. Disgusted with himself for exposing himself to the clerk's gibes; distressed because if that thing hadn't happened, then nothing was happening. He wasn't walking, and the night wasn't coming on, and there wasn't any estate or any bridge. He had a foreboding of a nervous breakdown. He was certain that he was wearing boots and trousers, and he was equally certain that that thing had happened. But there was the fact that it hadn't happened, and if it hadn't happened, then he wasn't wearing trousers, and the world was skidding sideways from him. He thought of the usual explanation of ghosts, but it couldn't, he thought, have been a ghostly haunting, because ghosts don't haunt a house before it has been fully built and lived in, and they don't wear the fashions of today. He went home puzzled, disgusted, irritated, and a little apprehensive; and it was three or four weeks, he says, before he shook off the damp memory of that afternoon.

Eight months later he came out of his school at midday and saw the contents bill of a special edition of one of the evening papers: NORTH LONDON MURDER. He saw it and noted it, but only as he noted other things that didn't interest him, such as TEST MATCH RESULT and

LATEST FROM GATWICK. The bill gave it no excited epithet, and he assumed that it had nothing to distinguish it from any other murder—it would be just one of those sordid affairs that happen in London four or five times a year. But while he was having his meal in a small eating house near the school, he picked up a copy of the paper left by a previous customer and found that most of its front page was given to the murder—a murder at Kettering Park, a suburb of North London. As you will guess, the combination of the words "murder" and "Kettering Park" started a mnemonic shuttle in his mind, and he began to read. Besides full details, the paper carried pictures of the victim and of the prisoner, who had been arrested and charged early that morning; and of course the pictures were what you were expecting them to be. He would have recognized anywhere the severe droop of the woman's mouth, or the fluffy mustache that was too big for the face. They were as familiar to him as the face of his dog or of the headmaster of his school, and he turned to the story with a feeling almost of relief.

That goblin memory, which at odd times of day and night had perched upon his brain, was now pulverized. The thing had happened; the idea had washed itself out in fact and was done with forever. What he had seen had indeed been a haunting, but with a difference. It had been not, as usually, a revisitation of the event, but a ghostly approach to it. He had not been suffering from nerves; he had simply seen something before it happened; and when he understood that that was the solution of his afternoon at Kettering Park, he felt easy and knew what the story would be.

It was all there. The very villa of Kettering Park, bordering the river, which the couple had occupied for about six months; the newspaper; the umbrella; the hour (half-past five) it was all there, just as in the—

And then, he says, he dropped the paper. For, though all the details were there, the keypoint of the thing was not. He picked up the paper and studied it again, and, as he read, that one missing thing brought the goblin back, and he felt again the damp and insubstantial sense of living in a world behind the moon. He felt as he had felt when the clerk called from the back room.

The body had been found in the upper back room of the villa.

(Right.) An umbrella and a newspaper were lying beside it. (Right.) The hat was off and the coat was torn open. (Right.) Death was by strangulation. (Right.) A neighbor had heard the man come home, and had heard him call: "Where are you?" and had heard the answer: "Upstairs. Back room." (Right.) And then the thing went all wrong. The picture of the victim was the picture of the man. The picture of the arrested murderer was the picture of the woman.

But that (said old Quong) is quite understandable. You see that something had happened in the interval between the approach to the event and the arrival at it, and, given all the circumstances of the first enactment of the affair, you can see what that something was. Intentions, good or bad, should be put into practice. Otherwise, they may float in the air and . . . Your move, I think.

HEINRICH VON KLEIST

The Earthquake in Chile

&•

Some literary authorities consider Kleist the greatest genius among the classic German writers. After reading this indescribably powerful story, you'll probably agree.

In Santiago, the capital of the kingdom of Chile, at the very moment of the great earthquate of 1647 in which many thousands of lives were lost, a young Spaniard by the name of Jeronimo Rugera, who had been locked up on a criminal charge, was standing against a prison pillar, about to hang himself.

A year or so before, Don Henrico Asteron, one of the richest noblemen of the city, had turned him out of his house, where he had been employed as a tutor, for falling in love with Donna Josepha, Don Henrico's only daughter. A secret rendezvous, held in defiance of the old man's express warning, and betrayed through the malevolent watchfulness of his proud son, made Don Henrico so angry that he sent his daughter away to the Carmelite convent of Our Lady of the Mountain. But, thanks to a lucky chance, Jeronimo was able to renew the attachment there and make the convent garden, one dark night, the scene of his perfect bliss.

It was on Corpus Christi Day, and the solemn procession of nuns, followed by the novices, was just starting out when the unfortunate Josepha, as the bells were pealing all around her, collapsed on the cathedral steps in the pangs of childbirth. This event caused a great outcry; the young sinner, without any attention being paid to her condition, was straightway imprisoned, and no sooner had she got up out of childbed than the Archbishop ordered her to be put on trial for her life: The scandal was talked about with such bitterness in the city, and the convent in which it had occurred was criticized so severely, that neither the pleas of the Asteron family nor even the wish of the abbess herself, who had grown fond of the young girl because of her otherwise irreproachable behavior, could mitigate the harsh punishment with which she was threatened by conventual law. The only thing they could do was to get the Viceroy to commute her sentence of being burned at the stake to one of beheading, much to the indignation of the matrons and virgins of Santiago. Windows were rented out along the route the sinner would follow to her execution, roofs were lifted off, and the pious daughters of the city invited all their friends to join them in watching the spectacle offered the divine wrath.

Meanwhile Jeronimo, who had been imprisoned too, nearly went out of his mind when he learned about the monstrous turn events had taken. He racked his brains in vain for a way to save her; everywhere his most audacious flights of thought bore him he ran into bolts and walls, and an attempt to file through the bars of his prison window only got him, when it was discovered, more closely confined. He prostrated himself before an image of the Holy Mother and with boundless fervor prayed to her from whom alone salvation now could come. But the dreadful day arrived, and with it the conviction that his situation was utterly hopeless. When he heard the air ring with the bells that accompanied Josepha's march to the scaffold, despair overwhelmed his soul. Life now seemed hateful to him and he made up his mind to hang himself with a rope that he found in his cell.

Just as he was standing next to a wall pillar, as we have said, tying to an iron bracket in the cornice the rope that was to snatch him from this wretched world, the greater part of the city suddenly collapsed with a roar, as if the firmament had given way, burying every living thing in its ruins. Jeronimo Rugera went rigid with terror; and, as if all his awareness of things had been destroyed, he now clung to the very pillar on which he had meant to die, to keep himself from falling. The ground swayed under his feet, great cracks suddenly appeared in all the prison walls, and the whole building leaned forward and would have come crashing down into the street if the building opposite had not fallen forward at the same time so that the two met and by a fluke formed a kind of arch over the street that saved it from being completely leveled.

Shaking uncontrollably, his hair standing on end and his knees nearly buckling under him, Jeronimo slid down the steeply slanting floor to the hole driven into the prison's front wall by the coming together of the two buildings. No sooner was he in the clear when a second tremor of the earth caused the already shattered street to collapse completely. Unnerved and at a loss as to how to save himself from the general destruction, he scrambled toward one of the nearest city gates over the rubble and beams, while death snatched at him from every side. Here another house crushed down, hurtling wreckage all around, and drove him into a neighboring street; here the flames were licking out of all the gables, flashing brightly through the clouds of smoke, and frightened him into another; here the Mapocho River, heaved out of its bed, bore down upon him in a flood and swept him with a roar into a third street. Here lay a heap of dead bodies, here a voice still groaned beneath the rubble, here people screamed from burning rooftops, here men and animals battled against the waves, here a brave man tried to rescue others; here another man, pale as death, mutely stretched his trembling hands to heaven.

When Jeronimo had passed through the gate and climbed a hill outside, he sank to the ground unconscious. He lay there for a quarter of an hour and more, in a deep swoon, before he finally awoke and pushed himself up on his knees, with his back to the city. He felt his forehead and chest, not knowing what to make of the state he was in, and an unutterable feeling of bliss possessed him when a west wind from the sea blew on the life stirring in him again and his eyes looked out on Santiago's flowering countryside. Only the bewildered crowds of people that he noticed everywhere made him feel uneasy; he could not understand what had brought him and them to this place, and only when he turned around and saw the prostrate city behind him did he remember the terrible time that he had just gone through. He stooped so low that his forehead touched the ground and thanked God for his miraculous escape; and just as if the last dreadful experience had effaced the recollection of everything before, he wept for joy that all the sweetness and vivid show of life should still be his. But, catching sight of a ring on his finger, he suddenly remembered Josepha, and, with her, his imprisonment, the bells he had heard in his cell, and the moment just before the collapse of the prison. A deep feeling of grief gripped him again; he began to regret his prayer of gratitude, and terrible to him seemed the being who ruled from above the clouds.

Jeronimo went down among the people who, busy saving whatever they could of their possessions, were streaming out of the gates, and ventured to ask them, very fearfully, about Asteron's daughter and whether she had been executed; but nobody was able to tell him anything very definite. A woman who was bent almost to the ground under the immense load of household goods on her neck, as well as the two children she carried at her breast, said as she went by, as if she had seen it with her own eyes, that Josepha had been beheaded.

Jeronimo turned back; he could not doubt, when he calculated the time, that the execution had been carried out before the earthquake struck; and he sat down in a solitary wood and gave way to his grief. He hoped that all of nature's destructive force would fall upon him anew. He did not understand why death, which his despairing soul craved, should have eluded him just when it seemed to be offering him deliverance of its own accord from every side. He was determined not to flinch and run if even now the oak trees were uprooted and their tops came crashing down on him. But when the torrent of his grief had at last subsided and hope returned to him amid his burning tears, he got up again and tramped the fields in every direction. He visited every hilltop on which people had gathered; he followed all the roads along which the streams of fugitives were still flowing; wherever a woman's dress blew in the wind, there his trembling limbs carried him, but none covered Asteron's beloved daughter.

The sun was already beginning to set, and all his hopes with it, when he came to the edge of a cliff, and a view into a broad valley, with just a soul here and there in it, was disclosed to him. His glance strayed over the solitary groups of figures as he hesitated about what to do next, and he was on the point of turning away when he suddenly noticed a young woman bathing an infant at the spring that watered the ravine. His heart jumped at this sight, he sprang down over the rocks full of hope, crying, "Holy Mother of God!" and recognized Josepha when she looked timidly around at the sound. How they hugged each other, with what bliss, the unhappy pair snatched from destruction by a miracle of heaven!

Josepha, on her death march, had almost reached the place of execution when the sudden crashing down of the buildings scattered the entire procession. Her first terrified steps took her toward the nearest gate; but soon recovering herself, she turned and ran back to the convent where she had left her helpless little boy. She found the whole place already in flames, and the abbess, who during the moments which were to have been Josepha's last ones had promised to take care of the infant, was standing at the door shouting for help to save him. Josepha plunged fearlessly through the smoke billowing out of the already collapsing building and soon afterward emerged unharmed from the portal again, with the boy in her arms, just as if all the angels of heaven were watching over her. She was about to fall into the arms of the abbess, who had thrown her hands up in amazement, when the latter, together with almost all her nuns, was killed by a falling gable. Josepha recoiled from the dreadful sight; hurriedly she closed the abbess' eyes and, full of terror, fled with the precious infant, whom heaven had returned to her arms, to save him from the destruction. She had only gone a few steps when she encountered the battered corpse of the archbishop, which had just been dragged out from under the wreckage of the cathedral. The viceroy's palace was a heap of rubble, the courthouse in which she had been sentenced was in flames, and on the spot where her father's house had stood there was now a lake whose boiling waters sent up reddish clouds of steam.

Josepha mustered all her strength to hold on. Putting aside her feelings of distress, she walked bravely through street after street with her prize in her arms, and was already nearing the city gate when she came upon the ruins of the prison in which Jeronimo had suffered. She tottered at the sight of it and would have fallen in a corner in a faint; but just then a building that had been rocked to its foundations by the quakes collapsed behind her and drove her on again, terror lending her new strength; she kissed her child, wiped the tears from her eyes, and disregarding the horrors all around her, reached the gate.

Once out in the open country, it soon became apparent to her that not everybody who had lived in a wrecked building must inevitably have died in its ruins. At the next crossroads she stopped and waited to see if the one who was dearest to her in the world after her little Philip would come along. But when there was no sign of him, and the press of people grew, she journeyed on, then turned back and waited again; and finally, shedding many tears, she crept into a dusky, pine-shaded valley to pray for his soul, which she believed had taken leave of this world; and found him here, her love, in this valley, and such bliss as made it seem like Eden. All this she now told Jeronimo, in a voice choked with emotion, and when her story was done she handed him the boy to kiss.

Jeronimo took him in his arms and petted him with a father's inexpressible delight, and, when his stranger's face made the infant cry, he stopped his mouth with endless kisses. Meanwhile such a night had fallen as only a poet could imagine, rich with a marvelous, mild fragrance, all silvery and still. Everywhere along the valley stream people had dropped down in the shimmering moonlight and were heaping soft beds for themselves of moss and leafy branches, to rest in after their harrowing day. And since the poor unfortunates were still lamenting what they had lost—one his house, another his wife and child, and a third the loss of everything—Jeronimo and Josepha crept away to where the woods were thicker lest the secret jubilation in their souls give pain to anyone. They found a marvelous pomegranate tree, with spreading branches full of fragrant fruit; and in its top the nightingale sang its sensual music.

Jeronimo sat down with his back against the trunk, with Josepha in his lap and Philip in hers, and his cloak around them all; and there they sat and rested. The checkered light and shade of the tree danced across them and the moon was already paling in the rosy dawn before they fell asleep. For there was no end of things they had to tell each other, about the convent and the prison and what they had suffered for each other's sake; and they felt it keenly when they thought of how much woe the world must suffer so that they should find their happiness! They made up their minds, as soon as the last quakes were over, to go to Concepción where Josepha had a close friend from whom they might hope to borrow a small sum with which to embark for Spain, where Jeronimo's relatives on his mother's side lived, and there they would live happily to the end of their lives. After this, and after many kisses, they fell asleep.

When they awoke the sun was already high in the sky, and not far off they noticed several families busy around a fire, getting a little breakfast for themselves. Jeronimo was just thinking how to get some food for his own family when a well-dressed young man with an infant in his arms came up to Josepha and diffidently asked her whether she would not give her breast to the poor little thing for a while, as the mother was lying injured under the trees over there. Josepha betrayed some confusion as she recognized him for somebody she knew; but when, misinterpreting her embarrassment, he continued, "It will only be for a little while, Donna Josepha—the child has had nothing since the hour that has made us all unhappy," she said, "I didn't answer for another reason, Don Fernando; in times like these no one refuses to share whatever he has with others"; and, taking the little stranger from him, while she handed her own child to its father, she gave him her breast. Don Fernando was very thankful for this kindness and asked them if they would not care to join his people at the fire, where they were just getting a little break-fast ready. Josepha said that she would be delighted to, and as Jeronimo had no objection, she followed Don Fernando to his family, where she was welcomed with the utmost cordiality and affection by his two sisters-in-law, whom she knew for very respectable young ladies. Donna Elvira, Don Fernando's wife, whose feet were badly injured, was lying on the ground; she drew Josepha down beside her with great friendliness when she saw her own drooping boy at her breast, Don Pedro, his father-in-law, who had a shoulder wound, also gave her an amiable nod.

Strange thoughts now began to stir in Jeronimo's and Josepha's breasts. When they saw themselves received with so much confidence and kindness, they did not know what to think about the past, the execution block, the prison, and the bells, and whether they had only dreamed it all. A universal reconciliation seemed to have followed the terrible stroke that had fallen on them all. No one seemed able to go farther back in his memory than to the earthquake. Only Donna Elizabeth, who had been invited by a friend to yesterday morning's spectacle, but had refused, occasionally allowed her glance to rest dreamily on Josepha; but the account of some new hideous mis-fortune soon recalled her briefly strayed attention to the present. Stories were told of how, immediately after the first main quake, the city had been crowded with women who gave birth right under the eyes of all the men; how monks with crucifixes in their hands had rushed wildly up and down screaming that the end of the world had come, and how a guard who had commanded everybody to leave a church at the viceroy's order, got for answer the shout that there was no viceroy in Chile any more; how the viceroy, when the disorder was at its height, had had to put up a gallows to stop the looting; and how an innocent man, escaping out of the back of a burning building, had been seized by the owner, who did not stop to ask any questions, and immediately lynched.

Donna Elvira, whose wounds Josepha was busy tending, used a moment when the stories were flying back and forth at their quickest to ask her what had happened to her on that terrible day. And when

Josepha, with a heavy heart, told her some of the most important things, she was intensely pleased to see tears start into the lady's eyes; Donna Elvira caught hold of her hand and squeezed it, and signed to her to say no more.

Josepha felt as if she were among the blessed. Try as she might, she could not help thinking that the preceding day, in spite of all the woe it had brought into the world, had been a blessing such as heaven had never vouchsafed her before. And indeed, at the very moment when all of men's earthly possessions had perished and even nature was threatened with being overwhelmed, the human spirit itself seemed to spring up like a lovely flower. In the fields, as far as the eye could see, people of all classes were jumbled together, princes and paupers, gentlewomen and peasant girls, state officials and day laborers, monks and nuns, commiserating with one another, helping one another, gladly sharing whatever they might have saved to keep themselves alive, as if the general disaster had united all the survivors into a single family. Instead of the empty chatter for which the world of tea tables used to furnish the subject matter, examples of prodigious deeds were now related: people whom one had hardly noticed in society had displayed a Roman virtue; examples without number of fearlessness, of cheerful contempt for danger, of self-denial and god-like self-sacrifices, of lives being thrown away, like some paltry little possession one could pick up again a few steps later on, without an instant's hesitation. Indeed, since there was not a soul on that day to whom something heart-stirring had not happened or who had not himself done some generous deed, the anguish in everybody's breast was mixed with so much sweet delight that it was impossible to decide, as she thought, whether the sum of general happiness had not increased on one side by as much as it had declined on the other.

Taking Josepha by the arm after they had both exhausted this theme in silent reflection, Jeronimo walked up and down with her, in a mood of inexpressible elation, in the shade of the pomegranate trees. He told her that the generous temper of mind that they saw everywhere, together with the revolution in social relations, had persuaded him to give up his purpose of sailing for Europe, that he would take the chance of going to see the viceroy (if he were still alive) and throwing himself at his feet, for he had always been favorably disposed toward his case, and that he hoped (and here he gave her a kiss) to remain with her in Chile.

Josepha said that she had been having similar thoughts; that if her father still lived she no longer doubted her becoming reconciled with him; but that she felt it would be better for them to go to Concepción and from there appeal in writing to the viceroy, rather than for Jeronimo to go and throw himself at his feet, since they would have the harbor near them at Concepción if worst came to worst, but that if all went well and their case took the direction they wished it to, they could easily return to Santiago. After a moment's reflection, Jeronimo applauded her prudence, strolled with her about the paths a little more while looking forward to their future happiness, and rejoined their friends.

Meanwhile the afternoon had arrived bringing an abatement of the earth shocks, so that the swarming refugees were a little easier in their minds, when the news spread that the abbot of the monastery himself was going to read a solemn mass in the Church of the Dominicans, the only one the earthquake had spared, imploring heaven to shield them against further calamities. From every region people were setting out and streaming into the city as fast as possible. In Don Fernando's group the question came up as to whether they should not join the throng, too, and attend the ceremony. Donna Elizabeth reminded them with some uneasiness of the trouble there had been in the church the day before; that many more such thanksgiving celebrations would be held; and that when the danger had receded more into the past, they would be able to give gladder and serener expression to their gratitude.

Josepha leaped enthusiastically to her feet and said that the wish to bow her face in the dust before her Maker had never been so strong in her as now, when He had given such proof of His unfathomable and supernal power. Donna Elvira empthatically endorsed Josepha's view. She absolutely insisted on their hearing the mass, and called on Don Fernando to lead them to the church, whereupon everybody, not excepting Donna Elizabeth, rose from his seat. But seeing how violently her breast was heaving and how hesitant she was about getting ready to go, they asked her what was wrong; she could not understand why, she said, she had such a deep foreboding of disaster. Donna Elizabeth then suggested that she should stay behind with her sick father and herself, and spoke reassuringly to her. Josepha said, "Since you are staying here, Donna Elizabeth, perhaps you will take this little darling off my hands, who, as you see, has crept back into my bosom again."

"Gladly," Donna Elizabeth answered and put her arms out for him; but when the infant wailed plaintively at the wrong being done to him and refused to be handed over, Josepha smiled and said that it looked as if she would have to keep him, and hushed him with kisses. Don Fernando, who was charmed by the dignity and grace of her demeanor, offered her his arm; Jeronimo, carrying little Philip, conducted Donna Constanza; the other members of the company followed after; and in this order they set off toward the city.

They had hardly gone fifty steps when they heard Donna Elizabeth, who meanwhile had been speaking aside to Donna Elvira with great concentration, call out, "Don Fernando!" and saw her hurry after them with anxious steps. Don Fernando halted and turned; waited for her without letting go of Josepha's arm; and, when she stopped some way off as if expecting him to come to her, asked her what she wanted. Donna Elizabeth then came closer, although apparently with some reluctance, and murmured in his ear so that Josepha could not hear her. "Well," said Don Fernando, "and where would be the harm in that?" Donna Elizabeth continued to whisper in his ear with a distraught look on her face. Don Fernando reddened with displeasure and said that that would do! Donna Elvira could put her mind at rest; and he went on with Josepha.

When they reached the Church of the Dominicans, the sonorous splendor of the organ could already be heard and a huge multitude swayed beneath the roof. The crowd overflowed the portal of the church far out into the square, and high up on the cathedral walls boys were clinging to the picture frames and squeezing their caps in their hands with looks of intense expectation. The chandeliers shed a brilliant light, the pillars cast mysterious shadows in the falling dusk, the great rose window of stained glass at the far end of the church glowed like the very evening sun by which it was illuminated; and when the organ left off playing, silence fell upon the whole assembly, as if no one there could make a sound.

Never did the flame of devotion leap more brightly toward heaven from a Christian cathedral than from the Dominican church of Santiago that day; and nobody's breast fed it with warmer fervor than Jeronimo's and Josepha's! The solemnity began with a sermon preached from the pulpit by one of the oldest canons of the church, attired in all his regalia. His trembling hands reaching toward heaven out of the flowing sleeves of his surplice, he began by giving praise and thanks that there were still men in this part of the world, which was collapsing into ruins, who were capable of lifting up their stammering voices to God. He described what, at a signal from the Almighty, had happened; Judgment Day could not be more fearful; and when he pointed to a crack in the cathedral wall and called yesterday's earthquake a mere herald of that coming time, a shudder ran through the entire congregation. His flow of priestly eloquence carried him on to the moral corruption of the city; he castigated it for abominations such as Sodom and Gomorrah had never known; and he ascribed it only to God's infinite forbearance that the city had not been wiped off the face of the earth.

But the hearts of our two unfortunates, already lacerated by this sermon, were stabbed as if by a sword when the canon seized the occasion to describe in detail the outrage that had been perpetrated in the convent garden of the Carmelites; called the tolerant attitude the world took toward it a piece of godlessness; and in an aside loaded with maledictions against the two miscreants, whom he named aloud, he consigned their souls to all the princes of hell! Donna Constanza tugged Jeronimo's arm and cried, "Don Fernando!" The latter, however, putting as much emphasis as could be combined with stealth into his reply, said, "Keep absolutely quiet, Donna, don't even blink your eyes, and make believe you have fainted; then we'll leave the church." But before Donna Constanza could carry out this clever ruse, a voice broke loudly into the canon's discourse: "Stand back, citizens of Santiago, the godless creatures are right here!"

"Where?" cried another voice, full of fear, a circle of dread spreading around it; a third man answered, "Here!" and, full of pious brutality, pulled Josepha by the hair, so that she would have fallen to the ground with Don Fernando's son if the latter had not held her up.

"Are you out of your mind?" the young man cried, putting his arm around Josepha. "I am Don Fernando Ormez, son of the commandant of the city, whom you all know."

"Don Fernando Ormez?" a shoemaker standing right in front of him called out, a man who had done work for Josepha and knew her at least as well as he knew her tiny feet. "Who is this child's father?" and he turned with insolent defiance to Asteron's daughter. Don Fernando turned pale at this question. First he looked hesitantly at Jeronimo, then around the congregation to see if there were anybody there who knew him. The terrible situation that had arisen forced Josepha to call out, "This isn't my child, Master Pedrillo, as you imagine," and she looked at Don Fernando with immense fear in her soul. "This young man is Don Fernando Ormez, son of the commandant of the city, whom you all know!"

The shoemaker asked, "Citizens, who among you knows this young man?" And several of those standing nearby repeated, "Who here knows Jeronimo Rugera? Let him come forward!" Now just at this moment little Juan, frightened by the noise, leaned out of Josepha's arms and stretched his hands toward Don Fernando. "He is too the father!" a voice yelled; "He is Jeronimo Rugera!" screamed another; "These are the blaspheming sinners!" a third—"Stone them! Stone them!" all the Christians assembled in the temple of Jesus roared.

Upon which Jeronimo: "Stop, you monsters! If you are looking for Jeronimo Rugera, here he is! Let that man go, he is innocent!" The enraged mob, confused by what Jeronimo had shouted, did not know what to do; several hands fell away from Don Fernando; and when a naval officer of high rank came running up at that moment, calling out, "Don Fernando Ormez! What has happened to you?" as he pressed through the tumultuous crowd, Don Fernando, now entirely set free, responded with truly heroic presence of mind, "Just look at them, those murderers, Don Alonzo! I would have been lost if this good man here had not pretended to be Jeronimo Rugera, to quiet the raging mob. Would you be good enough to arrest him, and also this young lady, for their own safety; and also this wretch here," and he seized Master Pedrillo, "who started the whole commotion!"

The shoemaker called out, "Don Alonzo Onoreja, I ask you on your conscience, isn't this girl Josepha Asteron?" When Don Alonzo, who knew Josepha quite well, hesitated in replying, and several voices, incensed anew by this, cried, "It's she, it's she!" and "Kill her!" Josepha put little Philip, whom Jeronimo had been carrying till then, in Don Fernando's arms, together with little Juan, and said, "Go on, Don Fernando, save your two children and leave us to our fate!" Don Fernando took both children and said he would sooner die on the spot than suffer anything to happen to his friends. After asking the naval officer for his sword, he gave Josepha his arm and called to the couple behind to follow. And they did indeed manage to leave the church, for the crowd gave way with grudging respect before them, and thought themselves saved.

But no sooner were they in the square, which was just as tightly packed with people, when a voice rang out of the frenzied mob that had pursued them: "Citizens, this is Jeronimo Rugera, for I am his own father!" and with a tremendous blow of his club, he struck him down at Donna Constanza's side. "Jesus Maria!" Donna Constanza screamed, running toward her brother-in-law; but already there was a cry of "Convent whore!" and a second blow, from another side, felled her lifeless to the ground beside Jeronimo.

"Monster!" a stranger cried out, "that was Donna Constanza Xares!"

"Then why did they lie to us!" the shoemaker retorted. "Find the right one and kill her!"

Don Fernando, when he caught sight of Donna Constanza's corpse, was maddened with rage; drawing his sword, he brandished it over his head and struck a blow that would have split the fanatical murderer who was the instigator of all these horrors in half if the shoemaker had not dodged out of its way. But since it was impossible for him to overcome the mob pressing in on him, Josepha cried out, "Farewell, Don Fernando and the children!"— and: "Here, murder me, you bloodthirsty tigers!" and plunged into their midst, to put an end to the struggle. Master Pedrillo felled her with his club. Then, spattered with her blood, he yelled, "Send the bastard to hell right after her!" and pressed forward afresh with still unsatisfied blood lust. Don Fernando now stood, heroic as a god, with his back to the church; his left hand held the children, his right his sword. With every lightning stroke he toppled somebody to the ground; a lion does not fight better. Seven of the bloodhounds lay dead in front of him, the leader of the satanic pack himself was wounded. But Master Pedrillo would not rest until he had pulled one of the children from Fernando's breast by the legs and, whirling it in the air, smashed it against the edge of a church pillar. Then silence fell upon the square and the crowd drew back.

When Don Fernando saw his little Juan lying there with his brains oozing out, he lifted his eyes, full of inexpressible woe, to heaven. The naval officer reappeared and tried to comfort him, and told him how sorry he felt about his own inaction, although there were several circumstances to explain it; but Don Fernando said he had nothing to reproach himself for, and only asked him to help remove the bodies. These were now carried through the darkness of the falling night to Don Alonzo's house, whither Don Fernando followed, raining tears on little Philip's face. He passed the night at Don Alonzo's, and for quite some time hid the full extent of the misfortune from his wife under a trumped-up story: for one thing, because she was ill, and then, too, because he did not know how she would judge his own behavior; but shortly after, learning the whole story by accident from a visitor, this good lady cried her maternal grief out in silence, and then one morning, throwing her arms around his neck, with a tear-drop shining in her eye, she kissed him.

Don Fernando and Donna Elvira took the little stranger for their own child; and when Don Fernando compared Philip with Juan, and the different ways the two had come to him, it almost seemed to him that he had reason to feel glad.

T. H. WHITE

Eccentrics

⟨

The author of The Once and Future King *was also an authority on eighteenth century England. This chapter is a highlight of his book* The Scandalmonger.

It may have been due to their bad teeth or to their rotten tonsils, before these forms of poisoning had been identified; or it may have been due to the quantities of alcohol consumed by many; or perhaps the root may have been podagral: whatever the explanation, the incidence of lunacy in the second half of the eighteenth century seems to have been high. Not only was the king himself a manic-depressive, but his first minister also, the elder Pitt, suffered during a great part of his administration from a toxic condition which produced the attitudes of melancholia.

Lord Chatham's state of health [wrote Mr. Whateley] is certainly the lowest dejection and debility that mind or body can be in. He sits all day leaning on his hands, which he supports on the table; does not permit any person to remain in the room; knocks when he wants anything; and having made his wants known, gives a signal, without speaking, to the person who answered his call to retire.

His sickly and uncertain appetite [wrote Walpole] was never regular, and his temper could put up with no defect: thence a succession of chickens were boiling and roasting at every hour, to be ready whenever he should call.

It was not only the politicians and the kings who suffered from imbecility—there were lunatic monarchs in Prussia, Russia, Denmark, Portugal, and perhaps elsewhere—but also the peerage and the landed gentry. Dukes like he of Bolton might suddenly sit on the floor and blow their brains out, causing Walpole to observe:

The Duke of Bolton the other morning—nobody knows why or wherefore, except that there is a good deal of madness in the blood, sat himself down upon the floor of his dressing-room, and shot himself through the head. What is more remarkable is, that it is the same house and the same chamber in which Lord Scarborough performed the same exploit. I do not believe that shooting oneself through the head is catching.

Earls like Ferrers might send for their stewards and shoot them down. Horace Walpole's own nephew, Lord Orford, who spent much of his life insane, would

do nothing but speak in the lowest voice, and would whisper to them at the length of the table, when the person next to him could not distinguish what he said. Every evening, precisely at the same hour, sitting round a table, he would join his forehead to his mistress's (who is forty, red-faced, and with black teeth, and with whom he has lived these twenty years), and there they would sit for a quarter of an hour, like two parroquets, without speaking.

The Townshend family, more metaphysical, would get into an argument about Life with a capital letter, with fatal results:

This boy [Lord William Townshend] from infancy had a tendency to insanity. Some years after his being in India, he was travelling in England with one of his brothers in a postchaise, when their conversation was whether life under all the evils that attended it was worth keeping? After a long discussion they were both of opinion that the evils so greatly outweighed the blessings that existence was not desirable: they therefore immediately determined to withdraw themselves from it, and taking out a pair of pistols they had in the carriage they intended each to shoot the other, or each to shoot himself. It was never ascertained which was the fact; one shot took effect, proving fatal instantaneously, I do not recollect upon which of them; the other pistol missed fire. The postilion stopping upon hearing the report, got off his horse and opening the door of the carriage found one of them fallen off his seat, weltering in his blood, the other sitting very composedly. Upon being asked what had happened to his brother he made no answer, nor would he even state a single circumstance relative to the transaction. He has ever since been confined as a lunatic.

WILLIAM HICKEY

In the republic of literature, moreover, there was scarcely a man who claimed to be of sound mind. Cowper, Smart, Gray, Johnson,

Boswell, Blake, and Lamb, all owned to the soft impeachment of mental affliction, sometimes homicidal, sometimes not.

Perhaps it was a sign of the times. Perhaps so eccentric a century was bound to have an abundance of examples, slightly more eccentric than the rest.

There was the odd duke of Queensberry. Born in 1725, and devoted to betting, to Newmarket or to "splendid vice, of almost oriental voluptuousness," it was he who "performed, in his own drawing room, the scene of Paris and the goddesses. Three of the most beautiful females in London presented themselves before him, precisely as the divinities of Homer are supposed to have appeared to Paris on Mount Ida: while *he,* habited like the Darden shepherd, holding a gilded apple in his hand, conferred the prize on her whom he deemed the fairest." In old age, according to Jesse

in fine sunny weather, it was the custom of the Duke of Queensberry to seat himself in his balcony in Piccadilly, where his figure was familiar to every person who was in the habit of passing through the great thoroughfare. Here (his emaciated figure rendered the more conspicuous from his custom of holding a parasol over his head) he was in the habit of watching every attractive form, and ogling every pretty face that met his eye. He is said, indeed, to have kept a pony and servant in constant readiness, in order to follow, and ascertain the residence of any fair girl whose attractions particularly caught his fancy.

The duke retained a doctor, whom he only paid when he was well, and died "with great firmness" in 1810, at the age of eighty-six, his deathbed being strewed

with billets and letters to the number of at least seventy, mostly, indeed, addressed to him by females of every description and of every rank, from duchesses down to ladies of the easiest virtue. Unable, from his extenuated state, to open or to peruse them he ordered them as they arrived to be laid on his bed, where they remained, the seals unbroken, till he expired [—unmarried].

There was the Chevalier d'Eon, the fencer and diplomat, who spent the first half of his life in breeches and the second half in petticoats. Hannah More met him in the latter garment:

On Friday I gratified the curiosity of many years, by meeting at dinner Madame la Chevalière d'Eon: she is extremely entertaining, has universal information, wit, vivacity, and gaiety. Something too much of the latter, (I have heard) when she has taken a bottle or two of Burgundy; but this being a very sober party, she was kept entirely within the limits of decorum. General Johnson was of the party, and it was ridiculous to hear her military conversation. Sometimes it was, *"Quand j'étais colonel d'un tel regiment!"* then again, *"Non, c'était quand j'étais secrétaire d'ambassade du Duc de Nivernois,"* or *"Quand je négociais la paix de Paris."* She is, to be sure, a phenomenon in history; and, as such, a great curiosity. But *one* d'Eon is enough, and *one slice* of her quite sufficient.

Walpole met the Chevalier in both forms, but was more amused by the feminine one:

I received a little Italian note from Mrs. Cosway, this morning, to tell me that, as I had at her house last week met an old acquaintance, without knowing her, I might meet her again this evening, *en connoissance de cause,* as Mademoiselle la Chevalière d'Eon, who, as Mrs. Cosway told me, had taken it ill that I had not reconnoitred her, and said she must be strangely altered—the devil is in it, if she is not!—but alack! I have found her altered again; adieu to the abbatical dignity that I had fancied I discovered; I now found her loud, noisy, and vulgar; indeed, I believe she had dined a little *en dragon.* The night was hot, she had no muff or gloves, and her hands and arms seem not to have participated of the change of sexes, but are fitter to carry a chair than a fan.

Lady Louvain wished to see Mademoiselle D'Eon [he wrote later], and Mr. Dutens invited her. The Lady asked her if she had ever been at Dijon, and said she herself had lain in there. "I have been there," said Miss Hector, "but did not lie in there, *car je suis vierge, et pour que les vierges accouchent, il faut qu'elles aillent à Jerusalem."* It was impertinent to Lady Louvain, and worse in a clergyman's house; but women of fashion should not go aboard Amazons.

She seems to have a noble, independent, as well as intrepid mind [wrote Anna Seward more kindly]—and the muscular strength and activity of her large frame at sixty-nine, are wonderful. She fences in the French uniform, and then appears an athletic, venerable, graceful man. In the female garb, as might be expected, she is awkwardly, though not vulgarly masculine.

Bets were laid on her sex, which were only decided at her death. Then Lady Jerningham wrote, in 1810:

It is a most extraordinary event. Père Elisé, who Called upon her every day during her illness, made his visit, about 2 hours after She had expired, and, going up to the Bed to Look at Her, and reflecting upon all the past Historys about Her, Lifted up the Sheet *Machinalement* and Screamed out to the dismay of the Femme de Chambre: *C'est un Homme!*

So far as mixed sexes went, there was a regular plethora of female soldiers in Walpole's century. Phoebe Hessel claimed to have been wounded at Fontenoy, and lived to be a hundred and eight. Mother Ross of the Second Dragoons was buried among the Chelsea pensioners with three grand volleys over her grave. Hannah Snell, who was known to her comrades as "hearty Jemmy," said that she had received five hundred lashes from the sergeant, and was wounded at Pondicherry. Mary Ann Talbot, the "British Amazon," was both soldier, cabin boy, and powder monkey but took to drink and ended as a domestic servant, though a tiresome one.

A major eccentric was Thomas Day, the author of *Sandford and Merton,* who, having been born in 1748 and bitten with the madness of Rousseau, determined to educate a wife for himself. The story may be found in Hesketh Pearson's *Doctor Darwin*:

Among other things, he wanted his wife to be as "simple as a mountain girl, in her dress, her diet, and her manners; fearless and intrepid as the Spartan wives and Roman heroines." . . .

With a barrister friend, Mr. Bicknel, he descended upon the town of Shrewsbury, and, armed with credentials of his moral probity, visited the Foundling Hospital there. From among the "prattling inmates of that institution" [to quote Blackman] he selected a girl aged eleven—Anna Seward describes her as "a clear, auburn brunette, with dark eyes, glowing bloom and chestnut tresses"—whom he called Sabrina Sidney. [She owed her Christian name to the River Severn and her surname to Day's hero, Algernon.] Day and Bicknel then visited the Foundling Hospital in London, where they selected another girl, aged twelve—described by Anna as "fair, with flaxen locks and light eyes"—and called her Lucretia.

Day proposed to keep whichever of these turned out to be the better, and to give a dowry to the other. He took them to France, and after two years of desperate trouble as a nursery maid, he started on the higher, the stoic education.

There were, he decided, two classes of cowards—those who shrank from immediate physical pain, and those who were terrified by the apprehension of danger. His methods were carefully selected to prove complete immunity from cowardice in both forms, should the patient survive the ordeal. First, he believed that the dropping of melted sealing wax on the neck and arms of Sabrina would, if she treated it as an ordinary occurrence, definitely signify her indifference to immediate physical pain. He tried it, but was disagreeably surprised to note that, as the wax sizzled and hardened on her flesh, she so far forgot herself as to scream.

But there was still hope. A woman who could not endure acute suffering, because of some inherited effeminacy, might yet be stoical under the threat of mortal danger. He informed her therefore that he had loaded his pistol and begged her to have sufficient faith in the accuracy of his aim, and his proved affection for herself, not to jump when he fired a bullet into her petticoats. Taking a careful aim at her legs, he then fired off a blank cartridge, and was shocked to observe that she not only jumped but emitted a howl of terror. He was not, however, callous enough to give her up in despair at the first failure. He wanted her to have every possible chance of gaining his good opinion; so he went on blazing away hopefully at her skirts . . . In the hope that hardening would come with time, he repeated these experiments, with others of a similar nature, at intervals during his year's residence at Lichfield; but Sabrina never really got used to them, and continually vexed him with her querulous complaints.

In the end, neither of the two young ladies proved to be acceptable as wives, and the enthusiast had to content himself with being painted by Wright of Derby.

Drawn as in the open air, the surrounding sky is tempestuous, lurid and dark. He stands leaning his left arm against a column inscribed to Hampden. Mr. Day looks upward, as enthusiastically meditating on the contents of the book, held in his dropped right hand. The open leaf is the oration of that virtuous patriot in the senate, against the grant of ship-money, demanded by King Charles the First. A flash of lightning plays in Mr. Day's hair, and illuminates the contents of the volume.

Another oddity was Maria Edgeworth's father, who according to Pearson, kept several terms at the Temple, read scientific books, constructed a carriage, played cards, made experiments . . . Some of his inventions were more curious than useful. One was a sailing carriage, which threatened to distribute the horse traffic on the roads about Reading in a most alarming manner. Another was a giant wooden horse, which, by a strange arrangement of front and rear legs, could carry him safely over any wall in the country. He experimented on this at intervals for forty years, but never achieved complete success. A third was a huge hollow wheel, by walking within which a man could travel much faster than his legs could naturally take him. This interesting novelty was wrecked before completion by a small boy, who got into it and began to ply his legs. The wheel, helped by a gentle incline, needed no human encouragement and dashed off in the direction of a chalk pit. The boy saved his life by jumping out, but the wheel refused to be saved and was picked up in small fragments the following morning by its sorrowful contriver, who had not enough capital to give the experiment a further trial.

There was Dr. Darwin himself, the grandfather of the biologist, who invented water closets—or reinvented them—luminous music, speaking machines, artificial birds, and even a plan by which,

if the nations who inhabit this hemisphere of the globe, instead of destroying their seamen and exhausting their wealth in unnecessary wars, could be induced to unite their labours to navigate the immense masses of ice in the polar regions into the more southern seas, two great advantages would result to mankind; the tropic countries would be much cooled by their solution, and our winters in this latitude would be rendered much milder for perhaps a century or two, till the masses of ice became again enormous.

In the year 1768 [wrote Anna Seward] Dr. Darwin met with an accident of irretrievable injury to the human frame. His propensity to mechanics had unfortunately led him to construct a very singular carriage. It was a platform, with a seat fixed upon a very high pair of wheels, and supported in the front, upon the back of the horse, by means of a kind of proboscis, which, forming an arch, reached over the hindquarters of the horse, and passed through a ring, placed on an upright piece of iron, which worked in a socket, fixed in the saddle. The horse could thus move from one side of the road to the other, quartering, as it is called, at the will of the driver, whose constant attention was necessarily employed to regulate a piece of machinery contrived, but *not well* contrived, for that purpose. From this whimsical carriage the doctor was several times thrown, and the last time he used it, had the misfortune, from a similar accident, to break the patella of his right knee, which caused, as it must always cause, an incurable weakness in the fractured part, and a lameness, not very discernible, indeed, when walking on even ground.

Apart from those who were mechanically afflicted, there were eccentric misers like the pleasant Elwes, a favorite of Horace Walpole's, whose one amusement was partridge shooting, and who consequently had to live on partridges. Nollekens was so mean that he only owned one pair of smallclothes. Neild would not allow his clothes to be brushed because it destroyed the nap, but he left £500,000 to Queen Victoria. And Daniel Dancer, who bequeathed £3000 per annum, dressed mainly in hay-bands. The least sufferable of contemporary misers tried to cheapen his own daughter's funeral by pointing out that he had another daughter who would be dying soon, and that he would send her to the same undertaker.

The *Dictionary of National Biography* is embarrassed with a richness of oddities, flourishing in the Age of Scandal. The unusual viceprovost of Trinity College, Dublin, John Barrett (1752-1821), "would sometimes go down to the kitchen to warm himself, but to this the servants objected on account of his dirty and ragged condition." Jeremy Bentham (1748-1832)—whose skeleton in its original clothes is preserved at University College, London—invented what he called "auto-icons." Dead people were to be embalmed and used as their own monuments. "If a country gentleman have rows of trees leading to his dwelling, the auto-icons of his family might alternate with the trees; copal varnish would protect the face from the effects of rain—caoutchouc the habiliments." Nathaniel Bentley (1735-1809), known as Dirty Dick, refused to have his premises cleaned or dusted for forty years. The great philosopher and exponent of tar water, Bishop Berkeley (1685-1753), "induced his friend Contarini, Goldsmith's uncle, to hang him experimentally. He was cut down when nearly senseless, and exclaimed, 'Bless my heart, Contarini, you have rumpled my band!'" Joseph Black (1728-1799), an eminent and precise chemist, died with his accustomed precision. "Being at table with his usual fare, some bread, a few prunes, and a measured quantity of milk diluted with water, and having the cup in his hand when the last stroke of the pulse was to be given, he appeared to have set it down on his knees, which were joined together, and in the action expired without spilling a drop, as if an experiment had been purposely made to evince the facility with which he departed." The famous Ladies of Llangollen—Lady Eleanor Butler and Sarah Ponsonby—retired to Wales and lived in seclusion and semi-masculine costume. Chatterton's father could put his clenched fist in his mouth. Romeo Coates (1772-1848) drove round Bath in a carriage shaped like a kettledrum "and across the bar of his curricle was a large brazen cock, with this motto, 'Whilst I live I'll crow.'" Cornwall, the Speaker of the House of Commons (1735-1789), kept a replenished mug of beer in the House and caused inconvenience by going to sleep from its effects. Patrick Cotter (1761-1806) was eccentric enough to be eight feet seven inches high—while Joseph Borulwaski (1739-1837) was content with thirty-nine inches and lived to be nearly a hundred. Cracherode (1730-1799), the timid bibliophile, held a manor of the king subject to the service of presenting a coronation cup, and the dread "lest he should at any time be called upon to undertake this service embittered his life." John Crofton the antiquary (1732-1820) read the whole of *Don Quixote* to his wife in Spanish, although she did not understand a word of that language. John Dalton (1766-1844), chemist and natural philosopher, ascended Helvellyn between thirty and forty times, and, when asked the reason why he had not married, replied, "I never had time." Daniel Day (1683-1767) "left directions that his body should be conveyed to the grave by water, in consequence of the number of accidents he had met with while traveling on land, and that it should be accompanied by six pump-and-block makers." John Deare the sculptor (1759-1798) "caught a fatal cold by sleeping on a block of marble of peculiar shape, expecting to get inspiration in his dreams for carving it." Thomas Dermody the poet (1775-1802) "abandoned himself to vice, saying, 'I am vicious because I like it.'" Robert Deverell, formerly Pedley (1760-1841), wrote a book to show that all the characters in Shakespeare were merely references to the moon. Lamb's friend George Dyer (1755-1841), on being told that a man called Williams had murdered two whole families, observed that Williams "must have been rather an eccentric character." An actor called John Edwin (1768-1805), who had received an adverse criticism, wrote to a friend, "Come and help me to destroy myself with some of the most splendid cogniac [sic] that I have ever exported to cheer a breaking heart," and duly destroyed himself by that means. The Duke of Bridgewater (1736-1803) would talk of nothing but canals, rooted up all the flowers in his garden, and would not allow any woman servant to wait upon him. The Earl of Bridgewater (1756-1829) had a house filled with cats and dogs, "some of which were dressed up as men and women, and were driven out in his carriage, and fed at his table." John Fransham the freethinker (1730-1810) lived on a farthing's worth of potatoes a day, considered that to make his bed more than once a week was "the height of effeminacy," thought dogs to be "noisy, mobbish, and vulgar," ate tarts till he got a headache in order to enjoy the contrasting pleasures of health, burned his hautboy to make tea, and "supplying its place with a 'bilbo-catch,' he persevered until he had caught the ball on the spike 666,666 times (not in succession; he could never exceed a sequence of two hundred)." Lord Gardenstone (1721-1793) had "an extreme fondness for pigs," which he kept in his bedroom, explaining: "It is just a bit sow, poor beast, and I laid my breeches on it to keep it warm all night." James Graham (1745-1794), the quack doctor who kept a not very respectable Temple of Health and Hymen visited by Horace Walpole, and who, incidentally, is said to have employed Nelson's Lady Hamilton there in her earlier years, was fond of "earth-bathing"; and "we are told that he and a young lady of Newcastle "stripped into their first suits" and were each interred up to the chin, their heads beautifully powdered and dressed, appearing not unlike two fine, full-grown cauliflowers." From December 31, 1792, to January 15, 1793, "he neither ate, drank, nor took anything but cold water, sustaining life by wearing cut-up turfs against his naked body, and by rubbing his limbs with his own nervous aethereal balsam." The mother of Thomas Greenhill (1681-1740) "had by one husband thirty-nine children, all (it is said) born alive and baptized, and all single births except one." John Henderson (1757-1788) would go to bed at daybreak "after putting on a shirt which he had made perfectly wet" at the pump. Orator Henley (1692-1756) invented a new way of making shoes—which was by cutting off the tops of boots. The eleventh Duke of Norfolk (1746-1815) was called "Dirty Jockey of Norfolk," and could only be washed by his servants when drunk in bed. Hortensia, one of the favorite whores of Dr. Johnson (*c.* 1778), would "walk up and down the Park, repeating a book of Virgil." John Howell the polyartist (1788-1863) broke his leg trying to fly and "having made at considerable expense, a model in the shape of a fish, he entered the machine, tried to swim under water at Leith, and was nearly drowned." Henry Constantine Jennings (1731-1819), virtuoso, was believed to keep an oven in his house for the cremation of his body, and, on getting up in the morning, he "mounted his chaise-horse, composed of leather and inflated like a pair of bellows, and took exactly one thousand gallops." Richard Kirwan (1733-1812) lived on ham and milk. "Flies were his especial aversion; he kept a pet eagle, and was attended by six large dogs." Daniel Lambert (1770-1809) "attained the acme of mortal hugeness." He weighed 52¾ stone and his coffin was built upon two axletrees and four wheels, being rolled down a gradual incline to the grave. Jane Lewson (1700-1816) would never allow water to be used in her house, for fear of catching cold, washed her hands with lard, and by these precautions lived to be about a hundred and sixteen. John Metcalf (1717-1810), though totally blind, was a jockey, swimmer, soldier, gallant, horse dealer, coach conductor, and road maker, who surveyed and laid out 180 miles of road without assistance. John Mitford (1782-1831), "took to journalism and strong drink." He lived for forty-three days in a gravel pit, with pen, ink, and paper, being allowed a shilling a day by his publisher, of which he expended tenpence on gin and twopence on bread, cheese, and an onion. Ann Moore (*fl.* 1813), the "fasting woman of Tutbury," was believed to live on air. Beau Nash (1674-1761) was accustomed to make bets "such as that he would ride through a village on cowback naked." William Paley of the *Evidences* (1743-1805) fell off his pony seven times on the road to Cambridge, "his father only turning his head on such occasions to say, 'Take care of thy money, lad.'" Sir Ralph Payne (1738-1807), governor of the Leeward Islands, "was attended by an army of servants, but he would not allow any of the black servitors about him to wear shoes or stockings, their legs being rubbed daily with butter so that they shone like jet; and he would not, if he could avoid it, handle a letter or parcel from their fingers. To escape the indignity, he designed a golden instrument, like a tongs, with which he held any article which was given him by a black servant." Robert Pigott (1736-1794) "fulminated against hats, arguing that they had been introduced by priests and despots, and that they concealed the face and were gloomy and monotonous." Richard Pockrich (1690-1757) proposed "to supply men-of-war with tin boats which would not sink, to secure immortality by the transfusion of blood, and to provide human beings with wings." The first person to have a glass pane in his coffin seems to have been Robert Robinson, D.D. (1727-1791), who also had an unlocked mausoleum and a watchman to see if he breathed on the glass. The only peer, perhaps the only gentleman of Great Britain, who wore a beard with his wig, was Lord Rokeby (1713-1800). He "lived chiefly on beef tea, and was an enthusiastic water drinker. He abhorred fires, and had a bath so constructed as to be warmed only by the rays of the sun, and passed much of his time in it." Sir Lumley Skeffington (1771-1850), a beau who was consulted on the subject of attire by Prinny and who invented a new color called Skeffington Brown, maintained that the secret of life lay in never stirring out of doors during the cold, damp winter months. He was known as "Skiffy Skipt-on," owing to his "wonted grace." The fourth Earl of Harrington (1780-1851) "designed the Petersham overcoat and the Petersham snuff mixture, and mixed his own blacking . . . His hats were also peculiar." Everybody knows that Lady Hester Stanhope (1776-1839), niece of the great earl of Chatham, settled on Mount Lebanon as a female sheikh. Walking Stewart (1749-1822), a general of Hyder Ali's and prime minister to the nabob of Arcot, covered most of the globe except China and Africa on foot, and at other times reposed in "trance-like reverie among the cows of St. James's Park, inhaling their balmy breath and pursuing his philosophical speculations." Benjamin Stillingfleet, the naturalist (1702-1771), was so modest that he always wrote of himself with a small "i." William Tatham (1752-1819) adopted an unusual mode of committing suicide, with a cannon. John Nicholas Thom (1799-1838) claimed first to be the Earl of Devon, later to be the king of

Jerusalem, and finally to be the Messiah. A butcher called Samuel Thorley, according to the *Eccentric Mirror,* "having frequently heard that human flesh resembled young pig in taste, curiosity prompted him to try if it was true." He consequently butchered a ballad singer named Ann Smith, cut her up, and sampled some of her boiled. She disagreed with him. "During his imprisonment and trial he behaved with the greatest indifference, and at the gallows only inquired if the executioner intended to strip him; when receiving an answer in the negative, he displayed a slight degree of satisfaction." The painter Varley (1778-1842), a powerful man, kept his own horoscope day by day, boxed for refreshment, and "when tired of boxing, he and his pupils would toss Mrs. Varley from one to the other across the table." The second Earl Verney (1712-1791) escaped from his creditors in his wife's hearse.

It is unwise to laugh at one's ancestors, for all that, and the reader will have noted that various ideas of unsinkable lifeboats, blood trans-fusion, aircraft, and submarines were mooted by the eccentrics of the Age of Scandal. The invention of the gramophone was by no means a monopoly of Edison's.

I promise to pay Dr. Darwin of Lichfield one thousand pounds upon his delivering to me (within two years of date hereof) an Instrument called an organ that is capable of pronouncing the Lord's prayer, the creed and ten Commandments in the vulgar tongue and his ceding to me and me only the property of the sd invention with all the advantages thereto appertaining.

M. BOULTON, Soho, Sep. 3rd 1777.
Witness: JAMES KEIR.
Witness: W. SMALL.

It was a dynamic age, through which there stalked the ghosts of great ideas: sometimes of real premonitions, some of them, perhaps, still to come. Jet propulsion, of which we make such a fuss today, was invented by George Medhurst (1759-1827), whose "Aeolian Engine" was to drive carriages on common roads by compressed air in a reservoir under the vehicle. Rocket-bombs were known to Wellington. A mysterious new weapon, no bigger than a duck egg, was invented by Samuel Warner (d. 1853), which was said to have utterly destroyed two French privateers with all hands; but, as the Admiralty would not pay him the £200,000 which he demanded, and as he would not reveal the secret without the money, it sank into oblivion. Perhaps the oddest of contemporary mysteries was the "secret war plan" of Admiral Cochrane (1775-1860). The nature of this "was never made public, though he repeatedly declared that it was capable of destroying any fleet or fortress in the world. He first proposed it as early as 1811, when it was referred to a secret committee, consisting of the duke of York, Lord Keith, Lord Exmouth, and two Congreves, who pronounced it to be infallible, irresistible, but inhuman. On this ground it was not adopted; but when the inventor entered the service of Chili he was pledged by the Prince Regent not to use it for any other country than his own." Cochrane ended as the Earl of Dundonald. "After his readmission to the English navy this secret plan was several times urged on the Admiralty and the government, and was brought prominently into notice during the Russian War of 1854-56; but on every occasion it was put on one side as too terrible and inhuman, though always with the clear admission that it was capable of producing the results which Dundonald claimed for it."

Perhaps it was appropriate to the eccentricity of the era that the only authentic instance of a prophetic vision should have visited a gentleman who was born in 1753. John Williams, a banker, on May 2 or 3, 1812, dreamed three times in one night that he saw a man shot in the lobby of the House of Commons, with which he was familiar, and he was informed in his dream that the victim was Mr. Spencer Perceval. On May 4 he actually consulted his business partners on the propriety of warning the Prime Minister. He was dissuaded from doing so. On May 11, Perceval was shot by the lunatic Bellingham, under all the circumstances of a successful Experiment with Time.

EDMUND PEARSON

Female Liars

Ᏸ✷

*Pearson was America's most famous true-crime writer. Here he is
dealing, for a change, with untrue crimes.*

A famous police official, once at the head of Scotland Yard, said
that he had sometimes wished that girls at the age of fourteen could
quietly be "put to sleep" by the state and allowed to remain unconscious until they were eighteen and ready to become normal and harmless women. Between those ages they caused altogether too much
trouble to the police.

The adolescent liar flourishes at about that time, although it is
hard to fix the limits. Ann Putnam was only twelve when she led
the little band of hellcats and kittens who caused nineteen persons to
be hanged, and one to be pressed to death, in Salem in 1692.

She and her friends began by dabbling in spiritualism and the
divination of dreams: today their amusement would be thought intelligent and even fashionable; it would be called psychic research and
Freudian interpretation. It is impossible to say how far they lost
control of themselves and were helpless hysterics, and to what extent
they knew they were swearing away the lives of innocent persons because they were in so deep they dared not turn back.

Elizabeth Canning, the first famous victim of an "abduction," was
eighteen. She became famous in London in 1753, but she died in
Wethersfield, Connecticut. She was carried off in a "hackney coach"
—and she is the spiritual ancestress of all the girls of today who come
back after a two or three days' escapade with tales of big, gray motor-
cars, masked ruffians, and imprisonment in dank cellar or dismal attic.
Their stories painfully lack originality.

The Canning sisterhood, however, have a definite object for lying.
It is not art for its own sake with them; they have need to account

for their mysterious absences. If they are inventive enough, if they can be carried into Mexico and be forced to walk for miles over the hot sands, they may even become romantic heroines.

The adolescent liar gets over it; the congenital liar may keep it up for long years. It is not, with her, an amusement of the golden years of youth. I know of a woman who apparently had not ceased her elaborate inventions at the age of thirty. She was, at first, an unattractive, quiet, well-behaved young woman of eighteen or nineteen, who was liked by a few women and by no men whatsoever. Dreadful disasters would happen to her, painful injuries of a peculiar nature, so that she would be forced to stay at home. But she would send as a substitute, to the place where she worked, her twin sister Violet. Her friends, and especially her friends' mothers and older relatives, were much attached to Violet—who dressed differently, was more animated, and even had different and heartier tastes in food than her sister Gertrude.

To this day, some of those older women refuse to believe what proved to be the truth: that Violet was merely Gertrude masquerading. They did not notice that they never saw the two together. How could they? Violet only appeared when Gertrude had had some fearful accident: had been in an explosion or been burned by acid. For this was not only a case of congenital lying; it was a double personality as well.

Violet, too, suffered grievously; she was present at naval disasters and subjected to terrible surgical operations. There was a tremendous craving for pity; hence these imaginary accidents. Both sisters were frequently on the verge of being wedded. Invitations were actually issued more than once for Gertrude's wedding, and gifts were received. All that prevented the marriage was the fact that the bridegrooms were as fictitious as sister Violet.

This, is of course, was pitiful—especially for relatives and friends to whom it brought acute embarrassment. What made it curious was that for three-quarters of the time Gertrude was a particularly correct, apparently normal, and totally uninteresting person.

These are usually cases for the physician or learned alienist, not for the law. All that the law should do is to take care that no innocent person suffers as a result of accusations made by one of these lying ladies. Since they almost invariably do make accusations, and usually against men; and since their accusations are almost always of a nature which four out of five persons are instantly ready to believe, whether the man is a saintly archbishop or a schoolboy, it is depressing to reflect how many men in the past have dangled at the end of a rope, or dragged out long years in prison, because of the glib inventions and detailed accusations of some girl of fifteen or sixteen.

The imaginary injuries and the imaginary betrothals in the case of Gertrude and Violet were duplicated in two trials, each famous in its day, in England and France. One was merely annoying and expensive to its victim, and amusing to everyone else. The other was extremely odd, but rather tragic.

On St. Valentine's Day, in 1846, Miss Mary Elizabeth Smith, then aged nineteen, brought suit in London for £20,000 against a peer of the realm, only a few years her senior. He was the Earl Ferrers, and he had been known, before his grandfather's death, as the Right Honorable Washington Shirley, Viscount Tamworth. And he—so said Miss Smith, through a formidable array of eminent lawyers—had most cruelly withered her young heart by marrying another, when he was engaged, betrothed, plighted, and sworn to love and marry only her—Miss Smith.

He had loved her, this wicked nobleman, for six years, or ever since she was a little maid of thirteen. He rode across country—on his great horse Zimro—from his estates to her more lowly home to pay court to her. He wrote her letters—dozens, scores of letters. They were produced in court. The date of the wedding had been set for the summer that Lord Ferrers came of age. The trousseau was ordered and so was the cake. The bridesmaids had been nominated, and everything was ready, when a notice appeared in the papers that the scoundrel earl had married somebody else.

How Miss Smith's lawyers came to take up with the case, and how such a great legal gun as the solicitor general for the Crown came into it on her side, it is hard to see. For when the tale of the aching heart was laid before the court, and all therein sat aghast at the wickedness of this peer of highest station, one of his lawyers arose and unfolded his defense. And this was that he had never written her a letter, had never ridden over on his great horse, Zimro, nor any other, and had never spoken to her, nor even seen her in his life.

And he proved it. Miss Smith had written all these dozens of love letters to herself; had arranged the marriage; hoaxing her parents, or at least her father; had bought millinery for the imaginary wedding —and concocted the whole business out of the depths of her fancy and her supernatural equipment as a liar.

In this suit, at all events, there was a material object: the cash damages. The romance had been built up—in her own mind—long before. But in the French case, the explanation is more difficult, and more certainly belongs in the class of abnormalities. This is not to say that it could not have been checked at the beginning by some simple physical remedy of one kind or another.

It was in 1834—one of those dull periods of history which may be interesting, and are often pleasant to live in. The scene was the cavalry school of the French army, at Saumur. The commandant was General the Baron de Morell, whose family lived in Paris, but came to Saumur in the summer. They were Madame de Morell; a son, aged twelve; and a daughter named Marie, aged sixteen.

The de Morells had been bothered in Paris by anonymous letters, and now, in this summer at Saumur, the plague broke out again. Everyone seemed to get them: the general, his wife, their daughter, and her English governess. Strange incidents began to happen: unknown men pushed notes in at doors or peered in at windows. No one seemed to notice that only Marie saw these unknown men; in fact, all the strange things happened to her.

She was insulted one evening, after a dinner party, by Lieutenant de la Roncière, who compared her beauty most unfavorably with that of her mother. This young subaltern was the son of another titled general, one of Napoleon's distinguished veterans.

The letters, which now began to come in a flood, were often signed by his initials—E. de la R. Sometimes they were avowals of affection for the mother; more often they were expressions of hatred for Marie.

Modern psychology would probably have explained this, quickly and correctly. It is strange that the explanation did not occur to anyone at the time.

Officers began to get the most outrageous letters, some of them containing words so shocking and indecent that nobody thought it possible that such words could even be known to "an innocent young girl."

Finally, at two o'clock one morning, the privacy of the virginal bedchamber was invaded by a man in deep disguise. He climbed in at the window, called out that he was bent on revenge, tied and gagged the terrified girl, stabbed her two or three times with a small knife, and bit her right wrist. The governess came, in response to the cries of Marie, and found her lying on the floor in her chemise, a handkerchief around her neck and a cord round her body. But the man had gone; the governess did not see him. Nobody saw him except the persecuted Mademoiselle de Morell. The glass from the broken windowpane, where the man had entered, had fallen *outside* instead of in. Mademoiselle told the governess that she thought she recognized M. de la Roncière. Later she was sure of it.

Marie was able to attend a dance two or three nights later, and did not tell her mother of the knife wounds for several weeks. Meanwhile her distracted father, the general, received a letter from the monster, in which he gloated over all the injuries he had inflicted upon the poor child. Some of them—so the letter said—were of a kind which in many countries are punished by death.

The anonymous messages continued; the lieutenant was involved in a duel with another officer; and finally, owing to the almost universal opinion of his brother officers that he was the letter writer, was coerced into signing a partial confession of guilt. He did this, believing the evidence against him was so overwhelming that it was his only hope of escape from a long sentence.

His trial became an enormous political sensation, which divided France into two camps and was notorious throughout Europe. A number of experts testified that the letters were not in his handwriting, and that they were unmistakably in the hand of Marie. Moreover, the paper on which one of the letters was written was conclusively shown to be of a peculiar kind, matching exactly with some which the girl used.

All this availed nothing against her testimony. By the time the trial came on she was having periodical "attacks" of a nervous character, which occurred at certain precise times each day. The only possible hour for her to testify was at midnight. So, with the same care for dramatic effectiveness, and the same protection against cross-examination which characterized the appearance of the pig woman at the Hall-Mills trial, Marie entered the court at a special midnight session and was conducted to a large armchair. She absolutely identified de la Roncière as the man who came into her room and treated her so cruelly.

As a result, he was found guilty of "attempting to commit an outrage" and of having willfully wounded her. He was sent to prison for ten years. He actually served eight. There was, later, after his release, a legal investigation, which seems to have been equal to a reversal of the sentence. He was made a commandant in the National Guard, and afterward held high appointments, retiring with the Legion of Honor. Here was a belated official apology, a resemblance to the Dreyfus case.

A few years after the trial, Marie married a marquis and lived in sanctity: a good mother and a gracious and bountiful lady. I wonder if she was ever troubled by thoughts of M. de la Roncière—his eight years in prison and his disgraced father. Her patient malice is hard to explain or excuse altogether on the ground of abnormality, and, however shocking to psychologists the suggestion may be, it is conceivable that, at the very beginning, the devils could have been cast out by three sound spankings.

RUDOLPH MARX, M.D.

Franklin Pierce

☙

A chapter from the book The Health of the Presidents. *The medical angle adds an interesting slant to a life that was fascinating to begin with.*

Franklin Pierce was one of those tragic figures who—born with all obvious advantages, which should add up to a successful and happy life, an influential family, wealth, good looks, intelligence, and personal magnetism—are beset by weakness of character and unfavorable circumstances. He was born in Hillsborough, New Hampshire, in 1804, in the same year as his lifelong friend Nathaniel Hawthorne.

His father was General Benjamin Pierce, a veteran of the Revolutionary War and famous for his hospitality. His big house was always filled with guests, like a tavern; he had to take out a liquor license on occasion. Thus Franklin grew up in an atmosphere of conviviality and alcohol and got to like the taste of both at an early age; however, he never learned to carry his liquor well. In later life he claimed that he had inherited his craving for, and intolerance of, alcohol from his mother—a confession which, true or not, reveals a rejection of his mother.

In 1824 he graduated from Bowdoin College, in Maine, and was admitted to the bar in 1827. In the same year, his father became governor of New Hampshire; he served two terms. Franklin was elected member of the state assembly in 1829, and in spite of his youth, became Speaker in 1831 and 1832.

Pierce's physical health seems to have been good until the summer of 1833, when he was stricken with a serious "bilious" attack, the nature of which is not described. It could have been a malaria, a gastrointestinal infection, or a combination of both. It does not appear to have been cholera, of which an epidemic was then raging in the

United States. It is reported that his life was despaired of by the doctors; however, he got well in spite of them. In 1833 he was elected to Congress, and after two terms became United States Senator in 1837. He enthusiastically supported Andrew Jackson and subsequently came under the influence of the southern Democrats.

In 1834 he married Jane Appleton, daughter of Reverend Jesse Appleton. She was a mousy woman, shy, inhibited, and straitlaced, and seemingly suffered from chronic tuberculosis. She presented a complete contrast to her buoyant, genial husband, whom she admired. On his part, he felt a protective love toward his helpless-looking little wife; and knowing that she needed him kept him from surrendering completely to his craving for alcohol.

During his first years in Washington, as a young congressman, he kept company with a hard-drinking crowd. Just because of his poor tolerance of alcohol he had to show his manliness by competing with his companions in drinking capacity. Again and again he awakened with a hangover of physical misery and mental agony, his wife looking at him with sad, reproachful eyes.

Once, when he had a bad cold, he went on one of his alcoholic sprees and got into a fight in a theater. He woke up in bed with a stabbing pain in his side and a high fever. A doctor was called, made the diagnosis of pleurisy, and took a pint of blood from his veins. Next day he drew twelve more ounces of blood, by making multiple scratches on the skin of the affected side and applying suction cups over them. The patient soon recovered, though for several weeks he remained mentally depressed, filled with self-reproach.

At thirty-three, Pierce was the youngest member of the Senate. His vivacity and brilliant conversation made him a refreshing exception from the majority of his dignified colleagues and a much sought-after dinner guest. However, the Washington climate—social and weather—did not agree with Mrs. Pierce, who usually begged off participating in social affairs with a real or pretended indisposition. Introverted and repressed, she grieved over the death of her first two children from sickness. In 1842, she left Washington for good, to give birth to another child in Concord, refusing to expose the new baby to the unhealthy weather of the capital.

To the father, the birth of a new son gave fresh purpose. He decided to mend his ways and to retire from the glitter and the temptations of Washington into his peaceful little country town. He seriously meant to devote the rest of his life to his family and his private law practice, and declined the governorship of the state, which his father had held, and the office of United States Attorney General in Polk's Cabinet. But he kept his hand in the local Democratic campaigns, and in 1846 was persuaded to accept the position of district attorney of New Hampshire, which permitted him to remain close to his family.

All during this time Pierce seemingly kept his drinking under control, until his peaceful life was interrupted by the Mexican War. Like other volunteers, he could not resist the adventure of war as an escape from the humdrum life. Like other unstable people with hidden conflicts, he could shed his responsibilities in the regimented life of the army and find solace in the thrill of danger. Appointed colonel and brigadier general, he distinguished himself for bravery and extraordinary coolness under fire, traits often displayed by neurotics with self-destructive drives.

In the battle of Contreras on August 19, he was severely injured when his horse, at the blast of a gun, reared and threw him on a jagged lava bed. The examining surgeon diagnosed his injury as a fracture of the pelvis and dislocation of the left knee. He reduced the dislocation of the knee and bandaged the pelvis. In spite of severe pains and his limp left leg, Pierce insisted on being helped on another horse and resuming his command. That he was able to remain in the saddle until far into the night argues against the pelvic fracture. However, Pierce's injuries were so severe that next day he collapsed in pain and fainted when he tried to lead his horse on foot across a ravine.

During September he was in a hospital, recovering from his injuries, but at this assembly point of all prevalent infections he contracted a tropical fever, probably a virulent form of malaria. This was followed by an infectious diarrhea, unavoidable in any hospital at the time. He returned to the army in time to participate in the crowning military event, the storming of Mexico City. The day before, the commander in chief, Winfield Scott, called a council of war. Robert E. Lee was for an indirect approach; Scott and Beauregard favored a frontal attack on Chapultepec, key to the city.

Pierce was won over for the latter plan. However, the next afternoon he collapsed from a recurrent spell of diarrhea and was unable to lead his brigade. His friend Colonel Ramson, who took his place, was killed at the head of his troops.

After the war Pierce returned to his law practice and became one of the most prominent and successful lawyers in New Hampshire, content to remain in Concord and stay out of the limelight of national politics. As the election of 1852 approached, both parties were looking around for presidential prospects unsoiled by outspoken convictions, records clear of embarrassing statements on controversial subjects—particularly the vexatious question of slavery. Pierce was named. He had been out of national politics for ten years, with the additional advantage of having been a general with an excellent war record. However, when some of his political friends approached him about his availability, he answered that the office of President "would be utterly repugnant to my tastes and wishes."

When the Democrats were unable in thirty-four ballots to agree on a candidate, Pierce's friends pressed him to be a good sport and, for the sake of the party and the nation, accept the nomination. Like President Warren G. Harding later, Pierce could not say "No," and he won the nomination on the forty-ninth ballot.

Against him the Whigs put up the pompous old war hero Winfield Scott, Pierce's former Commander in Chief, hoping to repeat with their general their prior victories with Generals Harrison and Taylor. Pierce made no speeches, presented no issues, yet won by the most decisive majority since the second election of Monroe.

Franklin Pierce's pattern of life did not permit him to taste the joy of victory for long. On January 6, 1853, two months before his inauguration, his only surviving son, Benjamin, eleven years old, an exceptional boy, was killed in a railroad accident before his parents' eyes when the car they were riding in was suddenly hurled from the roadbed. Themselves practically unharmed, the parents saw their son crushed under the wreckage.

Franklin Pierce entered the White House in a state of deep dejection. He sought escape from his overwhelming grief and the added burden of office in alcohol. Jane Pierce was never seen to smile again. Soon after Pierce's inauguration, on a trip through New England, one of the members of his party wrote of the President: "I deeply, deeply deplore his habits, he drinks deep. . . . A great mistake was made in putting him in at all."

During his residence in the White House Pierce suffered from a persistent cough, caused by a chronic bronchitis, perhaps of allergic origin —one of the allergens being alcohol. Possibly it was a smoldering form of tuberculosis from his wife. Doctors blamed it on dampness and insufficient heat in the executive mansion during the winter months, and so President Pierce installed the first furnace in the White House.

The new heating system warmed the air but not the spirit pervading the White House. Most of the time the President's wife sought seclusion in her room, sick in mind and body, scribbling pitiful little notes to her dead boy. The wives and daughters of Pierce's Cabinet members substituted as hostesses at White House social functions. After one such affair Charles Mason wrote in his diary: "Everything in that mansion seems cold and cheerless. I have seen hundreds of log cabins which contained more happiness."

In his first message to Congress on December 5, 1853, Pierce spoke of the "sense of repose and security" that had come as a result of the compromise of 1850, and vowed to oppose any move to upset it. Yet less than two months later he was closeted with his secretary of war, Jefferson Davis, and Senator Stephen A. Douglas, giving his approval to a measure that was not only to disturb this repose, but also precipitate the Civil War. It was the Kansas-Nebraska Bill, which gave the states and territories the right to decide for themselves all questions pertaining to slavery within their borders.

The summer of 1855 was unusually hot. An epidemic of Asiatic cholera struck the seaport cities, to add terror to the discomfort of the weather. The President suffered an episode of chills and fever, and Mrs. Pierce became so ill that vacation plans were postponed. During this time, bloody battles were taking place in Kansas over the issue of slavery. It was a dress rehearsal for the Civil War. The

President was powerless to turn back the forces of destruction he had conjured up. Finally, he sent federal troops to Kansas to suppress the warfare between the factions.

Pierce's friends entreated him to seek renomination as President. He was deeply hurt when James Buchanan won the nomination over him. However, another attack of malaria in the fall of 1856, his wife's continued illness, and the climate of the capital made him look forward to leaving the White House.

Like many American presidents, Pierce, released from responsibilities, took an extended trip through Europe. Returned home, he was alarmed by the threatening clouds of secession and wrote a ringing appeal to his southern friends to refrain from war. Up to the last he did not realize the strength of the anti-northern feeling in the South. He squarely took his place upon the outbreak of the war on the side of the North, but expressed his bitter opposition to Lincoln's dictatorial war measures. In taking an unpopular attitude in the midst of a Republican community, he showed more moral courage and consistency than he had ever shown as a practical politician.

Mrs. Pierce's health declined steadily. Her death in 1863, and that of his friend Hawthorne the following year, broke what was left of Franklin's spirit. All his life he had struggled against his addiction to alcohol; now he no longer resisted it, and became an uninhibited alcoholic.

The overconsumption of alcohol resulted in a chronic inflammation of the stomach, interfering with proper digestion. It may be assumed that, like most alcoholics, Pierce did not take sufficient food containing protein and vitamins. The result: liver damage, aggravated by his chronic bronchitis, which by this time had taken the aspect of a creeping tuberculosis. During 1864 and 1865 he had several acute exacerbations of his cough, with fever and night sweats. The climax came in the fall of 1865 when a recurrence brought him near death.

Up to that time, Franklin Pierce had merely paid lip service to religion. Now he looked for ultimate refuge in the inflexible tower of faith and became baptized in the Episcopal church. He stopped drinking altogether and lived a quiet, secluded existence. At last he gained the peace of mind he had been yearning for.

However, the change had come too late to stop the progress of the pathologic processes. In his last remaining years, Pierce suffered from ever increasing malaise, nausea, and pain in the stomach. During the last summer he developed dropsy, a distention of the abdomen by watery exudate. His symptoms were typical for a cirrhosis—shrinking of the liver—a condition in which the liver cells, bile ducts, and blood vessels are gradually strangulated by an increase of fibrous tissue, and the liver, which is the most important chemical plant of the body, fails in its function.

Alcoholism is a factor in 70 per cent of the patients suffering from liver cirrhosis. In the other 30 per cent a variety of other factors, among them malaria, can cause or contribute to the disease. Pierce died four years after he had given up alcohol, and many more years after his last malaria attack. However, cirrhosis of the liver takes a long time to reach a point incompatible with life. Once the disease had developed clinical symptoms, it could not be stopped.

At present it can be arrested up to a certain point, by proper diet and vitamins, eventually by surgery. In Pierce's time the condition of cirrhosis of the liver was well known to medical science but apparently not to his physicians. Even if they had known of it, they would not have been able to help him. Franklin Pierce died in a stupor, characteristic of liver failure, on October 8, 1869, friendless and forgotten in his sixty-fifth year.

JOSEPH KAY

The Frightful Extent of Infanticide Among Our Poor

&·

From The Social Condition and Education of the People of Europe *by Joseph Kay, M.A. of Trinity College, Cambridge, first published in 1850.*

A sad symptom of the condition of the poor of our own towns is the use they make of the "burial clubs." In some of our towns the degradation of many of the poor is such that parents often cause the death of their children in order to obtain the premiums from the societies.

The accounts of these "burial clubs," and of the extent to which infanticide is practiced in some parts of this country, may be found in Mr. Chadwick's able reports upon the sanitary condition of the poor.

It appears that in our larger provincial towns the poor are in the habit of entering their children in what are called "burial clubs." A small sum is paid every year by the parent, and this entitles him to receive from £3 to £5 from the club on the death of the child. Many parents enter their children in several clubs. One man in Manchester has been known to enter his child in *nineteen* different clubs. On the death of such a child, the parent becomes entitled to receive a large sum of money; and as the burial of the child does not necessarily cost more than £1, or, at the most, £1 10s, the parent realizes a considerable sum after all the expenses are paid!

It has been clearly ascertained that it is a common practice among the more degraded classes of poor in many of our towns to enter their infants in these clubs, and then to cause their death either by starvation, ill-usage, or poison! What more horrible symptom of moral degradation can be conceived? One's mind revolts against it, and would fain reject it as a monstrous fiction. But, alas! it seems to be but too true. Mr. Chadwick says,*

Officers of these burial societies, relieving officers, and others, whose administrative duties put them in communication with the lowest classes in these districts [the manufacturing districts], express their moral conviction of the operation of such bounties to produce instances of the visible neglect of children of which they are witnesses. They often say, "You are not treating that child properly; it will not live: *is it in the club?*" And the answer corresponds with the impression produced by the sight.

Mr. Gardiner, the clerk to the Manchester union, while registering the causes of death, deemed the cause assigned by a labouring man for the death of a child unsatisfactory, and staying to inquire, found that popular rumour assigned the death to wilful starvation. The child (according to a statement of the case) had been entered in at least *ten* burial clubs; *and its parents had had six other children, who only lived from nine to eighteen months respectively.* They had received from several burial clubs 20*l.* for *one* of these children, and they expected at least as much on account of this child. An inquest was held at Mr. Gardiner's instance, when several persons, who had known the deceased, stated that she was a fine fat child shortly after her birth, but that she soon became quite thin, was badly clothed, and seemed as if she did not get a sufficiency of food. . . . The jury, having expressed it as their opinion that the evidence of the parents was made up for the occasion, and entitled to no credit, returned the following verdict: "Died through want of nourishment, but whether occasioned by a deficiency of food, or by disease of the liver and spine, brought on by improper food and drink, or otherwise, does not appear."

Two similar cases came before Mr. Coppock, the clerk and superintendent-registrar of the Stockport union, in both of which he prosecuted the parties for murder. In one case, where three children had been poisoned with arsenic, the father was tried with the mother, and convicted, at Chester, and sentenced to be transported for life, but the mother was acquitted. In the other case, where the judge summed up for a conviction, the accused, the father, was, to the astonishment of everyone, acquitted. In this case the body was exhumed after interment, and *arsenic was detected in the stomach.* In consequence of the suspicion raised upon the death, on which the accusation was made in the first case, the bodies of two other children were taken up and examined, when *arsenic was found in their stomachs.* In all these cases payments on the deaths of the

* Sanitary Inquiry Report, 1843, p. 64.

children were insured from the burial clubs; the cost of the coffin and burial dues would not be more than about 1*l.*, and the allowance from the club is 3*l.*

It is remarked on these dreadful cases by the superintendent-registrar *that the children who were boys, and therefore likely to be useful to the parents, were not poisoned;* the female children were the victims. It was the clear opinion of the medical officers that infanticides have been committed in Stockport to obtain the burial money.

The town clerk of Stockport says,*

I have no doubt that infanticide, to a considerable extent, has been committed in the borough of Stockport.

I know it to be the opinion of some of the respectable medical practitioners in Stockport that infanticides have been commonly influenced by various motives—to obtain the burial moneys from the societies in question, and to be relieved from the burden of the child's support. The parties generally resort to a mineral poison, which, causing sickness, and sometimes purging, assumes the appearance of the diseases to which children are subject; and as they then take the child to a surgeon, who prescribes after a very cursory examination, they thus escape any suspicion on the part of their neighbours.

Mr. Chadwick again says,

At the Liverpool assizes in 1843, a woman named Eccles was convicted of the murder of one child, and was under the charge of poisoning two others with arsenic. Immediately the murders were committed, it appeared she went to demand a stated allowance of burial money from the employers of the children. The collector of a burial society, one of the most respectable in Manchester, stated to me strong grounds for believing that it had become a practice to neglect children for the sake of the money allowed.

The able author of the "Letters on Labour and the Poor in the Rural Districts," lately published in the Morning Chronicle, writing of the "burial clubs" in the eastern counties, says,

The suspicion that a great deal of "foul play" exists with respect to these clubs is supported, not only by a comparison of the different rates of mortality, but it is considerably strengthened by the facts proved upon the trial of Mary May. The Rev. Mr. Wilkins, the vicar of Wickes, who was mainly instrumental in bringing the case before a court of justice,

* Sanitary Inquiry Report, 1843, p. 235.

stated to me that from the time of Mary May coming to live in his parish he was determined to keep a very strict watch upon her movements, as he had heard that *fourteen of her children had previously died suddenly.* A few weeks after her arrival in his parish, she called upon him to request him to bury one of her children. Upon his asking her which of the children it was, she told him that it was "Eliza," a fine healthy-looking child of ten years old. Upon his expressing some surprise that she should have died so suddenly, she said, "Oh, sir, she went off like a snuff; all my other children did so, too." A short time elapsed, and she again waited upon the vicar to request him to bury her brother as soon as he could. His suspicions were aroused, and he endeavoured to postpone the funeral for a few days in order to enable him to make some inquiries. Not succeeding in obtaining any information, which would warrant further delay in burying the corpse, he most reluctantly proceeded in the discharge of his duty. About a week after the funeral Mary May again waited upon him, to request him to sign a certificate to the effect that her brother was in perfect health a fortnight before he died, that being the time at which, as it subsequently appeared, she had entered him as nominee in the Harwich Burial Club. Upon inquiring as to the reason of her desiring this certificate, she told him that unless she got it, she could not get the money for him from the club. This at once supplied the vicar with what appeared to be a motive for "foul play" on the part of the woman. He accordingly obtained permission to have the body of her brother exhumed; doses of arsenic were detected, and the woman was arrested. With the evidence given upon the trial, the reader is, no doubt, perfectly conversant, and it will be unnecessary for me to detail it. She was convicted. Previously to her execution, she refused to make any confession, but said, *"If I were to tell all I know, it would give the hangman work for the next twelve months."* Undue weight ought not to be attached to the declaration of such a woman as Mary May, but coupled with the disclosures that took place upon the trial, with respect to some of her neighbours and accomplices, and with the extraordinary rate of mortality among the clubs, it certainly does appear that the general opinion with respect to the mischievous effects of these societies is not altogether without foundation.

Although there are not in Essex, at present, any burial clubs in which children are admitted under fourteen years of age, as members or nominees, still, as illustrating the evils arising from these clubs, I may state that many persons who are fully conversant with the working of such institutions have stated that they have frequently been shocked by hearing women of the lower classes, when speaking of a neighbour's child, make use of such expressions as, *"Oh, depend upon it, the child'll not live; it's in the burial club."* When speaking to the parents of a child who may be unwell, it is not unfrequently that they say, "You should do so and so," or "you should not do so and so"; *"you should not treat it in that way; is it in the burial club?"* Instances of the most culpable neglect, if not of graver offences, are continually occurring in districts where clubs exist in which children are admitted. A collector of one of the most extensive burial societies gave it as his opinion, founded upon his experience, that it had become a constant practice to neglect the children for the sake of the allowance from the clubs, and he supported his opinion by several cases, which had come under his own observation.

From a very remarkable letter published in *The Times* of the eighteenth of January, A.D. 1849, by that indefatigable and earnest man, the Rev. J. Clay, chaplain of the Preston House of Correction, I collect the following particulars, still further illustrating this horrible symptom of our social state. Mr. Clay says,

Let me recall to your recollection *some* of the murders for burial money perpetrated since the publication of Mr. Chadwick's admirable Report on interment in towns. 1. A Liverpool paper of April, 1846, gives the details of an inquiry before the coroner in a case of "infanticide, at Runcorn, to obtain funeral money." It appeared, in evidence, that James Pimlet, aged ten months, died on the 6th of March, and that on the 21st of the same month died Richard Pimlet, aged four years and a half. On the 27th of the same month a *third* child was taken ill. The medical man's suspicions were roused. The authorities caused the bodies of the two dead infants to be exhumed. It was found that the *mother* had purchased arsenic before the children's illness. Dr. Brett showed the presence of arsenic in the bodies "in quantities more than sufficient to cause death." The collector of the Liverpool Victoria Legal Burial Society proved that the three children were all enrolled members; that he had paid 1*l.* 5*s.* on the death of one child, and 5*l.* on the death of the other. The steward of another society proved the payment of 1*l.* 5*s.* and 1*l.* 15*s.* on the two deaths. Verdict, "wilful murder" against the mother.

2. At York assizes, in July, 1846, John Rodda was convicted of the wilful murder of his own child, aged one year. The evidence proved that the wretch poured a spoonful of sulphuric acid down his helpless infant's throat. It was proved that he did not care how soon the child died, for whenever it died, he should have 2*l.* 10*s.*, as it was in a "dead list." He said he had another that would have the same when it died, and two others that would have 5*l.* apiece when they died.

3. In June, 1847, Mary Ann Milner was charged with the wilful murder —by arsenic—of her mother-in-law, her sister-in-law, and her niece; her

father-in-law had also well nigh become her victim, and was reduced to imbecility from the effects of the poison. The only imaginable motive for the conduct of the prisoner, as suggested by the counsel for the prosecution, and as supported by the evidence, was the obtaining moneys from a burial society.

4. In July, 1848, Mary May took her trial for the murder of Spratty Watts, by the favourite means—arsenic. This horrible case will be still in the recollection of your readers. The woman had put her victim into a "death list," which lured her to her crime, by promising 9l. or 10l. on its perpetration. "The private confession of Mrs. May afforded"—I quote from "The Times" of September 21,—"a due clue to a system, *which it is feared is capable of most extensive proof, and will result in the conviction of a large number of women,* who have adopted the practice of poisoning their husbands and children for the purpose of obtaining the fees which are granted by what are, in this part of the country, termed *death lists.*"

5. I must add to this imperfect, but too full catalogue, the name of Ann Mather, against whom, in August 1847, a coroner's jury, at Warrington, returned a verdict of "wilful murder." Her husband's name being in three separate *"death lists,"* the usual means—arsenic—was resorted to, and the desperate gamestress won 20l. I shall merely name the "Essex poisonings"; their horrible notoriety has not yet subsided. Let it be remembered that we have here only a portion of the positive murders resulting from the temptations offered by burial clubs. No one can guess how many more victims—infants especially—have been poisoned, or otherwise destroyed, for the sake of the coveted burial money, though neither inquiry nor suspicion may have been excited; nor how many children, entered by their parents in burial clubs, are, when attacked by sickness, suffered to die without any effort being made to save their lives.

My report on the sanitary condition of Preston, given in the "First Report of the Health of Towns Commission," furnishes startling evidence of the wide prevalence of this feeling. A collector of cottage rents states, that *"almost all the children of the families where he collects are members of burial societies. . . . The children of the poor when sick are greatly neglected; the poor seldom seek medical assistance for sick children, except when they are at the point of death."* Another collector states, *"the poor people have often told me that they were unable to pay at that time; but when a certain member of the family—generally a child—died, they would be able to pay."* . . . A lady states that a young woman, whose services she required as wet nurse, having a child ill, she offered to send her own medical friend to attend it; the reply of the nurse was, *"Oh! never mind, ma'am, it's in two burial clubs."* It also appears, on the un-

impeachable authority of a burial-club official, that *"hired nurses speculate on the lives of infants committed to their care, by entering them in
burial clubs;"* that "two young women proposed to enter a child into his
club, and to pay the weekly premium alternately. Upon inquiring as to
the relation subsisting between the two young women and the child, he
learned that the infant was placed at nurse with the mother of one of
these young women." The wife of a clergyman told me that, visiting a
poor district just when a child's death had occurred, instead of hearing
from the neighbours the language of sympathy for the bereaved parent,
she was shocked by such observations as—"Ah! it's a fine thing for the
mother; the child's in two clubs!" . . . . As regards one town, I possess
some evidence of the amount of burial-club membership, and of infant
mortality, which I beg to lay before you. . . . The reports of this town refer
to 1846, when the population of the town amounted to about 61,000. I
do not name the town, because, as no actual burial-club murders are
known to have been committed in it, and as such clubs are not more
patronised there than in other places, it is, perhaps, not fair to hold it up
to particular animadversion; indeed, as to its general character, this
very town need not fear comparison with any other. Now, this place,
with its 61,000 people of all classes and ages, maintains at least eleven
burial clubs, the members of which amount in the aggregate to nearly
52,000; nor are these all. Such clubs, remember, act as burial clubs. Of
these there are twelve or fourteen in the town, mustering altogether, probably, 2000 members. Here, then, we have good data for comparing population with *"death lists;"* but it will be necessary, in making the comparison,
to deduct from the population all that part of it which has nothing to
do with these clubs; viz., all infants under two months old, and all persons
of unsound health (both of these classes being excluded by the club
rules); all those also of the working classes, whose sound intelligence
and feeling lead them to abhor burial-club temptations; and all the better
classes, to whom 5*l*. or 20*l*. offer no consolation for the death of a child.
On the hypothesis that these deductions will amount to one-sixth of the
entire population, it results, that the *death lists* are more numerous by far
than the entire mass—old, young, and infants—which support them;
and according to the statement of a leading death-list officer, THREE-
FOURTHS of the names on these catalogues of the doomed are the names
of children. Now, if this be the truth—and I believe it is—hundreds, if
not thousands, *of children must be entered each into* FOUR, FIVE, *or even*
TWELVE *clubs*, their chances of life diminishing, of course, in proportion
to the frequency with which they are entered. Lest you should imagine
that such excessive addiction to burial clubs is only to be found in one
place, I furnish you with a report for 1846, *of a single club, which then*

boasted 34,100 *members—the entire population of the town to which it belongs having been in* 1841 *little more than* 36,000!!!

I would now bespeak your attention to the infantile mortality in places where burial clubs flourish. In Dr. Lyon Playfair's "Report on the Sanitary Condition of large Towns in Lancashire," p. 53., it is stated, that *among the poor of Manchester, out of* 100 *deaths,* 60 *to* 65 *are of infants under five years old. One man put his children into nineteen clubs!* Dr. Lyon Playfair again shows (p. 54) that children die in Manchester, when wages are high, at a rate more than that at which they die among the poverty-stricken laborers of Dorsetshire. . . .

I have now before me communications from five medical gentlemen, resident in the town of 61,000 inhabitants above alluded to (four of them surgeons to the union, and the fifth the medical officer of an institution furnishing gratuitous medical aid to the poor), showing their attendance on poor children under five years old, contrasted with their attendance on the poor above that age. The older patients, for whom medical aid was sought, constitute 87 per cent., the younger ones 13 per cent. Poor little creatures! 56 per cent. die, but only 13 per cent. of them have the doctor's help, though it may be had for asking. I extract the following from the communications alluded to:

"1. 'The above numbers (247 patients above five years of age, and 26 under five years of age) very strikingly illustrate what I have frequently remarked otherwise,—the great indifference displayed by parents and others in the lower ranks of life with regard to infant life.'

"2. 'With respect to the attendance which the poorer classes give to their children in sickness, I am sorry to say it is generally anything but what it ought to be. . . . If they seek medical aid at all, it is too often when there is not the slightest chance of recovery.'

"3. 'My impression is that very few of the children of the operative class, in sickness, fall under the notice of the medical men of the town. But latterly there has been a disposition to call us in, in the last stage of disease, *for the purpose of obtaining a certificate of death* for the registrar.'

"4. 'My general impression, derived from three years' experience at this institution, compels me to admit, what is very painful to acknowledge, that there is *among the poorer classes a manifest and cold* indifference to the health of infants, and especially so when suffering from disease.'

"The above extracts are from letters written in 1846. Since then, the medical certificate necessary to the registration of death has been more stringently required, and it was hoped would produce better attention to sick children. How far that hope has been realised, is shown in the following extract from a letter, written by the present medical officer of the charitable institution adverted to, a gentleman of distinguished zeal and ability:—"The return rather understates the mortality of infantile life; for in several instances, where very gross neglect has been apparent, and where our aid has only been requested in extremes, I have declined to give certificates, and such cases do not appear in the list. The whole number of patients admitted during the year 1847, was 3052: of these 341 were under five years of age, 2711 were about five years of age. It would thus appear, that although one half of all the deaths in the town consists of children under five years of age, the proportion of those who become patients of the only charitable medical institution in the place is only one-eighth of that above five years! Of the cases under five years, 1 in 6 proved fatal; of those above five years, 1 in 19¼. . . . The difference between a mortality of 1 in 6 and 1 in 19¼ is too great to be accounted for on any other supposition than that of the existence of great neglect on the part of the parents."

These accounts are really almost too horrible to be believed at all; and were they not given us on the authority of men of such great experience and benevolence, we should totally discredit them.

But, alas, they are only too true! There can be no doubt that a great part of the poorer classes of this country are sunk into such a frightful depth of hopelessness, misery, and utter moral degradation that even mothers forget their affection for their helpless little offspring, and kill them, as a butcher does his lambs, in order to make money by the murder, and therewith to lessen their pauperism and misery!

SIR OSBERT SITWELL

The Ghost in the Green Mask

&bkl;

This is truth rather than fiction; but of course it's up to you whether you want to believe it or not.

The story of Dr. Goodfellow's visitation is of interest; for the occurence, however slight, and of however familiar a type, has unusual features, one of which is the reliability and intelligence of the person to whom it happened, and another the curious insistence—seemingly quite beyond the necessities of the case—with which the apparition sought to attract the doctor's attention.

One evening I was sitting at dinner alone with Dr. Goodfellow. Upstairs a relation, of whom I happened to be extremely fond, was lying ill; and this serious illness had, during the last two or three months, formed the foundation for a friendship between the doctor and myself.

Knowing, as I did, this invalid, it was impossible not to admire the combination of tact and wisdom, the tempering of firmness with intuition, which the doctor had displayed. He lacked, too, the professional optimism of the English practitioner. He was about forty years af age, and a giant in stature; altogether he seemed a rather remarkable person.

The talk turned on the progress made recently in mental healing and the understanding of nervous disorders, and finally I inquired whether, among the many incidents of a medical career, there had ever occurred to him any event of which no ordinary explanation could be furnished.

Dr. Goodfellow at first denied any belief in the phenomena of thought transference or apparitions. Indeed, so strong was his conviction that it seemed completely to have banished from his memory for the moment the singular event which might have caused him to abandon it.

He was silent for some seconds, and I could see in his eyes a memory trying to rise, like a fish, to the still surface of his consciousness. At last it reached him, and rather unwillingly he admitted that, once, something unusual had happened to him.

As a student, at the age of seventeen, Dr. Goodfellow had worked in the smallpox hospital at Glasgow. It was at the time of that alarming outbreak which coincided with the Boer War.

To lessen the risks of catching or spreading this virulently infectious disease, it was the rule for workers among these cases to wear a special uniform, consisting of loose white coat and trousers and a green mask, with a beak-like nose, attached to a close-fitting cap. However necessary it may have been, this livery must have added a grotesque touch of further horror to the scene, dehumanizing the doctors and workers as they glided in and out of the carefully shaded rooms, making them seem, in the delirium of the poor disfigured victims, rather the personification of the disease—as though the deadly microbes responsible for it had for the moment been allowed to assume quasi-human form in order to plague and torture the wretched sufferers—than what they were, courageous and sympathetic volunteers for its combat.

Working with Goodfellow was a student named Fairfax, whose most intimate friend he became. But such friendships of adolescence are apt to be volatile, and when Goodfellow left his comrade behind in Glasgow in order to study medicine in Paris, his letters to Fairfax, his letters from Fairfax, became more and more infrequent, and finally, after a year, stopped altogether.

Goodfellow's new life, coming at the very moment when his vitality was at its greatest, and the transforming of the scene which framed it, filled him with the intoxication of existence which comes —if at all—but once in a lifetime, and completely obliterated for him the thought of anything but the actual moment. Fairfax was forgotten, absolutely forgotten.

The young Englishman was working in the medical college which was under the charge of the famous Monsieur Blois. For a year a room was found for him in the establishment, and then he was allowed to move out into a lodging of his own.

He was singularly fortunate in the one he now rented, for it was a delightful room, the paneling of which was painted a soft, clear gray, and, what was more important, it had three wide windows looking out on to a garden.

It was the sort of room that exercises an influence, both invigorating and calming, on the mind of its occupant, however unconscious he may be by nature of his environment.

The door faced one of the end windows, and between them was a very charming mantelpiece. The bed stood with its head against the other wall opposite the chimney, but there was a considerable space on each side of it.

The only drawback that Goodfellow found to his new lodging was the absence of electric light. But this deprivation was in the daytime fully compensated by the light which poured in.

Here the young man lived for some years; during this period he never heard from Fairfax, nor could the latter have been aware of his present address.

One night, during his fourth summer in Paris, Goodfellow came in about eleven o'clock. The windows stood wide open, and from the garden below drifted the warm air of May, scented by the pale, Persian shapes of the lilacs as they were fanned by their gentle slaves, the winds.

The room was drenched in moonlight, so pearly bright that it was as though daylight were being filtered through deep, clear waters.

A sense of rest and contentment seized on him, and, puffing out the candle, he swiftly fell asleep. Out of this peaceful but heavy slumber he was awakened suddenly, and with a feeling of disturbance. What had happened? . . . The clock struck two, and he looked around.

In an armchair by the window, facing him, and very distinct in the milky light, was a motionless figure in gleaming white clothes, and with a green beaked mask; an unearthly Punchinello, it seemed. Even apart from this sad, fantastic uniform, the build and poise of the visitor proclaimed it as his forgotten friend Fairfax.

Goodfellow knew that he had locked the door before going to bed. Fairfax was certainly ignorant of his address, and in any case would hardly call on him, in the middle of the night, clad in the garb of the Glasgow smallpox hospital.

The figure remained there motionless. His friend called him by name, asked him what he wanted; but he sat on there under the moonlight without moving.

Fear overcame Goodfellow; he could not find the matches, and the figure sat on. He feared that it was a hallucination, that he might be going mad. He buried his head in the blankets, and turned over toward the wall. It was some minutes before he dared open his eyes.

When he did so, the figure was opposite him once more, had moved to take up its position on a chair by the wall near him. There the masked creature sat, again rigid and immovable. Goodfellow fainted: but when he came round his visitor was no longer with him.

The next morning he made sure that his door was still locked.

But the concierge complained, when he came downstairs, that a funny, stiff figure in fancy dress had knocked him up in the middle of the night and asked for the young Englishman upstairs: so that the apparition was able, evidently, in the illogical way of ghosts, to enter certain rooms without human aid.

Goodfellow was so perturbed by the whole occurrence that he contrived to sit next to Dr. Blois at luncheon—for the head of the college often lunched with the students—and confided in him.

The old Frenchman inquired laughingly what he had eaten for dinner, when, just at that moment, a telegram was brought informing Goodfellow that Fairfax had died the previous night, shortly before two o'clock.

Under the will of the dead man he was appointed executor. Could he return to England as soon as possible?

Fairfax had died of pneumonia, following on influenza, and had left behind him a wife and child of whose existence the new executor had been ignorant. But why had he adopted that strange, ominous uniform for his appearance; why had he not spoken?

Dr. Goodfellow had never had an experience of this kind before, and has never had one since.

ALAN HYND

The Great Tooth Tycoon

ဦ

*I always thought that "Painless Parker" was a fictional char-
acter. But I was quite wrong.*

The American Dental Association heaved a loud sigh of relief when, in November, 1952, death removed from its profession a chopper expert who had been a pain in its jaw for half a century. The departing bone of contention was a dressy, sharp-tongued little character of eighty with a Vandyke beard, snapping blue eyes, and a love for bouncing his name around. He advertised himself in newspapers, magazines, on the radio, on the walls of abandoned warehouses, and by means of human flies walking up skyscraper fronts. He let everyone who could read, look, or listen know that he was Painless Parker.

The fact that Painless advertised wasn't the only thing the ethical dentists held against him. Many of them were jealous of the old boy. When Painless cashed in his chips he was the most widely known tooth tycoon in the land, with a string of twenty-seven offices employing seventy-five dentists and grossing three million dollars a year.

At various times in the course of Parker's turbulent career, the ethicals, as Painless scornfully referred to his colleagues, banded together and tried to drive him from the profession. The ethicals charged that Parker's work was not only shoddy but a menace to life and mouth, and that Painless wasn't painless at all. They offered as exhibits the false teeth in the mouths of Parker patients, which sometimes looked like stacks of date pits framed by sickly grins, and pointed accusing ears in the direction of the bloodcurdling screams that frequently jetted out of Parker offices.

"The ethicals are just damned liars!" Parker once said to a newspaper man, tugging at his ginger-colored beard and fixing the interviewers with a con man's stare. "Look at the record, son. Look at the record."

The record reveals that Painless Parker did more than any other single individual to make people conscious of the importance of oral hygiene. It was Painless who put dental work within reach of the average man by originating group dentistry, a practice whereby a patient could get everything from X ray to his uppers and lowers under one roof. Parker's group technique was adopted by the United States Navy in World War II.

"The sharks stole the idea from me," Painless proclaimed to his dying day. "And they never gave me a word of credit."

A born exhibitionist, Painless Parker was the first man to pull teeth in the middle of a busy street. It's a pretty safe bet to say he was also the last. In his early days, practicing in New York City, he went around town in a wagon equipped with a dental chair and a set of nippers. After collecting a crowd, Painless lectured it on the horrors of tooth decay, stopping every once in a while to fix some listener with a fishy stare.

"Come up here, my good man," he'd say, "and let me take a look into that mouth of yours."

Parker then clapped the victim in the chair, stared into his mouth, shook his head, and muttered a string of high-sounding gibberish that sounded like the voice of doom. Inevitably that would cause the poor dope to decide that, unless he let Painless pull his tooth immediately, he might not live to see another sunrise. Parker, a lightning-fast worker who never got a finger caught between molars, popped in and out of the man's mouth in a twinkling and triumphantly held up the tooth for the crowd to gape at.

When business was dead, Painless brought it to life by slipping in a ringer. Climbing out of the crowd, the ringer jumped up on the wagon, holding his jaw and moaning. As he squatted in the chair, Painless, his hands moving with the deceptive dexterity of a magician, went through the motions of yanking a tooth. Then, while the patient still sat there with his mouth open, the beaming Parker held up a palmed tooth to the crowd.

"Take it out!" the ringer would start yelling. "Take my tooth out and get it over with."

"But it *is* out, my good fellow," Parker would say. "Here, take a look at the rotten thing."

To make sure the message took hold, the ringer, feigning surprise, would thereupon shout, "Gee, I didn't feel a *thing!*"

Painless, who charged fifty cents an extraction while his colleagues were soaking their patients a dollar, boasted a standing reward of ten dollars to anyone who felt so much as a twinge of pain when he yanked a tooth. Only a con man would have dared make such an offer because at that time the local anesthetic was a practically useless substance called hydrocain. Parker rubbed a little hydrocain on a patient's gum, and then, before the stuff had a chance to work, went in after the tooth. When the patient let out a piercing shriek, Parker fixed him with a stare, a smile, and a clap on the back.

"It didn't really hurt at all, my friend," he'd trumpet. "It was only your imagination."

Edgar Rudolph Randolph Parker entered what he always called this vale of rubes in 1872, in the hamlet of Tynemouth Creek, New Brunswick. His parents were rock-ribbed citizens from an old line of Baptist shipbuilders. They were hell-bent for Edgar, their only child, to grow up into a minister. Although possessed of a strikingly rich voice and a convincing manner, Edgar displayed early signs of singular unsuitability for the cloth. When he was ten, he was expelled from school for drawing on the blackboard pictures far too advanced for his age.

At eighteen, young Parker shipped out as assistant cook on a freighter bound round Cape Horn. During the cargo stop in Buenos Aires, he got into a brawl and wound up in a hospital with a cracked skull. While recuperating, Edgar noticed that all the doctors seemed to be doing was walking around looking wise and dosing the patients with castor oil. Concluding that he could look just as wise, especially in a spanking white coat, Edgar decided to be a doctor.

He picked New York as the place to study, and when he finally hit the town, took a painful gander at medical requirements. Even a wise man, he reasoned, would be a fool to go in for anything that tough. So he settled for a trade that would let him wear the white coat and the wise smile at a cut-rate investment in time—the tooth-tending course called for only three years.

After graduating, Parker returned to his Canadian home country and became a traveling dentist. Then, lured by the Alaska gold rush, he checked into Sitka, all decked out in frock coat, polka-dot cravat, gray top hat, and striped pants, and opened an office in the back room of a combination saloon and dance hall. He made out fine pulling what teeth the roughnecks hadn't knocked out of one another, and they paid liberally in gold dust and were usually so drunk they felt no pain. Parker spent his gold on dames and drink until, getting into a squabble over a girl, he was offered the bum's rush from the Klondike, which he accepted.

Well, if Alaska didn't like him, New York would treat him all right. But he wasn't ready to crack Manhattan yet, so, in 1896, when he was twenty-four, he set up shop in Brooklyn. Renting three rooms over a German saloon on Flatbush Avenue, he began to pull teeth at half a buck a yank. He also fell for a neighbor girl named Frances Wolfe, who was to become—much to his surprise—the one steady love of Painless Parker's life. Frances and he were married within the year and took up housekeeping in part of his office.

Business was slow, and Parker occupied himself with anything he could find, such as playing his cornet. Hour after hour he sat in his office tootling away. Finally it got too much even for Frances, to say nothing of the neighbors.

"You're playing that horn practically all the time, dear," she said to him one day. "Where are your patients? We're almost starving."

The question and the empty cupboard set Parker to thinking. Next day he began buttonholing people on the street and asking why they avoided dentists. The answer was always the same and it was very simple—they were afraid of getting hurt. That little poll of Parker's was to have a far-reaching effect on American dentists. It had never occurred to them before that nobody loves a torturer.

"I've made a great discovery," Parker told his wife that night. "Now I know why people hate dentists—they're painful. So I'm going to change my name from Doctor Parker to Painless Parker."

"Painless!" repeated Frances, in pain. "Why Edgar, everybody would talk about such a silly name."

"Let 'em talk!" shrilled Parker. "That's just what I want."

To make sure the word got around he put up a big sign in front of his office:

PAINLESS PARKER
DENTIST
HE WON'T HURT YOU

That sign was pure magic. People walking along Flatbush Avenue stopped to gawk at it even when they didn't have toothaches. While they were catching flies, Parker wearing his white coat, stuck his head out the window, beamed down at them, and pointed to the door below.

"It's true!" he'd yell. "You won't get hurt here. Come on up."

Painless was soon extracting an average of thirty teeth a day, so that he was raking in ninety dollars a week strictly on a cash basis. Since he was paying only fifteen dollars a month rent for his office-living quarters, and sirloin steak was selling at twenty cents a pound, and a good whiskey was ninety cents a fifth, and nobody had yet thought of income taxes, he did all right.

Since the sign in front of his office was paying off so well, Parker decided to expand the message. He hired a couple of sandwich men to tramp the streets of Flatbush proclaiming his revolutionary dentistry. In a short while the sandwich advertising doubled his business.

That convinced him that teeth were filled with gold. So, feeling that he had only scratched the surface, Painless hit the streets himself. He put a Morris chair in a big red wagon and drove around hunting a likely spot. Then he blatted out with his cornet until he collared a crowd for his pitch.

One day a heckler piped up: "Friend of mine says when you pulled his tooth it hurt like hell."

Parker paused to give the boy a withering stare, and went on.

But the heckler was not to be downed. He bellowed the charge again, and Parker turned his full attention to him.

"How much, my good man," he asked, "are the high-priced dentists paying you to come here and deceive these fine people"—he waved his hand toward the crowd—"and get them away from me so they can *overcharge* them?"

It just *could* have been that there was something to that crack. By now the ethical dentists in Brooklyn were all aware of Painless' presence. Most of them were against him because he advertised— and advertised what he obviously didn't deliver. There was only a small minority who realized that he was making people dentistry conscious and indirectly driving trade their way.

When he had been in Brooklyn for a year, Parker had so much

business that he couldn't keep up with the work alone. So he put on an assistant. By the end of another year he had two dentists working for him and four men tramping the streets wearing his sandwich boards.

Four year after he arrived in Brooklyn, Painless Parker was doing so well that he took over half a floor in a Flatbush office building, employed eight dentists, and grew a goatee.

If misery loves company, it was probably some consolation for Brooklyn's ethicals that, a little later, Parker decided Manhattan was now ripe for plucking. He opened offices on Lower Broadway, but business didn't come. So he took to the wagon again. Even then, standing up there on the wagon behind his Morris chair, shouting for patients to jump aboard and have their teeth pulled, he still didn't make a dent.

"Maybe the people in New York are too sophisticated," one of Parker's dentists suggested.

"The hell they are," said Painless. "There are just as many rubes on Broadway as in Flatbush, and I'll get them yet. I've got an idea."

He went to a theatrical agency and hired a clown, a couple of chorus girls wearing tights, an Irish tenor, and a three-piece brass band. Driving this troupe around town, Painless put on free shows at street corners.

It never took long to gather a crowd. Then Parker popped up and began his spiel. A host of trusting faces looking up at Painless always brought out the best in the man. Soon he would have a line of achers waiting to get their teeth pulled out. It doesn't seem possible, but in short order Painless was pulling more teeth on the streets of Manhattan than he was in his Brooklyn office.

First, however, he had had to overcome a slight difficulty. One day when he yanked a molar on the street, his patient let out a screech that could be heard across the Hudson River in New Jersey. Parker tugged his goatee impatiently as he watched the crowd go out like a dam that had burst.

"We'll fix that," he told his band. "Hereafter, every time you see me going into somebody's mouth, play *Poet and Peasant* loud as all hell."

That seemed to work, because then the Manhattan office started to prosper, too. By 1905, when he was thirty-three, Parker felt solid enough to raise his goatee to a Vandyke and his price from fifty cents to a dollar. He had twenty-six dentists on the payroll in Manhattan and Brooklyn.

It ought to be admitted that, technically, Painless was probably no worse than the average dentist of his era. It was his personality, his ballyhoo, and his speed that set him apart. A bear for work, he labored right along with the dentists he employed.

In his prosperity, Painless took to wearing swallowtails every evening and to frequenting the leading Broadway saloons. One night he was bellying up to a bar when Bob Fitzsimmons, the ex-heavyweight champ, came in to plant a foot on the rail. Fitzsimmons joked with the bartender and as he laughed, Parker could see the former champ's big, white strong front teeth.

In a little while Painless turned to Fitz and handed him his card.

"I'd like to fix up that mouth of yours, Champ," he said. "In fact, I'll do it for nothing—just for the advertising."

Fitzsimmons, puzzled, pointed out that his teeth were in fine shape.

"Oh," said Painless, "you're teeth look healthy enough. What I have in mind is to make them more *attractive*."

"How?"

"I'll put diamonds in them—free of charge."

"Diamonds!" Fitz exclaimed. "I never heard of such a thing."

"Oh course not," Painless agreed. "But if you let me put three or four diamonds in those front teeth, everybody in town will be talking about you."

Fitz bought the idea. Soon half a hundred of the city's sports were walking around with diamonds in their choppers and telling people that Painless Parker had put them there. Every time one of these jokers drew a laugh, Painless got free advertising, and more money.

He needed the stuff. Frances had given him a family of three girls and a boy, and for them he bought a fifty-acre estate on Long Island. There he populated the grounds with blooded horses and began to throw elaborate parties. No man ever hated his own parties more, and Parker seldom patronized them. When he did, he didn't participate in the festivities but circulated among the guests looking for business.

Parker didn't realize it, but he hated parties because he couldn't take his mind off business. And like a lot of successful men, he had to pay for it. What with shuttling back and forth between Manhattan and Brooklyn, staging ballyhoo, counting cash, and chasing dolls, Painless cracked up. He was in bed for almost a year. Then, in 1907, his wife persuaded him to sell out and go to California.

Landing in the Golden State with three million dollars, Parker and his family settled down on a big orange grove just outside Los Angeles. At first, Parker was content. Walking around under the orange trees with his wife, he assured her that he had never been happier in his life. But that mood didn't last long.

"Dear," Frances said to him one day. "I know you're not happy. What'll we do?"

Painless couldn't very well give her an honest answer. But besides the old urge, the inactivity of no work was driving him to the point of chewing fingernails. As an outlet for his energy, he bought a big, bright-red touring car and began to plan trips. He was driving the buggy around downtown Los Angeles one afternoon, when it broke down at a busy street intersection. A crowd collected to ogle the handsome vehicle, and the sight of it was too much for Parker. Before he knew what he was doing, he was lecturing the group on the horrors of tooth decay. In a couple of weeks he was back in business.

Within a few years Painless had several offices in Los Angeles and employed more than a score of dentists. He could honestly say that he was pretty painless now—gas, chloroform, and local anesthetics were available, and he used them. But so did his competitors. Consequently, Painless went into conference with himself. He concluded that if the ethicals had stolen his thunder, he would have to find some other means of attracting attention to himself.

With that thought in the back of his mind, he was sitting at home one night reading the evening paper when he came on an item that caused him to lean back, close his eyes, and speculate. The item said that a little one-ring circus was stranded on the outskirts of Los Angeles.

In the morning Painless went out to look the circus over. He took a quick look at the tent and the equipment, a somewhat longer look at the animals and the freaks, and a fine enjoyable stare at the curvy half of the trapeze performers. By nightfall he had bought the circus for fifty thousand dollars in cash.

Leaving his offices in charge of his assistants, Parker proceeded to deck himself out in green satin suit and pink hat and, as ringmaster, hit the road for a tour of one-night stands up and down the Pacific Coast. When the circus played a town, Painless, heading the street parade astride an elephant, waved the hat graciously and peeled an eye for business. Tooth business, not show business.

Every so often he slid off the elephant and ran along the line of spectators, looking for likely prospects. When he found one, he made a lightning examination and went into his pitch.

"Better see me at the show and get those bad teeth out," he wound up. Then, to make sure the spectator would come, Painless gave him a pass to the show. Each pass let its bearer into a special section reserved for those who were to have their teeth yanked— for the price of admission.

During the show, Ringmaster Parker introduced the acts. Between acts, Dentist Parker pulled teeth. After a performance, Romeo Parker made the rounds.

A showman at heart, Painless put the circus on its feet and had a wonderful time at it. But when his business mind said he'd milked the show for all it was worth in money and advertising, he sold it at a profit and returned to office dentistry.

One day a friend in the know gave Parker a tip.

"The ethicals are going to court," he said, "to make you stop using that name 'Painless.' They claim it's misrepresentation."

Parker promptly figured the thing to do was beat his enemies to the punch. He hustled into court and had his name legally changed from Edgar Rudolph Randolph Parker to Painless Parker.

"You can go back," he told the friend who had tipped him off, "and tell those bastards to do something about my name *now*."

Late one afternoon, about closing time, a gorgeous-looking doll came in and said she had a toothache. The receptionist tried to turn her over to one of the assistants, but she insisted on being handled by Painless himself.

The girl seated herself in Parker's chair and, after a few pleasantries, he turned around to select an instrument. When he turned back, there the babe was, shedding her slip. She grabbed up her clothes and ran screaming from the office, down the stairs, and out into the street in her bra and panties.

"Painless Parker attacked me!" she yelled to the startled pedestrians. "Painless Parker *attacked* me!" she screeched again.

The story hit the front pages. When the newspapers tried to pursue it, however, they found the girl had dropped from sight. But the damage was done. People said it simply wasn't safe for a pretty girl to let Painless operate on her.

Soon practically every shyster in Los Angeles, knowing that Parker was loaded with dough, went gunning for him. Within a few months he was snowed under by more than a score of suits ranging from fraud to malpractice, and the air outside Parker's office was white with subpoenas.

Painless, yelling that he was being framed, laid his work tools aside and turned investigator. Around the clock he labored gathering evidence to defend himself. One former patient, for example, claimed that Painless, in on orgy of extractions, had broken his neck. Parker discovered that the man had fallen off a ladder while painting his house. The case went out the window.

Another ex-patient came into court asserting that Painless had committed assault and battery on his molars. The patient's lawyer introduced before-and-after X rays to prove the charge. Painless, suspecting a fast one, requested a recess.

"What for?" asked the judge.

"I want to bring an X-ray machine into the courtroom," said Painless, "and take pictures of this man's mouth."

Against frantic legal objections, Parker got permission to get the machine. With it he took shots of the plaintiff's teeth. The pictures proved that those exhibited by the lawyer were fakes—X rays of an unknown mouth—and that case was thrown out of court.

Next, Parker had to face a suit instituted by a redhead who claimed that her virtue was worth a hundred thousand dollars, and that, since Painless had confiscated it and couldn't very well return it, she wanted the cash. Parker put a magnifying glass to the redhead's past. Then, when the case came to trial, he introduced five gentlemen who testified that the plaintiff had round heels from way back. And that settled that.

Soon the shysters who had joined the cause against Parker saw the handwriting on the wall and withdrew their actions. Painless wound up beating every case in one way or another, and didn't pay a single dollar to anybody.

The flood of suits in the City of the Angels, however, left a hangover flavor in Parker's mouth, and shortly he moved his headquarters to San Francisco. For a home there he bought a three-hundred-acre showplace in Santa Clara Valley, and at his wife's urging turned respectable. For several years Painless was comparatively ethical, doing no advertising in San Francisco and eating stuffed lobster with stuffed shirts at the luncheon clubs.

Toward the end of this period a man walked into the office one day and got Painless, himself, to pull three of his teeth. Then the man pointed to the vacancies.

"Put three back in their place," he said.

Painless had had similar requests before. And he had always given the same answer: "I only pull teeth."

"Seems to me," said the patient, "that somebody could make a lot of money by doing everything in one place—pulling teeth and making them, too. Then people wouldn't have to run all over town to get their mouths fixed up."

"Brother," said Parker, "you've just given me a great idea."

That was how Painless Parker came to originate assembly-line dentistry, by which patients could get every kind of dental work done under one roof. Up until then a patient had been hit pretty hard in the pocketbook traveling to one dentist for an X ray, to a second for an extraction, to still another for drilling and filling, and to yet another man for a set of false teeth. But Parker, doing everything together, was able to cut the price. A patient who might have paid two hundred dollars under the old system now got the whole package from Painless for as little as fifty dollars and saved a lot of shoe leather in the process.

Parker made out so well with his factory-type business that he opened branch offices in Washington and Oregon, and set up a big shop just for manufacturing dental plates. While many of his plates wobbled, there is little doubt that he kept a lot of people chewing and saved thousands from severe infections.

With all that lovely money, though, Painless was practically wiped out when Wall Street laid an egg. As if that weren't bad enough, his business fell off to almost nothing. People weren't spending hard cash just for fixing teeth. Drastic measures were called for.

Parker took to spending his nights pacing the living room at home while he squeezed his brain for ideas. The evening finally came when he stopped abruptly and snapped his fingers, and the old pitchman's light came into his eyes.

"Frances," he said, "I'm going to hit the pavements again."

Almost immediately Painless was in the midst of generating the biggest promotional campaign of his career. He had human flies walking up the front of the building housing his San Francisco headquarters. His name was on billboards all over the coast and on banners flying from blimps. He himself roamed the streets, reaching into mouths while trapeze artists flew through the air and a brass band drowned out the cries of the wounded.

The ballyhoo soon paid off. Nobody can stall a toothache indefinitely, and Painless, working cheaper and faster than the ethicals, had a decided advantage over them. His competitors in Oregon were particularly hard hit. Two dentists in Portland left the profession entirely, loudly laying their loss of patients to Parker's hoopla.

The commotion persuaded the Oregon board of dental examiners to draw a bead on Painless. He was vulnerable. Parker had never been required to take an examination in Oregon but had been given a license to practice there because he had passed dental exams in

New York and California. Now the examiners in Oregon decided to expose him to an examination. Painless crammed thoroughly, but the questions were so tough that he flunked.

"Those dirty ethicals loaded the questions!" Parker screamed. "I'm going to take my case to the people."

Painless hired an army of solicitors to go from door to door with a petition calling for a popular vote to determine whether a man who legally practiced dentistry elsewhere had to pass an examination to work in Oregon. He got more than a hundred thousand signers and raised a terrific furor. The examiners, fearing public opinion, granted Painless his license. The only catch was that Parker had to abstain from his customary antics.

By the mid-thirties Painless Parker was a millionaire again, and, as such, a good ethical target. This time the newspapers fell on Painless. They accused him of making a mockery of his profession. Painless countered by stumping the coast charging that the ethicals were behind the attacks. And why? Because he was the people's dentist—giving everything from X rays to plates at reasonable cost.

The ethicals retaliated by pushing a law through the California legislature making street dentistry illegal. That hit Parker hard, especially when state legislators throughout the country quickly followed suit. Painless began to feel hemmed in.

He wasn't really in a straitjacket, though, until California and other states made it a legal offense for a corporation to practice dentistry. Since Painless had incorporated himself, he construed this as a move against him and nobody else. He made several legal maneuvers to circumvent the law, but none of them succeeded and his California license was revoked. So he tried his final gimmick— he leased his holdings to his employees, and they agreed to kick back the gravy.

Barred from practice, Painless had nothing to do through the war years but weigh the incoming gravy and cuss the navy for stealing his stuff. Then in 1945, when Painless was seventy-three, his wife died and his three-hundred-acre estate was suddenly too big. He moved into two rooms over his business office, but even they were lonely because he had so little to do. A close friend, millionaire A. P. Giannini, founder of the Bank of America, decided he needed his trade back and got California's governor Sunny Jim Rolfe to restore Parker's license. Painless eagerly picked up his nippers and started all over again.

And until he died, at the age of eighty, Painless Parker kept his three interests in life—pulling teeth, looking at a pretty leg, and railing against the ethicals.

"That'll be only ninety bucks, brother," he said—shortly before he dropped off—to a customer for whom his office had done a big reconstruction job. "One of those ethical bastards would've charged you a *thousand*."

CHARLES DICKENS

The Hospital Patient

✌

Dickens was in his early twenties when he wrote the magazine articles later published as Sketches by Boz. *They're still immortal.*

In our rambles through the streets of London after evening has set in, we often pause beneath the windows of some public hospital, and picture to ourselves the gloomy and mournful scenes that are passing within. The sudden moving of a taper as its feeble ray shoots from window to window, until its light gradually disappears, as if it were carried farther back into the room to the bedside of some suffering patient, is enough to awaken a whole crowd of reflections: the mere glimmering of the low-burning lamps, which, when all other habitations are wrapped in darkness and slumber, denote the chamber where so many forms are writhing with pain, or wasting with disease, is sufficient to check the most boisterous merriment.

Who can tell the anguish of those weary hours, when the only sound the sick man hears is the disjointed wanderings of some feverish slumberer near him, the low moan of pain, or perhaps the muttered, long-forgotten prayer of a dying man? Who, but they who have felt it, can imagine the sense of loneliness and desolation which must be the portion of those who in the hour of dangerous illness are left to be tended by strangers; for what hands, be they ever so gentle, can wipe the clammy brow, or smooth the restless bed, like those of mother, wife, or child?

Impressed with these thoughts, we have turned away, through the nearly deserted streets; and the sight of the few miserable creatures still hovering about them has not tended to lessen the pain which such meditations awaken. The hospital is a refuge and resting place for hundreds, who but for such institutions must die in the streets and doorways; but what can be the feelings of some outcasts when they are stretched on the bed of sickness with scarcely a hope of recovery? The wretched woman who lingers about the pavement, hours after midnight, and the miserable shadow of a man—the ghastly remnant that want and drunkenness have left—which crouches beneath a window ledge, to sleep where there is some shelter from the rain, have little to bind them to life, but what have they to look back upon in death? What are the unwonted comforts of a roof and a bed, to them, when the recollections of a whole life of debasement stalk before them; when repentance seems a mockery, and sorrow comes too late?

About a twelvemonth ago, as we were strolling through Covent Garden (we had been thinking about these things overnight), we were attracted by the very prepossessing appearance of a pickpocket, who having declined to take the trouble of walking to the police office, on the ground that he hadn't the slightest wish to go there at all, was being conveyed thither in a wheelbarrow, to the huge delight of a crowd.

Somehow, we never can resist joining a crowd, so we turned back with the mob, and entered the office, in company with our friend the pickpocket, a couple of policemen, and as many dirty-faced spectators as could squeeze their way in.

There was a powerful, ill-looking young fellow at the bar, who was undergoing an examination, on the very common charge of having, on the previous night, ill-treated a woman with whom he lived in some court hard by. Several witnesses bore testimony to acts of the grossest brutality; and a certificate was read from the house surgeon of a neighboring hospital, describing the nature of the injuries the woman had received, and intimating that her recovery was extremely doubtful.

Some question appeared to have been raised about the identity of the prisoner; for when it was agreed that the two magistrates should visit the hospital at eight o'clock that evening to take her deposition, it was settled that the man should be taken there also. He turned pale at this, and we saw him clench the bar very hard when the order was given. He was removed directly afterward, and he spoke not a word.

We felt an irrepressible curiosity to witness this interview, although it is hard to tell why, at this instant, for we knew it must be a painful one. It was no very difficult matter for us to gain permission, and we obtained it.

The prisoner, and the officer who had him in custody, were already at the hospital when we reached it, and waiting the arrival of the magistrates in a small room below stairs. The man was handcuffed, and his hat was pulled forward over his eyes. It was easy to see, though, by the whiteness of his countenance, and the constant twitching of the muscles of his face, that he dreaded what was to come. After a short interval, the magistrates and clerk were bowed in by the house surgeon and a couple of young men who smelt very strong of tobacco smoke—they were introduced as "dressers"—and after one magistrate had complained bitterly of the cold, and the other of the absence of any news in the evening paper, it was announced that the patient was prepared; and we were conducted to the "casualty ward" in which she was lying.

The dim light which burnt in the spacious room increased rather than diminished the ghastly appearance of the hapless creatures in the beds, which were ranged in two long rows on either side. In one bed, lay a child enveloped in bandages, with its body half consumed by fire; in another, a female, rendered hideous by some dreadful accident, was wildly beating her clenched fists on the coverlet, in pain; on a third, there lay stretched a young girl, apparently in the heavy stupor often the immediate precursor of death: her face was stained with blood, and her breast and arms were bound up in folds of linen. Two or three of the beds were empty, and their recent occupants were sitting beside them, but with faces so wan, and eyes so bright and glassy, that it was fearful to meet their gaze. On every face was stamped the expression of anguish and suffering.

The object of the visit was lying at the upper end of the room. She was a fine young woman of about two or three and twenty. Her long black hair, which had been hastily cut from near the wounds on her head, streamed over the pillow in jagged and matted locks. Her face bore deep marks of the ill-usage she had received: her hand was pressed upon her side, as if her chief pain were there; her breathing was short and heavy; and it was plain to see that she was dying fast. She murmured a few words in reply to the magistrate's inquiry whether she was in great pain; and, having been raised on the pillow by the nurse, looked vacantly upon the strange countenances that surrounded her bed. The magistrate nodded to the officer to bring the man forward. He did so, and stationed him at the bedside. The girl looked on, with a wild and troubled expression of face; but her sight was dim, and she did not know him.

"Take off his hat," said the magistrate. The officer did as he was desired, and the man's features were disclosed.

The girl started up, with an energy quite preternatural; the fire gleamed in her heavy eyes, and the blood rushed to her pale and sunken cheeks. It was a convulsive effort. She fell back upon her pillow, and covering her scarred and bruised face with her hands, burst into tears. The man cast an anxious look toward her, but otherwise appeared wholly unmoved. After a brief pause the nature of their errand was explained, and the oath tendered.

"Oh, no, gentlemen," said the girl, raising herself once more, and folding her hands together; "no gentlemen, for God's sake! I did it myself—it was nobody's fault—it was an accident. He didn't hurt me; he wouldn't for all the world. Jack, dear Jack, you know you wouldn't!"

Her sight was fast failing her, and her hand groped over the bed-clothes in search of his. Brute as the man was, he was not prepared for this. He turned his face from the bed and sobbed. The girl's color changed, and her breathing grew more difficult. She was evidently dying.

"We respect the feelings which prompt you to this," said the gentleman who had spoken first, "but let me warn you not to persist in what you know to be untrue until it is too late. It cannot save him."

"Jack," murmured the girl, laying her hand upon his arm, "they shall not persuade me to swear your life away. He didn't do it, gentlemen. He never hurt me." She grasped his arm tightly, and added, in a broken whisper, "I hope God Almighty will forgive me all the wrong I have done, and the life I have led. God bless you, Jack. Some kind gentleman take my love to my poor old father. Five years ago he said he wished I had died a child. Oh, I wish I had! I wish I had!"

The nurse bent over the girl for a few seconds, and then drew the sheet over her face. It covered a corpse.

ARTHUR TRAIN

The Human Element

ઠ્ર

One of the most simon-pure surprise stories of all time.

Although men flatter themselves with their great actions, they are not so often the result of great design as of chance.

—LA ROCHEFOUCAULD

"He says he killed him, and that's all there is about it!" said Tutt to Mr. Tutt. "What are you going to do with a fellow like that?"

The junior partner of the celebrated firm of Tutt & Tutt, attorneys and counselors at law, thrust his hands deep into the pockets of his yellow checked trousers and, balancing himself upon the heels of his patent-leather shoes, gazed in a distressed, respectfully inquiring manner at his distinguished associate.

"Yes," he repeated plaintively. "He don't make any bones about it at all. 'Sure, I killed him!' says he. 'And I'd kill him again, the ——!' I prefer not to quote his exact language. I've just come from the Tombs and had quite a talk with the defendant in the counsel room, with a gum-chewing keeper sitting in the corner watching me for fear I'd slip his prisoner a saw file or a shotgun or a barrel of poison. I'm all in! These murder cases drive me to drink, Mr. Tutt. I don't mind grand larceny, forgery, assault, or even mayhem—but murder gets my goat! And when you have a crazy Italian for a client who says he's glad he did it and would like to do it again—please excuse me! It isn't law, it's suicide!"

He drew out a parti-colored silk handkerchief and wiped his forehead despairingly.

"Oh, indeed!" remarked Mr. Tutt with entire good nature. "He's glad he did it and he's quite willing to be hanged!"

"That's it in a nutshell!" replied Tutt.

"What is our client's name?"

"Angelo Serafino."

" 'Not Angles but Angels'!" mused Mr. Tutt.

The senior partner ran his bony fingers through the lank gray locks over his left temple and tilted ceilingward the stogie between his thin lips. Then he leaned back in his antique swivel chair, locked his hands behind his head, elevated his long legs luxuriously, and crossed his feet upon the fourth volume of the *American and English Encyclopedia of Law,* which lay open upon the desk at "Champerty and Maintenance." Even in this inelegant and relaxed posture he somehow managed to maintain the air of picturesque dignity which always made his tall, ungainly figure noticeable in any courtroom. Indubitably Mr. Ephraim Tutt suggested a past generation, the suggestion being accentuated by a slight pedantry of diction somewhat out of character with the rushing age in which he saw fit to practice his time-honored profession. "Cheer up, Tutt," said he, pushing a box of stogies toward his partner with the toe of his congress shoe. "Have a weed?"

Since in the office of Tutt & Tutt such an invitation, like that of royalty, was equivalent to a command, Tutt acquiesced.

"Thank you, Mr. Tutt," said Tutt, looking about vaguely for a match.

"That conscienceless brat of a Willie steals 'em all," growled Mr. Tutt. "Ring the bell."

Tutt obeyed. He was a short, brisk little man with a pronounced abdominal convexity, and he maintained toward his superior, though but a few years his junior, a mingled attitude of awe, admiration, and affection such as a dickey bird might adopt toward a distinguished owl.

This attitude was shared by the entire office force. Inside the ground glass of the outer door Ephraim Tutt was king. To Tutt the opinion of Mr. Tutt upon any subject whatsoever was law, even if the courts might have held to the contrary. To Tutt he was the eternal fount of wisdom, culture, and morality. Yet until Mr. Tutt had finally elucidated his views Tutt did not hesitate to hold conditional, if temporary, opinions of his own. Briefly their relations were symbolized by the circumstance that while Tutt always addressed his senior partner as "Mr. Tutt," the latter accosted him simply as "Tutt." In a word there was only one Mr. Tutt in the firm of Tutt & Tutt.

But so far as that went, there was only one Tutt. On the theory that a lily cannot be painted, the estate of the one, seemingly, was as good as that of the other. At any rate there never was and never had been any confusion or ambiguity arising out of the matter since the day, so long ago, when Tutt had visited Mr. Tutt's law office in search of employment. Mr. Tutt was just rising into fame as a police-court lawyer. Tutt had only recently been admitted to the bar, having abandoned his native city of Bangor, Maine, for the metropolis.

"And may I ask why you should come to me?" Mr. Tutt had demanded severely from behind the stogie, which even at that early date had been as much a part of his facial anatomy as his long ruminative nose. "Why the devil should you come to me? I am nobody, sir,—nobody! In this great city there are certainly thousands more qualified than I to further your professional and financial advancement."

"Because," answered the inspired Tutt with modesty, "I feel that with you I should be associated with a good name."

That had settled the matter. They bore no relationship to one another, but they were the only Tutts in the city and there seemed to be a certain propriety in their hanging together. Neither had regretted it for a moment, and as the years passed they became indispensable to each other. They were the necessary component parts of a harmonious legal whole. Mr. Tutt was the brains and the voice, while Tutt was the eyes and legs of a combination that at intervals made the law tremble, sometimes in fear and more often with joy.

At first, speaking figuratively, Tutt merely carried Mr. Tutt's bag, —rode on his coattails, as it were; but as time went on his activity, ingenuity, and industry made him indispensable and led to a junior partnership. Tutt prepared the cases for Mr. Tutt to try. Both were well versed in the law if they were not profound lawyers, but as the origin of the firm was humble, their practice was of a miscellaneous character.

"Never turn down a case," was Tutt's motto.

"Our duty as sworn officers of the judicial branch of the government renders it incumbent upon us to perform whatever services our clients' exigencies demand," was Mr. Tutt's way of putting it.

In the end it amounted to exactly the same thing. As a result, in addition to their own clientele, other members of the bar, who found themselves encumbered with matters which for one reason or another they preferred not to handle, formed the habit of turning them over to Tutt & Tutt. A never-enduring stream of peculiar cases flowed through the office, each leaving behind it some residuum of golden dust, however small. The stately or—as an unkind observer might have put it—the ramshackly form of the senior partner was a constant figure in all the courts, from that of the coroner on the one hand to the appellate tribunals upon the other. It was immaterial to him what the case was about—whether it dealt with the "next eventual estate" or the damages for a dog bite—so long as he was paid and Tutt prepared it. Hence Tutt & Tutt prospered. And as the law, like any other profession, requires jacks-of-all-trades, the firm acquired a certain peculiar professional standing of its own, and enjoyed the good will of the bar as a whole.

They had the reputation of being sound lawyers if not over-afflicted with a sense of professional dignity, whose word was better than their bond, yet who, faithful to their clients' interests, knew no mercy and gave no quarter. They took and pressed cases which other lawyers dared not touch lest they should be defiled—and nobody seemed to think any the less of them for so doing. They raised points that made the refinements of the ancient schoolmen seem blunt in comparison. No respecters of persons, they harried the rich and taunted the powerful, and would have as soon jailed a bishop or a judge as a pickpocket, if he deserved it. Between them they knew more kinds of law than most of their professional brethren, and, as Mr. Tutt was a bookworm and a seeker after legal and other lore, their dusty old library was full of hidden treasures, which on frequent occasions were unearthed to entertain the jury or delight the bench. They were loyal friends, fearsome enemies, high chargers, and maintained their unique position in spite of the fact that at one time or another they had run close to the shadowy line which divides the ethical from that which is not. Yet Mr. Tutt had brought disbarment proceedings against many lawyers in his time and—what is more —had them disbarred.

"Leave old Tutt alone," was held sage advice, and when other lawyers desired to entertain the judiciary they were apt to invite Mr. Tutt to be of the party. And Tutt gloried in the glories of Mr. Tutt.

"That's it!" repeated Tutt as he lit his stogie, the cub of a Willie having foraged successfully in the outer office for a match. "He's willing to be hanged or damned or anything else just for the pleasure of having put a bullet through the other fellow!"

"What was the name of the unfortunate deceased?"

"Tomasso Crocedoro—a barber."

"That is almost a defense in itself," mused Mr. Tutt. "Anyhow, if I've got to defend Angelo for shooting Tomasso, you might as well give me a short scenario of the melodrama. By the way, are we retained or assigned by the court?"

"Assigned," chirped Tutt. "And—if he's convicted, as of course he will be—we stand a good chance of losing our reputation as successful trial counsel. Why not beg off?"

"Let me hear the story first," answered Mr. Tutt. "Angelo sounds like a good sport. I have a mild affection for him already."

He reached into a lower compartment of his desk and removed a tumbler and a bottle of malt extract, which he placed at his elbow. Then he leaned back again expectantly.

"It is a simple story," began Tutt, seating himself in the chair reserved for paying clients—that is to say, one which did not have the two front legs sawed off an inch or so in order to make lingering uncomfortable—"a plain, unvarnished tale. Our client is one who makes an honest living by blacking shoes near the entrance to the Brooklyn Bridge. He formed an attachment for a certain young lady who had previously had some sort of love affair with Crocedoro, as a result of which her social standing had become slightly impaired. In a word, Tomasso jilted her. Angelo saw, pitied, and loved her, took her for better or for worse, and married her."

"For which," interjected Mr. Tutt, "he is entitled to everyone's respect."

"Quite so!" agreed Tutt. "Now Tomasso, though not willing to marry the girl himself, seemed to have resented the idea of anyone else doing so, and accordingly seized every opportunity which presented itself to twit Angelo about the matter."

"Dog in the manger, so to speak," nodded Mr. Tutt.

"He not only jeered at Angelo for marrying Rosalina, but he began to hang about his discarded mistress again and scoff at her choice of a husband. But Rosalina gave him the cold shoulder, with the result that he became more and more insulting to Angelo. Finally one day our client made up his mind not to stand it any longer, secured a revolver, sought out Tomasso in his barber shop, and put a bullet through his head. Now however much you may sympathize with Angelo as a man and a husband, there isn't the slightest doubt that he killed Tomasso with every kind of deliberation and premeditation."

"If the case is as you say," replied Mr. Tutt, pouring out a tumbler of malt extract and flicking a stogie ash from his waistcoat, "the honorable justice who handed it to us is no friend of ours."

"He isn't," assented his partner. "It was Babson, and he hates Italians. Moreover, he stated in open court that he proposed to try the case himself next Monday and that we must be ready without fail."

"So Babson did that to us!" growled Mr. Tutt. "Just like him. He'll pack the jury and charge our innocent Angelo into the middle of hades."

"And Bloodhound O'Brien is the assistant district attorney in charge of the prosecution," mildly added Tutt. "But what can we do? We're assigned, we've got a guilty client, and we've got to defend him. Bonnie Doon says it's the toughest case he ever had to handle in which to find any witnesses for the defense. There aren't any. Besides, the girl bought the gun and gave it to Angelo the same day."

"How do you know that?" demanded Mr. Tutt, frowning.

"Because she told me so herself," said Tutt. "She's outside if you want to see her."

Tutt retired and presently returned half leading, half pushing a shabbily dressed young Italian woman. She wore no hat and her hands and fingernails were far from clean, but from the folds of her black shawl her neck rose like a column of slightly discolored Carrara marble, upon which her head with its coils of heavy hair was poised with the grace of a Roman empress.

"Come in, my child, and sit down," said Mr. Tutt kindly. "No, not in that one; in *that* one." He indicated the chair previously occupied by his junior. "You can leave us, Tutt. I want to talk to this young lady alone."

The girl sat sullenly, with averted face, showing in her attitude her instinctive feeling that all officers of the law, no matter upon which side they were supposed to be, were one and all engaged in a mysterious conspiracy of which she and her unfortunate Angelo were the victims. A few words from the old lawyer and she began to feel more confidence, however. No one, in fact, could fail to realize at first glance Mr. Tutt's warmth of heart. The lines of his sunken cheeks, if left to themselves, automatically tended to draw together into a whimsical smile, and it required a positive act of will upon his part to adopt the stern and relentless look with which he was wont to glower down upon some unfortunate witness in cross-examination.

Inside, Mr. Tutt was a benign and rather mellow old fellow, with a dry sense of humor and a very keen knowledge of his fellowmen. He made a good deal of money, but not having any wife or child upon which to lavish it, he spent it all either on books or on surreptitious quixotic gifts to friends or strangers, whom he secretly admired or whom he believed to be in need of money. There were vague traditions in the office of presents of bizarre and quite impossible clothes made to office boys and stenographers; of ex-convicts re-outfitted and sent rejoicing to foreign parts; of tramps gorged to repletion and then pumped dry of their adventures in Mr. Tutt's comfortable, dingy old library; of a fur coat suddenly clapped upon the rounded shoulders of old Scraggs, the antiquated scrivener in the accountant's cage in the outer office, whose alcoholic career, his employer alleged, was marked by a trail of empty rum kegs, each one flying the white flag of surrender.

And yet old Ephraim Tutt could on occasion be cold as chiseled steel, and as hard. Any appeal from a child, a woman, or an outcast always met with his ready response. He would burn the midnight oil with equal zest to block a crooked deal on the part of a wealthy corporation or to devise a means to extricate some no less crooked rascal from the clutches of the law, provided that the rascal seemed the victim of hard luck, inheritance, or environment. His weather-beaten conscience was as elastic as his heart. He had, indeed, when under the expansive influence of a sufficient quantity of malt extract or ancient brandy from the cellaret on his library desk, been heard to enunciate the theory that there was very little difference between those in jail and those who were not.

He would work for weeks, without compensation, to argue the case of some guilty rogue before the Court of Appeals, in order, as he said, to "settle the law," when his only real object was to get the miserable fellow out of jail and send him back to his wife and children. He went through life with a twinkling eye and a quizzical smile, and when he did wrong he did it—if such a thing be possible—in a way to make people better. He was a dangerous adversary and judges were afraid of him, not because he ever tricked or deceived them, but because of the audacity and novelty of his arguments, which left them floundering. He had the assurance that usually comes with age and with a lifelong knowledge of human nature, yet apparently he had always been possessed of it.

Now as he gazed at the tearstained cheeks of the girl-wife whose husband had committed murder in defense of her good repute, he vowed that so far as he was able he would fight to save him. The more desperate the case, the more desperate her need of him—the greater the duty and the greater his honor if successful.

"Believe that I am your friend, my dear!" he assured her. "You and I must work together to set Angelo free."

"It's no use," she returned less defiantly. "He done it. He won't deny it."

"But he is entitled to his defense," urged Mr. Tutt.

"He won't make no defense."

"We must make one for him."

"There ain't none. He just went and killed him."

Mr. Tutt shrugged his shoulders.

"There is always a defense," he answered. "Anyhow, we can't let him be convicted without making an effort. Will they be able to prove where he got the pistol?"

"He didn't get the pistol," retorted the girl with a glint in her black eyes. "I got it. I'd ha' shot him myself if Angelo hadn't. I said I was goin' to, but he wouldn't let me."

"Dear, dear!" sighed Mr. Tutt. "What a case! Both of you trying to see which can get hanged first!"

The inevitable day of Angelo's trial came. Upon the bench the Honorable Mr. Justice Babson glowered down upon the defendant flanked by his distinguished counsel, Tutt & Tutt, and upon the two hundred good and true talesmen who, "all other business laid aside," had been dragged from the comfort of their homes and the important affairs of their various livelihoods to pass upon the merits of the issue duly joined between The People of the State of New York and Angelo Serafino, charged with murder.

Each of them, as his name was called, took his seat in the witness chair and perjured himself like a gentleman in order to escape from service, shyly confessing to an ineradicable prejudice against the entire Italian race and this defendant in particular, and to such an antipathy against capital punishment as, he unhesitatingly averred, would render him utterly incapable of satisfactorily performing the functions of a juryman. Hardly one, however, but was routed by the Machiavellian Babson. Hardly one, however ingenious his excuse,—whether about to be married or immediately to become a father, whether in the last stages of illness or obliged to be present at the bedside of a dying wife—but was browbeaten and ordered back to his place amidst the waiting throng of citizens so disinclined to facilitate that system of trial by jury, the failure of which they so loudly at other times condemned.

This trifling preliminary having been concluded, the few jurymen who had managed to wriggle through the judicial sieve were allowed to withdraw; the balance of the calendar was adjourned; those spectators who were standing up were ordered to sit down and those already sitting down were ordered to sit somewhere else; the prisoners in the rear of the room were sent back to the Tombs to await their fate upon a later day; the reporters gathered rapaciously about the table just behind the defendant; a corpulent Ganymede, in the person of an aged court officer, bore trembling an opaque glass of yellow drinking water to the bench; O'Brien, the prosecutor, blew his nose like a fish horn; Mr. Tutt smiled an ingratiating smile which seemed to clasp the whole world to his bosom—and the real battle commenced, a game in which every card in the pack had been stacked against the prisoner by an unscrupulous pair of officials whose only aim was to maintain their record of convictions of "murder in the first" and who laid their plans with ingenuity and carried them out with skill and enthusiasm to habitual success.

They were a grand little pair of convicters, were Babson and O'Brien, and woe unto that man who was brought before them. It was even alleged by the impious that when Babson was in doubt what to do or what O'Brien wanted him to do, the latter communicated the information to his conspirator upon the bench by a system of preconcerted signals. But no such system was necessary, for the judge's part in the drama was merely to sustain his colleague's objections and overrule those of his opponent, after which he himself delivered the *coup de grâce* with unerring insight and accuracy. When Babson got through charging a jury the latter had always in fact been instructed in brutal and sneering tones to convict the defendant or forever after to regard themselves as disloyal citizens, oath violators, and outcasts; although the stenographic record of his remarks would have led the reader thereof to suppose that this same judge was a conscientious, tender-hearted, merciful lover of humanity, whose sensitive soul quivered at the mere thought of a prison cell, and who sought to surround the defendant with every protection the law could interpose against the imputation of guilt. He was, as Tutt put it, "a dangerous old cuss."

O'Brien was even worse. He was a bull-necked, bullet-headed, young ruffian with beery eyes, who had an insatiable ambition and a still greater conceit, but who had devised a blundering way of conducting himself before a jury that deceived them into believing that his inexperience required their help and his disinterestedness their loyal support. Both of them were apparently fair-minded, honest public servants; both in reality were subtly disingenuous to a degree beyond ordinary comprehension. In a word, they were a precious pair of crooks, who for their own petty and selfish ends played fast and loose with libety, life, and death.

Both of them hated Mr. Tutt, who had more than once made them ridiculous before the jury and shown them up before the Court of Appeals, and the old lawyer recognized the fact that these two legal wolves were, in revenge, planning to tear him and his helpless client to pieces, having first deliberately selected him as a victim and assigned him to officiate at a ceremony which, however just so far as its consummation might be concerned, was nothing less in its conduct than judicial murder. Now they were laughing at him in their sleeves, for Mr. Tutt enjoyed the reputation of never having had a client convicted of murder, and that spotless reputation was about to be annihilated forever.

He well knew that although the defense had thirty peremptory challenges, Babson would sustain the prosecution's objections for bias, until the jury box would contain the twelve automata personally selected by O'Brien in advance from what Tutt called "the standing army of the gibbet." Yet the old war horse outwardly maintained a calm and genial exterior, betraying none of the apprehension which in fact existed beneath his mask of professional composure. The court officer rapped sharply for silence.

"Are you quite ready to proceed with the case?" inquired the judge with a courtesy in which was ill concealed a leer of triumph.

"Yes, Your Honor," responded Mr. Tutt in velvet tones.

"Call the first talesman!"

The fight was on, the professional duel had begun between traditional enemies, in which the stake—a human life—was in truth the thing of least concern. Yet no casual observer would have suspected the actual significance of what was going on or the part that envy, malice, selfishness, and ambition were playing in it. He would have seen merely a partially filled courtroom flooded with sunshine from high windows, an attentive and dignified judge in a black silk robe sitting upon a dais, below which a white-haired clerk drew little slips of paper from a wheel and summoned talesmen to a service which outwardly bore no suggestion of a tragedy.

He would have seen a somewhat unprepossessing assistant district attorney lounging in front of the jury box, taking apparently no great interest in the proceedings, and a worried-looking young Italian sitting at the prisoner's table between a rubicund little man and a tall, grave, longish-haired lawyer with a frame not unlike that of Abraham Lincoln, over whose wrinkled face from time to time played the suggestion of a smile. Behind a balustrade were the reporters, scribbling on rough sheets of yellow paper. Then came the rows of benches, upon the first of which, as near the jury box as possible, sat Rosalina in a new bombazine dress and wearing a large imitation gold cross furnished for the occasion out of the legal property room of Tutt & Tutt. Occasionally she sobbed softly. The bulk of the spectators consisted of rejected talesmen, witnesses, law clerks, professional court loafers, and women seeking emotional sensations which they had not the courage or the means to satisfy otherwise. The courtroom was comparatively quiet, the silence broken only by the droning voice of the clerk and the lazy interplay of question and answer between talesman and lawyer.

Yet, beneath the casual, almost indifferent manner in which the proceedings seemed to be conducted, each side was watching every move made by the other with the tension of a tiger ready to spring upon its prey. Babson and O'Brien on the one hand were engaged in forcing upon the defense a jury composed entirely of case-hardened convicters, while upon the other Tutt & Tutt were fighting desperately to secure one so heterogeneous in character that they could hope for a disagreement.

By recess thirty-seven talesmen had been examined without a foreman having been selected, and Mr. Tutt had exhausted twenty-nine of his thirty challenges, as against the prosecution's three. The court reconvened and a new talesman was called, resembling in appearance a professional hangman with a predilection for the execution of Italians. Mr. Tutt examined him for bias and every known form of incompetency, but in vain—then challenged peremptorily. Thirty challenges! He looked on Tutt with slightly raised eyebrows.

"Patrick Henry Walsh—to the witness chair, please!—Mr. Walsh!" called the clerk, as he drew another slip from the box.

Mr. Walsh arose and came forward heavily, while Tutt & Tutt trembled. He was the man they were most afraid of—an old-timer celebrated as a bulwark of the prosecution, who could always be safely counted upon to uphold the arms of the law, who regarded with reverence all officials connected with the administration of justice, and from whose composition apparently all human emotions had been carefully excluded by the Creator. He was a square-jawed, severe, heavily built person, with a long relentless upper lip, cheeks ruddy from the open air; and he had a brogue that would have charmed a mavis off a tree. Mr. Tutt gazed hopelessly at Tutt.

Babson and O'Brien had won.

Once more Mr. Tutt struggled against his fate. Was Mr. Walsh sure he had no prejudice against Italians or foreigners generally? Quite. Did he know anybody connected with the case? No. Had he any objection to the infliction of capital punishment? None whatever. The defense had exhausted all its challenges. Mr. Tutt turned to the prospective foreman with an endearing smile.

"Mr. Walsh," said he in caressing tones, "you are precisely the type of man in whom I feel the utmost confidence in submitting the fate of my client. I believe that you will make an ideal foreman. I hardly need to ask you whether you will accord the defendant the benefit of every reasonable doubt, and if you have such a doubt will acquit him?"

Mr. Walsh regarded Mr. Tutt suspiciously.

"Sure," he dryly responded. "Oi'll give him the benefit o' the doubt, but if Oi think he's guilty Oi'll convict him."

Mr. Tutt shivered.

"Of course! Of course! That would be your duty! You are entirely satisfactory, Mr. Walsh!"

"Mr. Walsh is more than satisfactory to the prosecution!" intoned O'Brien.

"Be sworn, Mr. Walsh," directed the clerk; and the filling of the jury box in the memorable case of People versus Serafino was begun.

"That chap doesn't like us," whispered Mr. Tutt to Tutt. "I laid it on a bit too thick."

In fact, Mr. Walsh had already entered upon friendly relations with Mr. O'Brien, and as the latter helped him arrange a place for his hat and coat the foreman cast a look tinged with malevolence at the defendant and his counsel, as if to say: "You can't fool me. I know the kind of tricks you fellows are all up to."

O'Brien could not repress a grin. The clerk drew forth another name.

"Mr. Tompkins—will you take the chair?"

Swiftly the jury was impaneled. O'Brien challenged everybody who did not suit his fancy, while Tutt & Tutt sat helpless.

Ten minutes, and the clerk called the roll, beginning with Mr. Walsh, they were solemnly sworn a true verdict to find, and settled themselves to the task.

The mills of the gods had begun to grind, and Angelo was being dragged to his fate as inexorably and as surely, with about as much chance of escape, as a log that is being drawn slowly toward a buzz saw.

"You may open the case, Mr. O'Brien," announced Judge Babson, leaning back and wiping his glasses.

Then as his fellow conspirator undertook to tell the jury what it was all about, he surreptitiously began to read his mail. One by one the witnesses were called—the coroner's physician, the policeman who had arrested Angelo with the smoking pistol in his hand outside the barber shop, the assistant barber who had seen the shooting, the customer who was being shaved. Each drove a spike into poor Angelo's legal coffin. Mr. Tutt could not shake them. The evidence was plain. He had come into the shop, accused Crocedoro of making his wife's life unbearable, and—shot him.

Yet Mr. Tutt did not lose any of his equanimity. With the tips of his long fingers held lightly together in front of him, he smiled benignly down upon the customer and the barber's assistant as if these witnesses were merely unfortunate in not being able to disclose to the jury all the facts. His manner indicated that a mysterious and untold tragedy lay behind what they had heard, a tragedy pregnant with primordial passions, involving the most sacred of human relationships, which when known would rouse the spirit of chivalry of the entire panel.

On cross-examination the barber testified that Angelo had said: "You maka small of my wife long enough!"

"Ah!" murmured Mr. Tutt, waving an arm in the direction of Rosalina. Did the witness recognize the defendant's young wife? The jury showed interest and examined the sobbing Rosalina with approval. Yes, the witness recognized her. Did the witness know to what incident or incidents the defendant had referred by his remark —what the deceased Crocedoro had done to Rosalina—if anything? No, the witness did not. Mr. Tutt looked significantly at the row of faces in the jury box.

Then, leaning forward, he asked: "Did you see Crocedoro threaten the defendant with his razor?"

"I object!" shouted O'Brien, springing to his feet. "The question is improper. There is no suggestion that Crocedoro did anything. The defendant can testify to that if he wants to!"

"Oh, let him answer!" drawled the judge.

"No—" began the witness.

"Ah!" cried Mr. Tutt. "You did not see Crocedoro threaten the defendant with his razor! That will do!"

But, forewarned by this trifling experience, Mr. O'Brien induced the customer, the next witness, to swear that Crocedoro had not in fact made any move whatever with his razor toward Angelo, who had deliberately raised his pistol and shot him.

Mr. Tutt rose to the cross-examination with the same urbanity as before. Where was the witness standing? The witness said he wasn't standing. Well, where was he sitting, then? In the chair.

"Ah!" exclaimed Mr. Tutt triumphantly. "Then you had your back to the shooting!"

In a moment O'Brien had the witness partially rescued by the explanation that he had seen the whole thing in the glass in front of him. The firm of Tutt & Tutt uttered in chorus a groan of outraged incredulity. Several jurymen were seen to wrinkle their foreheads in meditation. Mr. Tutt had sown a tiny—infinitesimally tiny—seed of doubt, not as to the killing, but as to the complete veracity of the witness.

And then O'Brien made his coup.

"Rosalina Serafino—take the witness stand!" he ordered.

He would get from her own lips the admission that she had bought the pistol and given it to Angelo! But, with an outburst of indignation that would have done credit to the elder Booth, Mr. Tutt was immediately on his feet protesting against the outrage, the barbarity, the heartlessness, the illegality of making a wife testify against her husband! His eyes flashed, his disordered locks waved in picturesque synchronization with his impassioned gestures. Rosalina, her beautiful golden cross rising and falling hysterically upon her bosom, took her seat in the witness chair like a frightened, furtive creature of the woods, for one brief instant gazed, with those great black eyes of her, upon the twelve men in the jury box, and then with burning cheeks buried her face in her handkerchief.

"I protest against this piece of cruelty!" cried Mr. Tutt in a voice vibrating with indignation. "This is worthy of the Inquisition. Will not even the cross upon her breast protect her from being compelled to reveal those secrets that are sacred to wife and motherhood? Can the law thus indirectly tear the seal of confidence from the confessional? Mr. O'Brien, you go too far! There are some things that even you—brilliant as you are—may not trifle with."

A juryman nodded. The eleven others, being more intelligent, failed to understand what he was talking about.

"Mr. Tutt's objection is sound—if he wishes to press it," remarked the judge. "You may step down, madam. The law will not compel a wife to testify against her husband. Have you any more witnesses, Mr. District Attorney?"

"The People rest," said Mr. O'Brien. "The case is with the defense."

Mr. Tutt rose with solemnity.

"The court will, I suppose, grant me a moment or two to confer with my client?" he inquired. Babson bowed and the jury saw the lawyer engage his partner in what seemed to be a weighty discussion.

"I killa him! I say so!" muttered Angelo feebly to Mr. Tutt.

"Shut up, you fool!" hissed Tutt, grabbing him by the leg. "Keep still or I'll wring your neck."

"If I could reach that old crook up on the bench, I would twist his nose," remarked Mr. Tutt to Tutt with an air of consulting him about the year books. "And as for that criminal O'Brien, I'll get him yet!"

With great dignity Mr. Tutt then rose and again addressed the court:

"We have decided upon all the circumstances of this most extraordinary case, Your Honor, not to put in any defense. I shall not call the defendant——"

"I killa him—" began Angelo, breaking loose from Tutt and struggling to his feet. It was a horrible movement. But Tutt clapped his hand over Angelo's mouth and forced him back into his seat.

"The defense rests," said Mr. Tutt, ignoring the interruption. "So far as we are concerned the case is closed."

"Both sides rest!" snapped Babson. "How long do you want to sum up?"

Mr. Tutt looked at the clock, which pointed to three. The regular hour of adjournment was at four. Delay was everything in a case like this. A juryman might die suddenly overnight or fall grievously ill; or some legal accident might occur which would necessitate declaring a mistrial. There is always hope in a criminal case, so long as the verdict has not actually been returned and the jury polled and discharged. If possible he must drag his summing up over until the following day. Something might happen.

"I shall need about two hours, Your Honor," he replied.

The jury stirred impatiently. It was clear that they regarded a two-hour speech from him under the circumstances as an imposition. But Babson wished to preserve the fiction of impartiality.

"Very well," said he. "You may sum up until four-thirty, and have half an hour more tomorrow morning. See that the doors are closed, Captain Phelan. We do not want any interruption while the summations are going on."

"All out that's goin' out! Everybody out that's got no business with the court!" bellowed Captain Phelan.

Mr. Tutt with an ominous heightening of the pulse realized that the real ordeal was at last at hand, for the closing of the case had wrought in the old lawyer an instant metamorphosis. With the words "The defense rests" every suggestion of the mountebank, the actor, or the shyster had vanished. The awful responsibility under which he labored; the overwhelming and damning evidence against his client; the terrible consequences of the least mistake that he might make; the fact that only the sword of his ability, and his alone, stood between Angelo and a hideous death by fire in the electric chair—sobered and chastened him.

For his client was foredoomed—foredoomed not only by justice, but also by trickery and guile—and was being driven slowly but surely toward the judicial shambles. For what had he succeeded in adducing in his behalf? Nothing save the unsupported speculation that the dead barber might have threatened Angelo with his razor and that the witnesses might possibly have drawn somewhat upon their imaginations in given the details of their testimony. A sorry defense! Indeed, no defense at all. All the sorrier in that he had not even been able to get before the jury the purely sentimental excuses for the homicide, for he could only do this by calling Rosalina to the stand, which would have enabled the prosecution to cross-examine her in regard to the purchase of the pistol and the delivery of it to her husband—the strongest evidence of premeditation. Yet he must find some argument, some plea, some thread of reason upon which the jury might hang a disagreement or a verdict in a lesser degree.

With a shuffling of feet the last of the crowd pushed through the big oak doors which were closed and locked. An officer brought a corroded tumbler of brackish water and placed it in front of Mr. Tutt. The judge leaned forward with malicious courtesy. The jury settled themselves and turned toward the lawyer with a defiant attention, hardening their hearts already against his expected appeals to sentiment. O'Brien, ostentatiously producing a cigarette, lounged out through the side door leading to the jury room and prison cells. The clerk began copying his records. The clock ticked loudly.

And Mr. Tutt rose and began going through the empty formality of attempting to discuss the evidence in such a way as to excuse or palliate Angelo's crime. For Angelo's guilt of murder in the first degree was so plain that it had never for one moment been in the slightest doubt. Whatever might be said for his act from the point of view of human emotion only made his motive and his responsibility under the statutes all the clearer. There was not even "the unwritten law" to appeal to. Yet there was a genuine defense, a defense that could not be urged even by innuendo: the defense that no accused ought to be convicted upon any evidence whatever, no matter how conclusive, when his trial has been conducted with essential unfairness.

Such was the case of Angelo. No one could demonstrate it, no one could with safety even hint at it; any charge that the court was anything but impartial would prove a boomerang to the defense; and yet the fact remained that the whole proceeding from start to finish had been conducted with illegality, that the jury had been duped and deceived, and that the pretense that the guilty Angelo had been given an impartial trial was a farce. Every word of the court had been an accusation, a sneer, an acceptance of the defendant's guilt as a matter of course, an abuse far more subversive of the administration of justice than the mere acquittal of a single criminal, for it struck at the very foundations of liberty—the guarantees of the presumption of innocence and "due process of law."

Unmistakably the proceedings had been conducted throughout upon the theory that the defendant must prove his innocence and that presumably he was a guilty man; and this, as well as his own impression that the evidence was conclusive, the judge had subtly conveyed to the jury in his tone of speaking, his ironical manner, and his facial expression. Guilty or not, Angelo was being railroaded. That was the real defense—a defense that could never be established even in any higher court.

And so Mr. Tutt, boiling with suppressed indignation, weighed down with the sense of his responsibility, fully realizing his inability to say anything in behalf of his client based on the evidence, rose with a genial smile upon his puckered old face and with a careless air, which however seemed to indicate the utmost confidence and determination, and with a graceful compliment to his arch enemy upon the bench and the yellow dog who hunted with him, assured the jury that the defendant had had the fairest of fair trials and that he, Mr. Tutt, would now proceed to demonstrate to their satisfaction his client's entire innocence; nay, would indeed show them that he was a man not only guiltless of any wrongdoing, but worthy of their hearty commendation.

With anecdotes not too unseemly for the occasion he overcame their preliminary distrust and put them in a good humor. He gave a historical dissertation upon the law governing homicide, on the constitutional rights of American citizens, on the laws of naturalization, marriage, and the domestic relations; waxed eloquent over Italy and the Italian character, mentioned Cavour, Garibaldi, and Mazzini in a way to imply that Angelo was their lineal descendant; lauded Mussolini; and quoted from D'Annunzio back to Horace, Cicero, and Plautus.

"Bunk! Nothing but bunk!" muttered Tutt, studying the twelve faces before him. "And they all know it!"

But Mr. Tutt was nothing if not interesting. These prosaic citizens of New York County, these saloon and hotel keepers, these contractors, insurance agents, and salesmen were learning something of history, of philosophy, of art and beauty. They liked it. They felt they were hearing something worthwhile, as indeed they were, and they forgot all about Angelo and the unfortunate Crocedoro in their admiration for Mr. Tutt, who had lifted them out of the dingy sordid courtroom into the sunlight of the Golden Age. And as he led them through Greek and Roman literature, through the early English poets, through Shakespeare and the King James Version, down to John Galsworthy and Rupert Brooke, he brought something that was noble, fine, and sweet into their grubby materialistic lives.

"Bang!" went Babson's gavel just as Mr. Tutt was leading Mr. Walsh, Mr. Tompkins, and the others through the winding paths of the Argonne forests, with tin helmets on their heads, in the struggle to make the world safe for democracy.

"You may conclude your address in the morning, Mr. Tutt," said the judge with supreme unction. "Adjourn court!"

Gray depression enveloped Mr. Tutt's soul as he trudged homeward. He had made a good speech, but it had had absolutely nothing to do with the case, a fact which the jury would perceive as soon as they thought it over. It was a confession of defeat. Angelo would be convicted of murder in the first degree and electrocuted, Rosalina would be a widow, and he would be in a measure responsible for it. The tragedy of human life appalled him. He felt very old, as old as the dead-and-gone authors from whom he had quoted with such remarkable facility. He belonged with them; he was too old to practice his profession.

"Law, Mis' Tutt," expostulated Miranda, his ancient Negro hand-maiden, as he pushed away the chop and mashed potato, and even the glass of claret, untasted, in his old-fashioned dining room on West Twenty-third Street, "you ain't got no appetite at all! You's got a misery, Mis' Tutt."

"No, no, Miranda!" he replied weakly. "I'm just getting old."

"You's mighty spry for an old man, yit," she protested. "You kin make dem lawyer men hop mighty high when you tries. Heh, heh! I reckon dey ain't got nuffin' on ma Mistah Tutt!"

Upstairs in his library, Mr. Tutt strode up and down before the empty grate, smoking stogie after stogie, trying to collect his thoughts and devise something to say upon the morrow, but all his ideas had flown. There wasn't anything to say. Yet he swore Angelo should not be offered up as a victim upon the altar of unscrupulous ambition.

The hours passed and the old banjo clock above the mantel wheezed eleven, twelve; then one, and two. Still he paced up and down, up and down, in a sort of trance. The air of the library, blue with the smoke of countless stogies, stifled and suffocated him. Moreover he discovered that he was hungry. He descended to the pantry and salvaged a piece of pie, then unchained the front door and stepped forth into the soft October night.

A full moon hung over the deserted streets of the sleeping city. In divers places, widely scattered, the twelve good and true men were snug in their beds. Tomorrow they would send Angelo to his death without a quiver. He shuddered, striding on, he knew not whither, into the night. His brain no longer worked. He had become a peripatetic automaton self-dedicated to nocturnal perambulation.

With his pocket bulging with stogies, and with one glowing like a headlight in advance of him, he wandered in a sort of coma up Tenth Avenue, crossed to the Riverside Drive, mounted Morningside Heights, descended again through the rustling alleys of Central Park, and found himself at Fifth Avenue and Fifty-ninth Street just as the dawn was paling the electric lamps to a sickly yellow and the trees were casting strange unwonted shadows. He was utterly exhausted. He looked eagerly for some place to sit down, but the doors of the hotels were dark and tightly closed, and it was too cold to remain in the open air without moving.

Down Fifth Avenue he trudged, intending to go home and snatch a few hours' sleep before court should open, but each block seemed miles in length. Presently he approached the cathedral, whose twin spires were tinted with reddish gold. The sky had become a bright blue. Suddenly all the street lamps went out. He told himself that he had never realized before the beauty of those two towers reaching up toward eternity.

He remembered having heard that a cathedral was never closed, and looking toward the door he perceived that it was open. Wearily he climbed the steps and entered its dark shadows. A faint light came through the tops of the stained-glass windows. Down below, a candle burned on either side of the altar and a flickering gleam shone from the red cup in the sanctuary lamp. Worn out, drugged for lack of sleep, faint for want of food, old Mr. Tutt sank down upon one of the rear seats by the door, and resting his head upon his arms on the back of the bench in front of him, fell fast asleep.

He dreamed of a legal heaven, of a great wooden throne upon which sat Babson in a black robe and below him twelve red-faced angels in a double row with harps in their hands, chanting: "Guilty! Guilty! Guilty!" An organ was playing somewhere, and there was a great noise of footsteps. Then a bell tinkled and he raised his head and saw that the chancel was full of lights and white-surpliced priests. It was broad daylight. Horrified he looked at his watch, to find that it was ten minutes after ten. His joints creaked as he pulled himself to his feet, and his eyes were half-closed as he staggered down the steps and hailed a taxi.

"Criminal Courts Building—side door. And drive like hell!" he ordered the driver.

He reached it just as Judge Babson and his attendant were coming into the courtroom and the crowd were making obeisance. Everybody else was in his proper place.

"You may proceed, Mr. Tutt," said the judge after the roll of the jury had been called.

But Mr. Tutt was in a daze, in no condition to think or speak. There was a curious rustling in his ears and his sight was blurred. The atmosphere of the courtroom seemed to him cold and hostile; the jury sat with averted faces. He rose feebly and cleared his throat.

"Gentlemen of the jury," he began, "I—I think I covered everything I had to say yesterday afternoon. I can only beseech you to realize the full extent of your great responsibility and remind you that, if you entertain a reasonable doubt upon the evidence, you are sworn to give the benefit of it to the defendant."

He sank back in his chair and covered his eyes with his hands, while a murmur ran along the benches of the courtroom. The old man had collapsed! The defendant was cooked! Swiftly O'Brien leaped to his feet and began his summation. There had been no defense, he shouted. The case was as plain as a pikestaff. There was only one thing for the jury to do—return a verdict of murder in the first. It would not be pleasant, but that made no difference! He read them the statute, applied it to the facts, and shook his fist in their faces. They must convict—and convict of only one thing, nothing else—murder in the first degree. They gazed at him like silly sheep, nodding their heads, doing everything but bleat.

Then Babson, rising in dignity, expounded the law to the sheep in a rich mellow voice, in which he impressed upon them the necessity of preserving the integrity of the jury system and the sanctity of human life. He pronounced an obituary of great beauty upon the deceased barber—who could not, as he pointed out, speak for himself, owing to the fact that he was in his grave. He venomously excoriated the defendant, who had deliberately planned to kill an unarmed man peacefully conducting himself in his place of business, and expressed the utmost confidence that he could rely upon the jury, whose character he well knew, to perform their full duty no matter how disagreeable that duty might be. The sheep nodded.

"You may retire, gentlemen."

Babson looked down at Mr. Tutt with a significant gleam in his eye. He had driven in the knife to the hilt and twisted it round and round. Mr. Tutt did not look at the jury as they went out. They would not be long, and he could hardly face the thought of their return. Never in his long experience had he found himself in such a desperate situation. Heretofore there had always been some argument, some construction of the facts upon which he could base an appeal, however fallacious or illogical.

He leaned back and closed his eyes. The judge was chatting with O'Brien, the court officers were betting with the reporters as to the length of time it would take the twelve to agree upon a verdict of murder in the first. The funeral rites were all concluded except for the final commitment of the corpse to mother earth.

And then without warning Angelo suddenly rose and addressed the court in a defiant shriek.

"I killa that man!" he cried wildly. "He maka small of my wife! He no good! He bad egg! I killa him once—I killa him again!"

"So!" exclaimed Babson with biting sarcasm. "You want to make a confession? You hope for mercy, do you? Well, Mr. Tutt, what do you wish to do under the circumstances? Shall I recall the jury and reopen the case by consent?"

Mr. Tutt rose trembling to his feet.

"The case is closed, Your Honor," he replied. "I will consent to a mistrial and offer a plea of guilty of manslaughter. I cannot agree to reopen the case. I cannot let the defendant go upon the stand."

The spectators and reporters were pressing forward to the bar, anxious lest they should lose a single word of the colloquy. Angelo remained standing, looking eagerly at O'Brien, who returned his gaze with a grin like that of a hyena.

"I killa him!" Angelo repeated. "You killa me if you want."

"Sit down!" thundered the judge. "Enough of this! The law does not permit me to accept a plea to murder in the first degree, and my conscience and my sense of duty to the public will permit me to accept no other. I will go to my chambers to await the verdict of the jury. Take the prisoner downstairs to the prison pen."

He swept from the bench in his silken robes. Angelo was led away. The crowd in the courtroom slowly dispersed. Mr. Tutt, escorted by Tutt, went out in the corridor to smoke.

"Ye got a raw deal, Counselor," remarked Captain Phelan, amiably accepting a stogie. "Nothing but an act of Providence c'd save that Eyetalian from the chair! An' him guilty at that!"

An hour passed; then another. At half after four a rumor flew along the corridors that the jury in the Serafino case had reached a verdict and were coming in. A messenger scurried to the judge's chambers. Phelan descended the iron stairs to bring up the prisoner, while Tutt to prevent a scene invented an excuse by which he lured Rosalina to the first floor of the buildinlg. The crowd suddenly reassembled out of nowhere and poured into the courtroom. The reporters gathered expectantly round their table. The judge entered, his robes gathered in one hand.

"Bring in the jury," he said sharply. "Arraign the prisoner at the bar."

Mr. Tutt took his place beside his client at the railing, while the jury, carrying their coats and hats, filed slowly in. Their faces were set and relentless. They looked neither to the right nor to the left.

O'Brien sauntered over and seated himself nonchalantly with his back to the court, studying their faces. Yes, he told himself, they were a regular set of hangmen—he couldn't have picked a tougher bunch if he'd had his choice of the whole panel.

The clerk called the roll, and Messrs. Walsh, Tompkins, et al., stated that they were all present.

"Gentlemen of the jury, have you agreed upon a verdict?" inquired the clerk.

"We have!" replied Mr. Walsh sternly.

"How say you? Do you find the defendant guilty or not guilty?"

Mr. Tutt gripped the balustrade in front of him with one hand and put his other arm round Angelo. He felt that now in truth murder was being done.

"We find the defendant not guilty," said Mr. Walsh defiantly.

There was a momentary silence of incredulity. Then Babson and O'Brien shouted simultaneously: "What!"

"We find the defendant not guilty," repeated Mr. Walsh stubbornly.

"I demand that the jury be polled!" cried the crestfallen O'Brien, his face crimson.

And then the twelve reiterated severally that that was their verdict and that they hearkened unto it as it stood recorded and that they were entirely satisfied with it.

"You are discharged!" said Babson in icy tones. "Strike the names of these men from the list of jurors—as incompetent. Haven't you any other charge on which you can try this defendant?"

"No, Your Honor," answered O'Brien grimly. "He didn't take the stand, so we can't try him for perjury; and there isn't any other indictment against him."

Judge Babson turned ferociously upon Mr. Tutt.

"This acquittal is a blot upon the administration of criminal justice; a disgrace to the city! It is an unconscionable verdict; a reflection upon the intelligence of the jury! The defendant is discharged. This court is adjourned."

The crowd surged round Angelo and bore him away, bewildered. The judge and prosecutor hurried from the room. Alone, Mr. Tutt stood at the bar, trying to grasp the full meaning of what had occurred.

He no longer felt tired; he experienced an exultation such as he had never known before. Some miracle had happened! What was it?

Unexpectedly the lawyer felt a rough warm hand clasped over his own upon the rail and heard the voice of Mr. Walsh with its rich brogue saying: "At first we couldn't see that there was much to be said for your side of the case, Mr. Tutt; but when Oi stepped into St. Patrick's on me way down to court this morning and spied you prayin' there for guidance, I knew you wouldn't be defendin' him unless he was innocent, and so we decided to give him the benefit of the doubt."

HANS ZINSSER

The Influence of Epidemics on History

••

A rodent's view of history, taken from the famous book Rats, Lice and History.

If it were not for the fact that so many utterly uninterested people die of disease or are killed in them, wars would not be taken so seriously. It is of course true that rapacity for territory, commercial rivalry, and all other expressions of that avarice which is as instinct-ive to the human species as the sexual and intestinal functions, have always been present as the underlying causes of war. But it is doubtful whether these more or less realistic reasons would fulminate to the actual point of explosion as often as they do if mankind did not, in spite of repeated demonstration, obstinately harbor a totally erroneous conception of what actually constitutes a war in terms of experience. It is not, of course, the propaganda of glory, the *dulce est pro patria mori,* and so forth, that influence men so deeply. These and similar "residues" are only moderately effective rationaliza-tions of more fundamental impulses. Much more deeply significant are the boredom with the unutterably dull peacetime occupations of most people, and the childish but universal delight men take in playing soldiers. Until they actually suffered from dirt, lousiness, fatigue, terror, disease, or wounds, most men enjoyed the last war. Think of the man who has lived meagerly in a frame house on the outskirts of Somerville or Weehawken, and for ten years—except for two weeks in August—has regularly caught the eight-fifteen, spent the rest of the day floorwalking, and then caught the six-twenty back to what he came from in the morning! Think of his feelings of release and self-satisfaction when he is marching up Broadway behind the band, between files of cheering garment workers. Think of his pride in a renewed manhood, standing guard at dawn or lying behind a pile of sandbags pot-shooting his fellowman, or drinking beer with his comrades—knowing that the world approves him as a hero, and that his family has the government to look out for it forever and ever!

But beyond the release from boredom there is the joy in uniforms which stimulates war. The instinct for fancy dress is hard to kill, as anybody knows who has been in a town where the Mystic Knights or the Shriners or the Red Indians were holding a convention; or even in Boston, when the Ancient and Honorables are blocking traffic on Beacon Hill. And, further, there is the applause of the women—not women in general, but each man's own women—who, as instinctively as the men like to play soldiers, have the hereditary longing to glorify the brave brutalities that their heroes write home about: "I threw a hand grenade into a dugout, and blew up six Germans. I'm going to be kissed by the general." "Isn't he wonderful? Just a big, brave boy!" One can hear the devil's grandmother, adoringly watching him turn a squealing sinner on the spit, saying: "Oh, Beelzebub—you're nothing but a great big boy!"

We might expostulate on the minor causes of war in a more convincingly thorough manner if we were writing a tract for a peace foundation instead of the biography of a disease. But since we are primarily interested in the subject of typhus fever, we cannot give too much space to these matters. The point is that war is visualized —even by the military expert—as a sort of serious way of playing soldiers. In point of fact, the tricks of marching and of shooting and the game called strategy constitute only a part—the minor, although picturesquely appealing part—of the tragedy of war. They are only the terminal operations engaged in by those remnants of the armies which have survived the camp epidemics. These have often determined victory or defeat before the generals know where they are going to place the headquarters' mess.

To the average professional officer, the military doctor is an unwillingly tolerated noncombatant who takes sick call, gives cathartic pills, makes transportation trouble, complicates tactical plans, and causes the water to smell bad. Of course he is useful after an action, to remove the debris, but otherwise he is almost, if not quite, a positive nuisance. There was a tempest of respiratory diseases and the threat of enteric fever in the Second American Army at the end of the war. The inspector general, Colonel O., neither knew nor cared about that. He reprimanded a weary chief sanitary inspector for saluting him with one hand in his pocket. We pitied this poor gentleman when we thought of all the buttons that were off and the puttees wrongly adjusted among a hundred thousand men. How he suffered and toiled! The same sanitary officer was trying to locate water points for the advancing troops in September 1918. "You don't exist for me," said Colonel H. of the Engineers. "You are not in the Tables of Organization." Occasionally there is a great soldier who knows, like General Bullard. He stands out by contrast. However, this may seem like spleen. But not at all; it leads up to our theme that soldiers have rarely won wars. They more often mop up after the barrage of epidemics. And typhus, with its brothers and sisters—plague, cholera, typhoid, dysentery—has decided more campaigns than Cæsar, Hannibal, Napoleon, and all the inspector generals of history. The epidemics get the blame for defeat, the generals the credit for victory. It ought to be the other way round—perhaps someday the organization of armies will be changed, and the line officer will do what the surgeon general lets him do. Among other things, this plan would remove about 90 per cent of the expenses of the pension system.

Before we go on to the special military exploits of typhus, it may be interesting to discuss the decisive influence of disease upon battle in a more general manner, and so justify our contentions with a few facts.

The difficulty is not to find evidence, but to select from the dreadful abundance. Von Linstow, a military surgeon of the Prussian army, who thought along similar lines, has culled the literature for some of the most enlightening examples in common historical records. We cite freely from his studies and from the writings of historians and military surgeons who have accompanied great armies in campaigns.

Herodotus, in the eighth book of his *History,* tells us about the saving of Greece by λοιμός (possibly plague and dysentery) when Xerxes entered Thessalia with an army estimated at about eight hundred thousand men. Soon after Greek territory was entered, supplies began to fail, and disease stepped upon the heels of undernourishment and hardship. The campaign was abandoned, and the Persian king swept back into Asia with less than half a million followers.

It was the plague of Athens which laid low for a time the power of Athens on land. In the second year of the disease, three hundred knights, forty-five thousand citizens, and ten thousand free men and slaves died. Pericles himself succumbed, and the Lacedæmonians were left free to roam over the peninsula.

That the sieges of Syracuse by the Carthaginians in 414 and 396 B.C. were relieved by a disease probably identical with that of Athens is likely. There is no telling what might have been the outcome of the Punic Wars and of the future power of Rome if Hannibal had found his fleet and armies firmly established in Sicily.

In the civil struggles of Rome, in 88 B.C., the victory of Marius was decided by an epidemic which killed seventeen thousand men in the army of Octavius.

In 425 A.D. the Huns gave up their otherwise unimpeded advance upon Constantinople because a plague of unknown nature decimated their hordes.

What might have been the future of the power of the Saracen empire if the king of Abyssinia had not been turned back from Mecca by the "sacred fire," no one can tell. This was what is commonly spoken of as the "Elephant War." The Abyssinian army of sixty thousand men was completely disorganized by the ravages of a disease which, in description, sounds either like a severe form of smallpox or like a combination of erysipelas and general staphylococcus infection.

That the Crusades were turned back by epidemics much more effectively than they were by the armed power of the Saracens can hardly be questioned. The history of the Crusades reads like the chronicle of a series of diseases, with scurvy as potent as infections. In 1098 a Christian army of three hundred thousand men besieged Antioch. Disease and famine killed so many and in such a short time that the dead could not be buried. The cavalry were rendered useless within a few months by the death of five thousand of their seven thousand horses. Nevertheless, the city was captured, after a nine months' siege. On the march to Jerusalem, the hosts were accompanied by an enemy more potent than the heathen. When Jerusalem was taken, in 1099, only sixty thousand of the original three hundred thousand were left, and these, by 1101, had melted to twenty thousand.

The story of the second Crusade, led by Louis VII of France, is sadly similar. Of half a million men, only a handful—most of them without horses—managed to get back to Antioch, and few returned to Europe.

Antioch seems to have been the spot where all the Christian armies were ambushed by pestilence. Error in the road taken beyond this city, through the treachery of a Turkish guide, led the crusading army of 1190 into the desert. Famine, plague, and desertions reduced an army of one hundred thousand to a mere five thousand.

The fourth Crusade, under the doge of Venice and Baldwin of Flanders, never reached Jerusalem because of a dreadful outbreak of bubonic plague which started during the hottest part of the summer, soon after the Crusaders left Constantinople.

When Frederick II of Germany took ship at Brindisi in 1227, dysentery came aboard with his army; the fleet turned back when the emperor himself was taken sick, and the expedition was a flat failure.

Scurvy is not an infectious disease and has no proper place, therefore, among the relatives of typhus fever, whose influence on history we are discussing. However, it was an almost constant menace to armies whenever the food supply ran low or became restricted. Under such circumstances, which were common in besieged cities and during long marches through devastated territories, scurvy not infrequently became decisive in itself or so weakened large bodies of men that subsequent infectious disease found them without normal powers to resist. In this way it was often a powerful ally of our disease. We have no intention of further digressing from our main theme into the interesting military history of scurvy, but cite a single episode only, to illustrate the formidable influence of scurvy in determining the outcome of campaigns.

Until the first Friday in Lent of 1250, the crusading army of St. Louis was reasonably holding its own against the Saracens. Shortly after this, Joinville tells us, "the host began to suffer very grievously." He attributes the nature of the illness to the stench of dead bodies and to the eels from the river that "ate the dead people, for they are a gluttonous fish." The disease was, without question, scurvy: "There came upon us the sickness of the host, which sickness was such that the flesh of our legs dried up, and the skin upon our legs became spotted; black and earth color like an old boot; and with us who had this sickness, the flesh of our gums putrefied; nor could anyone escape from this sickness but he had to die. The sign of death was this, that when there was bleeding of the nose, then death was sure."

The Turks at about this time managed to blockade the river against the supply ships, fresh food became still more scarce, and many of the leaders fell sick. "The sickness began to increase in the host in such sort, and the dead flesh to grow upon the gums of our people, that the barber surgeons had to remove the dead flesh in order that the people might masticate their food and swallow it. Great pity it was to hear the cry throughout the camp of the people whose dead flesh was being cut away; for they cried like women laboring of child." The disease made prompt retreat imperative, and the king decided upon a desperate effort to break through the Saracen blockade. Failure, defeat, and the capture of the king with all his knights followed.

On the second attempt, Louis got no farther than Tunis, where he and his son, the Duc de Nevers, died of dysentery on August 3 and August 25, 1270.

A curious disease that cannot be precisely classified destroyed the army of Frederick Barbarossa in Rome in 1157. It is described by Kerner and also by Lersch. It might have been typhus, for it began with severe headaches, pain in the limbs and abdomen, heat, chills, and delirium. Many died within a few days. The mortality was so high and the terror so great that on August 6 of 1167, four days after the plague began, the army burned their tents and started northward. Rome was abandoned, and the greater part of the host perished on its march.

The centuries of struggles between Spain and France were again and again decided by disease. Philip III of France was turned back from his campaign into Aragon in 1285 by a plague of uncertain nature that killed large numbers of the soldiers, most of the officers, and, eventually, the king himself. In the subsequent military history of Spain, typhus itself played a devastating role.

In 1439, on October 1, the German emperor, Albrecht, reached the walls of Bagdad. By the thirteenth of the same month, the emperor was dead and the army in retreat, defeated by dysentery.

In the sixteenth century, the story is the same in principle, and though typhus and plague now begin to be cast for the leading roles, dysentery, typhoid, and smallpox no doubt contributed their share. The siege of Metz by Charles V was raised by scurvy, dysentery, and typhus, and the army retreated from the city after thirty thousand men had died.

One of the earliest really decisive typhus epidemics was that which dispersed the army of Maximilian II of Germany, who was preparing with eighty thousand men to face the Sultan Soliman in Hungary. In the camp at Komorn, in 1566, a disease broke out which was undoubtedly typhus. It was so violent and deadly that the campaign agaist the Turks was given up.

The Thirty Years' War was in all its phases dominated by deadly epidemics. To follow them in detail would be to write the history of this war over again, for the pestilences roamed the Continent in the trains of the armed forces. There is one episode, however, which deserves particular mention, because typhus, single-handed, defeated both armies before they could join battle. In 1632, Gustavus Adolphus and Wallenstein faced each other before Nuremberg, which was the goal of both armies. Typhus and scurvy killed eighteen thousand soldiers, whereupon both the opposing forces marched away in the hope of escaping the further ravages of the pestilence.

It is not impossible that the fate of Charles I was sealed by typhus fever. In 1643 Charles was opposed at Oxford by the Parliamentary army under Essex, each general commanding about twenty thousand men. The king was forced to give up his plan of advancing upon London by an epidemic of typhus fever which ravaged both armies.

In 1708 the Swedes, having their own way in southern Russia, completely lost the fruits of their hard-fought battles and were rendered helpless by an outbreak of plague.

In November of 1741, Prague was surrendered to the French army because thirty thousand of the opposing Austrians died of typhus.

Frederick the Great, victorious over the troops of Maria Theresa, was forced out of Bohemia when violent dysentery attacked his troops.

The outcome of the French Revolution was to some extent decided by dysentery. In 1792, Frederick William II of Prussia, with Austrian allies, a total strength of forty-two thousand men, was marching against the armies of the Revolution. Dysentery, the Red, decided in favor of *Liberté, Égalité,* and *Fraternité,* and with only thirty thousand effectives remaining, the Prussians retreated across the Rhine.

The establishment of the Haitian republic, though usually attributed to the genius of Toussaint l'Ouverture, was actually brought about by yellow fever. In 1801 Napoleon sent General Leclerc with twenty-five thousand men to Haiti to put down the revolt of the Negroes. The French troops landed at Cap Français, defeated Toussaint, and drove him into the interior. The Negro army was rallied and reorganized by Dessalines, but could not have successfully opposed the well-disciplined and well-equipped French troops had not an epidemic of yellow fever disorangized the invader. Of twenty-five thousand Frenchmen, twenty-two thousand died. There were only three thousand left to evacuate the island in 1803.

Even the greatest general of them all, Napoleon, was helpless when pitted against the tactics of epidemic disease. We have accounts of the Russian campaign from Larrey. But records of more specific value for our subject are those of the Chevalier J. R. L. de Kerckhove (*dit* de Kirckhoff), a corps surgeon of the army of invasion, who—on the title page of his book—signs himself *Membre de la plupart des Académies savantes de l'Europe*. The army of upward of half a million men was mobilized in cantonments which extended from northern Germany to Italy. Until the main bodies were assembled, there was little sickness, and the hospitals established at Magdeburg, Erfurt, Posen, and Berlin had few patients. Kerckhove describes the miserable conditions encountered after the entry into Poland. He was shocked by the poverty, wretchedness, and slavishness of the people and the contrast of the conditions here found with those prevailing in other European countries. The villages consisted of insect-infected hovels; the army was forced to bivouac. Nutrition was bad; the days hot and the nights cold. New hospitals were now established at Danzig, Königsberg, and Thorn because of the rapidly increasing sick rates, at this time largely due to respiratory infections, including pneumonia and throat anginas—probably diphtheria. Typhus cases began to appear in small numbers at about the time that the Niemen was crossed, on June 24. In Lithuania, huge forests and wretched roads were encountered; towns and villages had been burned by the Russians; there was little shelter and less food. The water was bad, the heat intense, and the disease rate—now largely dysentery, enteric fevers, and typhus—became formidable. After the battle of Ostrowo, in late July, there were over eighty thousand sick. The army corps to which Kerckhove was attached was reduced to less than half of its original forty-two thousand men by the time the river Moskva was reached in early September. An enormous number of wounded—over thirty thousand—resulting from the battle fought near the river, further rendered the task of the medical officers an almost impossible one. By September 12, typhus and dysentery were becoming more and more intense. Moscow was entered on September 14. It was at this time a city of 300,000 people, but most of the population had fled before the French army entered. On the fifteenth, fires were started, first at the Bourse, then all over the city—set, presumably, under orders of Governor Rostoptchin, by liberated criminals who had been furnished with sulfur torches. Moscow contained a number of well-equipped hospitals, but these were soon filled with the sick and wounded, and since so large a part of the city was either in ashes or destroyed by bombardments, the thoroughly infected troops were crowded in unsatisfactory shelters and camped outside the city. Stores of food had been almost completely destroyed by the Russians.

From now on typhus and dysentery were Napoleon's chief opponents. When the retreat from Moscow was begun, on October 19, there were not more than 80,000 men fit for duty. The homeward march became a rout, and the exhausted and sick troops were constantly harassed by the pursuing enemy. The weather grew intensely cold, and a large number—exhausted by sickness and fatigue—were frozen. In early November, when Smolensk was reoccupied, only 2,000 of the cavalry were left, and there were about 20,000 patients in the hospitals of the city. Many typhus patients were left behind in Smolensk, which was evacuated on November 13. The disastrous crossing of the Beresina, in which Larrey was saved only by the grateful affection of soldiers who passed him over their heads across the bridge, cost the army an enormous number—not precisely recorded, but estimated at 40,000 men. While typhus remained the predominant disease, dysentery and pneumonia were also increasing. Fifteen thousand men are said to have been frozen on the way to Vilna, and when this city was reached, on December 8, the magnificent army had shrunken to 20,000 sick and disheartened men. Of the Third Army Corps commanded by Marshal Ney, only twenty men remained. In Vilna the hospitals were crowded, the men lay on rotten straw in their own refuse, hungry and cold, without care. They were driven to eat leather and even human flesh. The diseases, especially typhus, spread through all the cities and villages of the surrounding country. At one time, in December, the sick that had been evacuated to Vilna had accumulated to the number of 25,000. By the end of June, 1813, only 3,000 of these remained alive. The vestiges of the army which escaped from Russia were almost without exception infected with typhus.

It is suggested by de Kerckhove, whose book testifies to a lively interest in the strategy of his great chief, that if Napoleon had been content to occupy Poland and attend to reorganization, including sanitary control, his campaign might have been a success and his power permanently established.

It is perhaps the greatest testimony to the genius of Napoleon that, after this disastrous failure, he was again—in 1813—able to raise a new army of 500,000 men. These were mostly, for lack of available adult man power, young recruits, particularly suitable fuel for epidemic disease. By the time his new army faced the allies at Leipzig, preliminary battles at Bautzen, Dresden, and Karlsbad, together with disease, had reduced his forces to little more than 170,000 men with which to face 200,000 allies.* It is hardly debatable that the power of Napoleon in Europe was broken by disease more effectively than by military opposition or even by Trafalgar.

As far as the Crimean War is concerned, it is not possible to deduce the results of the struggle from disease, since the opposing armies suffered almost equally and disastrously from cholera, typhus, dysentery, and the lesser epidemic afflictions of armies. Nevertheless, this war is of unusual interest for our theme, because there are available unusually accurate records which demonstrate how much more destructive than the clash of armed conflict is the power of disease. We have reliable accounts of the army epidemics of this war from Jacquot's *Du Typhus de l'Armée d'Orient,* and Armand's *Histoire Medico-Chirugical de la Guerre de la Crimée.* There were two separate typhus outbreaks—one which started in December 1854, the other in December of the following year. The disease began among the Russians, then attacked the British and the French, penetrated into Constantinople, there spread to the fleets and the merchant

* Von Linstow states that 205,000 were lost for service by battle casualty; 209,000 by disease.

ships, and was distributed in all directions throughout Russia and Turkey. In 1855, after the battle of Alma, a severe cholera epidemic began which lasted through to April 1856. At the time of the greatest violence of the various diseases, 48,000 men were removed from the ranks by sickness within four months—or at the rate of 12,000 a month. According to Armand, the French sent something over 309,-000 men east. Of these, 200,000 were hospitalized—50,000 by wounds and 150,000 by disease. The following table, which we take from Von Linstow, summarizes the conditions which prevailed from 1854 to 1856.

	Wounded	Died of Wounds*	Sick	Died of Disease
French	39,869	20,356	196,430	49,815
English	18,283	4,947	144,390	17,225
Russians	92,381	37,958	322,097	37,454

* Including men lost in battle, and so forth.

SIR COMPTON MACKENZIE

Just Ordinary People

⃤

Some unforgettable real-life heroes—from the book Certain Aspects of Moral Courage.

From time to time the critics of television in the press have a crack at the BBC program *This Is Your Life* which attracts a weekly audience estimated to be about ten million. One will suggest that the public are growing tired of it or that, at any rate, if the public are not growing tired of it they ought to be because the critic himself

is growing tired of it. Another will suggest that the public are weary-
ing of Eamonn Andrews whose slickness of presentation and the way
he puts the subjects quickly at ease after they have recovered from
the first shock of surprise is too slick, and one or two of these critics
will hint that it's time somebody else took the place of Eamonn
Andrews if the BBC are determined to keep on with *This Is Your
Life*. Such critics do not of course express a positive opinion that they
would make excellent successors to Eamonn Andrews but faintly in
the tone of their criticism such a notion steals through. It does not
seem to occur to such critics that men like Eamonn Andrews, Ed
Murrow, Richard Dimbleby, and the late much lamented Gilbert
Harding could not draw their immense audiences unless the public
were aware of the sincerity at the back of such men and that mere
slickness is not enough to make a man a household face.

The critics of *This Is Your Life* go further. They profess to pity
the victims of it for the embarrassment the abrupt publicity must
cause them, and they even feel sorry for the embarrassment of an
audience unfairly compelled to display its own emotion over the
simple goodness of ordinary people. Can it really be embarrassing to
be made aware of how many good people there are in this world after
the reading of our daily paper has drawn our attention to the number
of bad people that there are?

The life of Henry Starling, a porter in Billingsgate Fish Market,
was one of those examples of simple courage and goodness.

Henry Starling was born in Edmonton in 1906, the third son in a
humble family of seven children. His father volunteered for Kitchener's army at the beginning of 1915, which meant that his wife and
family would have £1 a week on which to live while the war lasted.
Mrs. Starling was then expecting her youngest boy, and owing to some
delay in the army pay department no money at all arrived for five
weeks, which meant that Mrs. Starling had to pawn everything she
possessed, including the sheets from her own bed, to get food. Two
years later her husband was killed in action.

At fourteen Henry Starling found a job at a small wage in a factory
where they made attaché cases. At eighteen he fell in love with a girl
of his own age who for three years had been blind. In 1926 they

became engaged, but when Henry Starling asked his boss for a raise in order that he might get married, he was given the sack instead. Business was bad; unemployment was increasing; the dole queues were lengthening. Things were pretty difficult in Marigold Street, Rotherhithe, where the Starlings lived. Fred Fosbeary, whose sister Maud was engaged to Henry Starling, came out of the army and got engaged to Henry's sister Daisy. There was no work to be found.

In the program Fred Fosbeary declared that if it had not been for Henry's optimism he would have lost heart in that grim time.

To quote him:

As soon as there was a sniff of any work going, Henry was on to it like a bird. He'd be the first to learn if there were barges wanted unloading. If there was a fall of snow, well, that was good news because we was hired to sweep it away. Old Henry never gave up hope. Always wanted to be up and doing. I remember he'd walk four miles to the dock to get a hundredweight of coke and bring it home on his back.

Seven difficult years went by, until in the winter of 1933 Henry Starling managed to find himself with some fairly regular casual work. He and Maud were to be married on Christmas Day. Then on Christmas Eve for a wedding present he got the sack. However, this time he was determined that a seven-year engagement was long enough. He and Maud were married.

Mrs. Starling was asked what was her first week's housekeeping money to pay the rent and feed her husband and herself.

To quote her:

It was two and sevenpence. I gave Henry the penny back, and he put it in the gas-meter. The second week it was seven and ninepence; and the week after that it was the other way round—nine and sevenpence. We'd rented two rooms in Raymouth Street, Rotherhithe, but we were very lucky in our landlord. Mr. Weller got Henry a temporary job with his brother who was a builder.

It was not until 1939 that Henry Starling obtained a steady job in Leadenhall Market with regular wages. At last he was able to save and plan for the future. And then came the war, with all the destruction it brought to the homes of poor people in the East End. In September 1940 the Starlings were bombed out of their place in

Rotherhithe and went over to Fred and Daisy Fosbeary's. To quote Mrs. Starling again, and let it be remembered she is blind:

Next morning I was very worried about my cat, Whisky—so back we went for him. When we got there, they told us, "You can't go in there," but Henry said, "Well, we're going in." We weren't there five minutes when the warning went. So I picked up old Whisky and we went back to my brother's. We were there about a fortnight when they got worse damage than what we'd had. The windows were blown in right on top of us while we were in bed. Well, there was nothing else for it—back we had to go to *our* place. I'll never forget it. We looked *so* funny. There was my brother with the twins in a push-chair. There was someone else looking after the dog. I had Whisky in my arms. Henry had another push-chair with three cases in it—and of course he had to hold onto me with one arm. And Daisy was in between us with little Eileen in the bassinette. And there we were dodging the hose-pipes, and the dog chasing the firemen, and nearly being run in for it!

Then Henry joined the Gunners and was sent up to Yorkshire for many months until at last he was posted to a gun site in the London area and was able to see his wife more often.

Horace Lee who was on a gun with Henry Starling testified to him:

One of the best. A real cockney. He used to think Yorkshire people were foreigners. We used to share our two bob a day, and I'd go and spend many a week-end leave with Henry and Maud. And the cat. It's a funny thing about that cat. It really used to know when there was an air raid going to start. As soon as old Whisky got fidgety we knew there was something up. Why, we've even put off a visit to the pictures because of it. And sure enough he was always right. Yes, I had some wonderful times with old Henry and Maud. They're grand. I don't think you could find a more loving couple anywhere.

When the war was over Henry Starling obtained a regular job as a porter in Billingsgate Fish Market and he has found and earned the security his moral stamina deserves. The Starlings had no children of their own, but two members of the Blind Friends' Social Club came forward to say that their lives had been happier thanks to Henry and Maud Starling, who herself had been blind since she was fifteen years old.

The words spoken by Eamonn Andrews at the end expressed what some millions of viewers must have been feeling:

"Henry Starling, and you, Mrs. Starling, believe me, have been most welcome here on our stage and, we're sure, in the homes of our audience." Then turning to that audience he said:

"We have recalled no great achievements, but you have seen the affection and loyalty that are the mainspring of this jolly and unremarkable family, typical of thousands of others. Henry Starling is at once one and all those people, and we leave him, as we found him, working happily in Billingsgate Market. There he goes now, unnoticed, one of the many thousands of cheerful, ordinary people whom we hope we have saluted through you, Henry Starling."

Henry Starling may not have given a display of moral courage by seeking truth and justice at the cost of his own popularity, but we must not overlook that quieter aspect of moral courage which consists in going through life doing one's best.

It was difficult to decide whether two or three of the "lives" chosen as aspects of moral courage should not more accurately have been called examples of physical courage, and this set me off again wondering about that definition of moral courage by Sir James Stephen cited in the *Oxford English Dictionary:* "Moral courage is readiness to expose oneself to suffering or inconvenience which does not affect the body." Certainly we should always have to concede moral courage when a man acts or speaks without regard to the consequences for his career, his position, or his good name, but surely we must allow that often what may need physical courage to sustain demands high moral courage to face what may ensue from displaying it. Every deliberate martyr has required moral courage as well as physical. Every man who has done what he has considered it right to do has had to face the risk of being let down by his physical courage, which is a risk that needs moral courage to accept.

In due course we shall be relating the moral courage of those Germans who resisted the evil beliefs of the Nazis. That needed physical courage because there was no mercy for those who resisted those evil beliefs. At the same time, the will to resist was founded upon moral courage. Put the other way it was not necessarily physical cowardice that led so many Germans to display moral cowardice. The force of public opinion is often more deterring than the force of arms.

So, although well aware of the demand upon the physical courage of the examples chosen from the subjects of *This Is Your Life,* they are chosen primarily as illustrations of moral courage.

Sergeant Charles Coward of the Royal Artillery was recalled to his old regiment at the beginning of the Second World War and was taken prisoner after the hand-to-hand fighting at Calais when he was wounded in the leg and head by a German hand grenade. In the course of his time as a prisoner of war he made over half a dozen attempts to escape but was always recaptured. At last he was sent to a prisoner-of-war camp just outside the entrance to Auschwitz, where he heard the horrifying tales of what went on in that infamous concentration camp. Coward, without talking about it, made up his mind to do what he could to help the victims. He was an accomplished scrounger and he managed to exchange cigarettes and chocolates for the bodies of dead Jews who had been working as slave labor in the I. G. Farben factory. Somehow these bodies were smuggled out of the factory and hidden in a ditch beside the road leading to Birkenau, which was the camp with the gas chambers and crematoriums. Coward would then wait until the next batch of Jews were being marched along the road to the gas chambers. If he had four bodies in the ditch, then four men in the extermination party would somehow be warned in advance to drop out on the road and roll into the ditch, from which they were to push the dead bodies on to the road. The guards always marched at the head of the column and when they reached the gas chambers there was a count. Four being missing, a search party would be sent back along the road, when the four dead bodies would be found and thus the four missing Jews would be accounted for. This work of giving a chance of escape to the Nazi victims went on at intervals without the Germans having any suspicion of what Coward was doing.

Then came a signal act of courage. In 1943 Coward heard a rumor that a British naval officer was being held prisoner in the extermination camp and he smuggled himself into that hell in the hope of being able to help him to escape. Coward did not succeed in finding the prisoner but he did see what was going on in the camp and after the war he gave evidence about Auschwitz at the Nuremberg trials.

Just after Christmas 1944 the I. G. Farben factory was bombed twice by the Americans and three times by the Russians. Thirty-nine British prisoners of war were killed. Early in 1945 when the advancing Russian army was sweeping across Poland the British prisoners had hopes of freedom, but sudden orders came for them to be moved and they were marched some five hundred miles to Hanover by which time they were in a bad way. However, Sergeant Charles Coward was determined to escape again and at last he was successful, being picked up by American troops and flown back to England a few days later.

Not only did he testify at the Nuremberg trials, but in 1951 he volunteered to give evidence at a German trial in Frankfurt.

Norbert Wollheim, a German Jew living in Berlin, was arrested by the Nazis in March 1943. On the platform of the railway station at Auschwitz he he was separated from his wife and three-year-old son, neither of whom he ever saw again. Wollheim was employed as a slave laborer in the I. G. Farben factory until January 1945, and after the war he brought an action against the I. G. Farben Company for maltreatment. This was a test case and opened the way for thousands of others, some of which are still pending.

To Charles Coward the German court set on record his tribute:

> As a Chamber of the German Court, we regret that the German defendants and witnesses were so lacking in courage, and so debased in morale. It was left to a British prisoner of war to show them what moral courage means and involves.

One feels inclined to say that critics who sneer at a program which can tell a story like that are as "debased in morale" as those German defendants.

The Second World War provided no more tales of courage than every war before it, but being nearer to the present and therefore more easily imagined by a vast contemporary audience, it is natural that the series *This Is Your Life* should search among its chronicles for examples of courage that can hold their own with the heroic tales of the past.

Alfred Southon escaped from a prisoner-of-war camp in Italy in September 1943 and for a year fought side by side with the Italian

partisans who represented that Italy which in the days of the risorgi-
mento had captured so many British hearts, so many who could say
with Browning, "Open my heart, and you shall see graved inside of
it Italy."

On November 8, 1944, Alfred Southon and thirty-eight partisans
decided it was necessary to escape from Italy into France because
the Germans were becoming more and more active in the area in
which they were fighting as the Allies were pushing northward. It
was for them either escape or certain obliteration.

After two days of Alpine climbing Southon found himself trying
to shelter from a fierce blizzard under an overhanging rock. With him
was another escaped British prisoner of war. All the party except
two Italians had thought it wise to press on through the blinding
snow in the hope of getting help. Southon's companion was fast
growing weaker, and Southon himself knew he must keep him awake
and this he desperately tried to do. At the end of the third day no
food was left and Southon's legs and feet were numb. Carlo and
Giuseppe, the two Italian partisans who had stayed behind, had by
now pressed on like the others to seek help or find shelter.

By the end of the fifth day Southon's blistered hands began to
bleed, and suddenly his companion, driven crazy by hunger, attacked
him. Then on the seventh day Southon's companion died and he was
alone in the snow, still just alive, 8,700 feet up in the Galisia Pass.
Two more days went by. His only hope was that his thirty-seven comrades had reached a place from which they would be able to send
help. He mercifully did not know that nearly all of them were already
dead. From time to time he would try to shout for help into the savage
teeth of the blizzard. By now Southon's fingers were black, and
in his agony he began to fancy that he could hear voices. On the tenth
day these voices became real, and with what was left to him of strength
Southon shouted for help.

Gildo Bianchetti, an Alpine guide, who used to lead groups of
partisans from Italy into France, was exploring a path when he met
Aldo Grossotti who told him that as he was descending the mountain
he thought he had heard someone cry out. Bianchetti told him it must
have been imagination, and then one of his own companions declared

he could hear a voice calling. They went toward it and at last discovered Southon. He was now completely black and his hair was pasted with snow. One of the men who found him said the only thing that made them think he was alive was that his teeth were shining. Beside Southon was the dead body of his companion. His rescuers did not think it was possible to keep Southon alive; it was his twenty-fifth birthday when they found him. All night they massaged him and as his circulation came back he suffered an agony of pain. At last he was taken to a hospital at Aix-les-Bains, where he heard that every single one of those who had started with him to cross the mountains had perished in the blizzard. He was the sole survivor. Then he had to face the news that both his legs must be amputated and that he must lose all the fingers of his right hand. Back in England, he was in hospital for many months, and after he had been out of hospital for eight months he had to endure the ordeal of re-amputation.

So far this may seem a story of fantastic physical courage. There was, indeed, an abundance of that, but now Southon had to draw upon an equal abundance of moral courage. He was determined not to become a useless survivor of that fearful ordeal. With artificial legs and no fingers on his right hand he set out to get a job and in doing that job to drive a car. He married and had a son. When one hears the story of a man like Alfred Southon it is difficult not to feel a little impatient of people who can make life miserable for themselves and for other people by that self-pity which seems to be a malady that is on the increase with material progress.

There are many other stories of courage that might be told from that heartening series *This Is Your Life*. There is the tale of Mrs. Bloom who was married when the Japanese were closing in on Singapore. She and her husband were separated after the surrender for three and a half years, she to go with four hundred women and children into Changi Jail, he to an internment camp. For nearly two years Mrs. Bloom devoted herself to keeping up morale in various ways, and then came the Kempe Tai, the Japanese secret police, who suspected that messages were somehow being sent out of Changi to the Allies. The jail was ransacked for clues, and in Mrs. Bloom's cell the secret police found some Christmas cards in Braille which Mrs. Bloom was making for the blind children in the jail. At last the Japanese thought they had found something to justify their absurd suspicions. Mrs. Bloom was taken off for a brutal interrogation at the end of which she was shut in a wooden cage with fifteen men and made to sit cross-legged for fourteen hours a day on a stone floor without moving or speaking. This ordeal lasted for five months before she was sent back to Changi.

When the war came to an end, Dr. Bloom and his wife returned to England with nothing except the clothes they stood in.

In September 1946 a little girl was born to them, and perhaps as the result of those years of semistarvation and that ghastly ordeal in the wooden cage that little girl was born deaf. This gave to Mrs. Bloom's courage a fresh challenge, which was not only to get the best out of life for her own child but also for all deaf children, too many of whom, alas, are left shut off in that silence.

Miss Dorothy Brodie, the headmistress of the Ackmar School for Deaf Children, paid Mrs. Bloom this tribute:

She has been chairman of our Care Committee for the last two years, and what a difference she made from the moment she joined us. Energy and effort are not enough when one is working for deaf children. One must have understanding *and* compassion. Mrs. Bloom knew that deaf children because of the demands they make upon one's time and patience can so easily become neglected. When she entered the silent world of her own daughter she learned what was needed to make that world as happy and normal as possible. And what she had learned she was able to make others understand, especially the parents of other deaf children. They need to be taught just as much as their children.

Once upon a time Mrs. Bloom edited a paper in Changi Jail; it was called *Pow-wow,* and it was one of the ways in which she helped to keep up the morale of the other occupants. Now she edits a quarterly called *Talk,* which is the magazine of the National Deaf Children's Society and sums up in its title what should be the aim of every teacher and every mother, and that is to make the deaf child talk.

It was once my privilege to sit next Miss Helen Keller at lunch on the occasion of her receiving an honorary degree from Glasgow University. Helen Keller became deaf, dumb, and blind when nineteen months old. She was accompanied by the devoted friend who had performed the miracle of teaching her to speak. The tone of her voice as Miss Keller rose to thank the university for the honor she had received is still in my ears from thirty years ago, and reflection upon that miracle of courage and patience has been for me a moral refreshment ever since.

Surely one may feel that the sight of Mrs. Bloom's young daughter Virginia on television and the sound of her voice must have been a moral refreshment for many in that great audience of ten million.

Another moving story of courage was that of Madame Anne Brusselmans, a Belgian lady with a husband and two small children who lived in a flat over the offices of the gas company in Brussels. There during the five years of the German occupation she sheltered many airmen in her own flat or as *chef logeur* in the Belgian resistance arranged for their shelter elsewhere until the escape route was ready. She also conducted them herself for the first part of the journey along the Comet Line. This was a thread of escape stretching for nine hundred miles from Brussels, through Belgium and France, over the Pyrenees into Spain. Over six hundred airmen who had been shot down passed along it safely. Two hundred and twenty-seven Belgian and French patriots were shot by the Germans for helping those airmen on the way to safety.

Major Henry Sarnow of the United States Air Force flew from Chicago to add his tribute to the courage of Madame Brusselmans. Major Sarnow was hidden for five weeks in her own flat. He recalled the thoroughness with which she coached him for his escape. She made him do exercises to keep fit. She taught him how to hold a cigarette like a Belgian. She fixed him with a false identity card and with clothes to wear. She even made him carry a briefcase in order that by carrying it he would not swing his arms like an American airman and so give himself away.

During the occupation Madame Brusselmans sheltered under her own roof 176 Allied airmen, all of whom she sent on the road to safety and all of whom successfully escaped and flew again.

It would be an impertinence to praise the courage of a woman like Madame Anne Brusselmans, but at least the BBC can be praised for giving a vast public an opportunity to realize that these great women did exist outside a paragraph in a newspaper. It is so valuable for those millions who look at *This Is Your Life* to see for themselves that women like Mrs. Bloom or Madame Brusselmans are not obvious heroines but people they would not think were different from the other women in a train or a bus.

The third of a trio of courageous women is Mrs. Ellen Field. Her husband and his father were members of the Hong Kong Volunteer Defence Corps and after the surrender of the island were both prisoners in the dreadful Shamshuipo Camp on the mainland. Mrs. Field managed to escape internment by burning her passport and bluffing the Japanese into accepting her as Irish and therefore a neutral. During the years of the Japanese occupation with astonishing energy she with the help of Dr. Selwyn-Clarke, the chief medical officer, who was not interned at first, managed to convey parcels of food to the prisoners and also to help in the escape of some of them. It was a task that required constant courage. She was shot in the leg by a Japanese sentry on one occasion and had to hold her own with some completely intolerable Japanese officers, who were all condemned to various sentences of imprisonment at the war trials and one of whom was hanged. Yet there was one remarkable exception in the shape of a former Lutheran minister in Philadelphia who now had a church of his own in Japan. The Reverend Kinoshi Watanabe had been called up for service as an interpreter. He was a man of Christian saintliness and is now setting an example in his native land, having returned to his church in spite of losing his wife and children when the bomb obliterated Hiroshima.

Of Sir Selwyn Selwyn-Clarke I wrote at Hong Kong in my diary, *All Over the Place,* on March 21, 1947:

Went in to see Dr. Selwyn-Clarke who is acting as honorary director of medical services. He is an outstanding personality. I have rarely been as deeply impressed by the moral force of an individual. He is a barrister as well as a doctor and was sentenced by the Japs to rigorous confinement for many months in prison after severe torture and brutality. He is permanently lame from Jap kicking. His courage and humanity during the ordeal were continuous. Now he is repaying evil with good and tries all the time to help Jap prisoners here. I am told that at Easter he will present each of them with a toothbrush at his own expense.

In that year of 1947 Sir Selwyn Selwyn-Clarke was appointed governor of the Seychelles and there to my own knowledge showed the same outstanding moral courage he had shown in Hong Kong. It is easy for me to understand what an encouragement association with him must have been to Mrs. Field. She has written a full account of those years, in continuous danger with three little girls to look after, in a book called *Twilight in Hong Kong*. Yet if there were only her book from which to gauge her courage we should not have an intimate picture of a woman. In *This Is Your Life* her character revealed itself with perfect clarity, and those millions seeing and hearing her on television could understand why she had been able to defy those intolerable Japanese officers.

One last example of moral courage from *This Is Your Life*. This is Major Richard Carr-Gomm, formerly in the Coldstream Guards, who was thirty-five years of age when he was faced with an unexpected public appearance which he would probably have been glad to miss. As a subaltern he had been on active service in Normandy and after the war he had seen service in the Middle East and Cyprus. After fifteen years as a Coldstreamer he could look forward in due course to commanding his battalion. Then one evening in 1955 as Officer of the Guard in the Bank of England he asked Godfrey Winn to dine with him, and to him he announced that he was going to resign his commission because on his visits to Bermondsey where his family had property he had been struck by the number of old people who seemed to be wandering aimlessly and miserably about the streets or huddling in libraries and other public places for warmth. He felt that he could do something to provide them with some kind of companionship and help them in their sad loneliness. He felt that soldiering in peacetime was not good enough. He must do something to help people.

So in September 1955 Major Carr-Gomm turned down a War Office Staff appointment which would have led to promotion and resigned his commission. He went to consult the London County Council Home Help organizer. Miss Marie Monk had already had a letter from him offering his services as a home help, but she had paid no attention to his letter because it had seemed to her that a major in the Brigade of Guards was the last person in the world to become a scrubber of floors or a nurse to old people. Major Carr-Gomm wrote again and finally Miss Monk decided to give him an interview. She was so struck by the sincerity of his desire to become a home helper that she accepted him. And Miss Monk started him off as toughly as she could. She told those millions:

I well remember his first job because I went with him. We climbed the bare stairs to a shabby landing. We got no reply when we knocked on the door. Eventually we had to break in, and down on the floor lay the man we had called to see. He was an old-age pensioner who had had a stroke. Major Carr-Gomm picked him up and put him on the bed and got hold of a doctor and ambulance. Then he set about cleaning up the room. The place was filthy and I remember I had to show him how to wring out a swab in a bucket to wash the floor. But he was a quick learner and inside a week he could scrub floors as well as anybody.

So Major Carr-Gomm living in one room in Rotherhithe, from half-past nine in the morning until late at night devoted himself to scrubbing floors, cleaning windows, making beds, and running errands for lonely old people. Then he bought his first house for old people—50 Eugenia Road, Bermondsey.

One of his first two lodgers, Miss Dina Saunders, aged eighty-three, said:

I'd been living in the same room for fifty-three years, and suddenly I was told I had to get out. I didn't know what to do. I knew nobody who could help. I'd nowhere to go and I was very unhappy. Then the major heard about me and said I could have a front room in his house.

Major Carr-Gomm managed to acquire other houses, and the Abbeyfield Society was formed and registered as a charity. Contributions began to come in, but the problem of lonely old people became continually more urgent. He found one old man who was turned out of his lodging every day from ten to five, wet or fine. He found one old woman ill in bed with practically no food for a fortnight. He found another old woman who had spoken to nobody except an occasional passer-by for ten years.

Major Carr-Gomm's aim is to have a home for old people in every street of the district in which he works. This determination of his to cut himself off from his former life has been rigidly maintained. No doubt he was called a crank; somebody who had left the Coldstream Guards to fuss about lonely old people must be a crank. His mother said a few words which suggest what resolute moral courage Major Carr-Gomm must have:

I must admit it was a bitter disappointment to us all at first. Indeed, we simply could not understand his action. He had enjoyed so much his life in the Brigade. Of course I admired what he wanted to do, but I just couldn't understand why he had to give up everything to live in one room in a tiny house in Bermondsey with no hot water or even indoor sanitation.

In the end Major Carr-Gomm's singleness of heart silenced criticism.

Some may think it an exaggeration to claim high moral courage for the impulse which led a guards officer to renounce the world he knew because he desired to be useful in the world where poverty and old age and loneliness go hand in hand; the taboos imposed on a man educated at a public school are hardly appreciated by those who have not been subjected to that adamantine mold.

ROBERT LEWIS TAYLOR

Klondike Stef

⟨⟩

From a New Yorker *profile, written in 1941. Stefansson died in 1962 at the age of eighty-two, after enjoying his steak-and-bourbon diet to the very end.*

Vilhjalmur Stefansson announced his retirement as an active arctic explorer in 1919, when he was thirty-nine years old. He said that he intended to devote the rest of his life to consolidating his knowledge of the North for the benefit of the human race. That, in effect, is how he has spent the last twenty-two years. Soon after he retired, he came to New York and set up housekeeping in an apartment on West Eighty-ninth Street with Carl Akeley, the African explorer, and Herbert J. Spinden, the Central American explorer. The three men did considerable arguing, at the dinner table, about which of their respective stamping grounds was the most suitable for human life. Akeley would paint a pretty picture of the unclad aboriginals frolicking over the veldt, then Spinden would recall the languid Central Americans lying in hammocks, sipping rum, and plucking bananas from the nearby trees. After this, Stefansson would arise and salute the North. He generally warmed up with a superficial account of the foliage of northern Canada and proceeded from there toward the pole. In the course of his exposition he gave details of the carefree life led by the Eskimos in their winter playground and occasionally tapered off with sidelights on the history of Greenland and Iceland. He usually became so vehement that Akeley and Spinden had to forget their own differences and gang up on him in self-defense. As a clincher, Stefansson wrote a book called *The Northward Course of Empire,* in which he recommended that civilized man remove to the arctic, where he could live in luxury.

While some explorers, unsettled by Stefansson's irreverent approach to their profession, argue that he does not take his work seriously enough, the more detached scientists are inclined to consider him the most scholarly and honest man in the field. As a writer and lecturer, Stefansson, more than anybody else, has been responsible for the growing awareness that the arctic is habitable and possesses undeveloped resources of great value. He has also had a good deal to do with getting the government to establish air bases and weather stations in the arctic. Stefansson wrote his first book, *My Life with the Eskimos,* in 1913, after he had spent several years living among Eskimos in Alaska and Canada. It caused a distinct sensation, notably among explorers. Before the appearance of his book, living in the Far North had been considered a fairly cold proposition, but Stefansson put the Eskimos on a tropical basis. He claimed that their houses were heated to nearly a hundred degrees and that the temperature inside their airtight garments seldom dropped below that when they went outside. *My Life with the Eskimos* disagreed with practically everything that had been taught about the arctic and had a good sale. Stefansson wrote by far his most important and comprehensive book, *The Friendly Arctic,* in 1920, soon after his retirement. It is 784 pages long and sells for $6.50. Stefansson prepared it with his characteristic thoroughness and it is regarded by experts as a complete job, the text being supplemented by a preface, a foreword, an introduction, a hundred illustrations, nine maps, a lengthy appendix, and an index. The foreword is sprinkled liberally with tributes from various scientists to Stefansson. The introduction was written by Sir Robert Laird Borden, former prime minister of Canada, which country sponsored much of Stefansson's work. Sir Robert deals at length with Stefansson's last expedition, during which he went out on the ice floes for several months and maintained life solely by hunting, and notes with pleasure that as a result of the expedition the ovibos, or musk ox, may eventually be domesticated. *The Friendly Arctic* is now acknowledged by explorers to be the best handbook on travel in the Far North ever written. Russian explorers of the arctic, of whom there have been many lately, consider it a standard part of their equipment. Each member of the squadron of Russian fliers who made a nonstop flight to New York a few years ago had among his scanty belongings a copy of the book. One explorer recently said, after reading all 784 pages, that anybody over ten should be able to go to the North Pole with a copy of *The Friendly Arctic* and a rifle and reside there in feudal ease.

Several of Stefansson's books are nearly pure adventure. From *Hunters of the Great North, The Adventure of Wrangel Island,* and *The Three Voyages of Martin Frobisher,* for instance, one gets the feeling that the arctic is not quite the tranquil, friendly place that Stefansson has indicated it is in *The Friendly Arctic* and in his lectures. Some of his own activities even sound moderately dangerous to a layman. One time, Stefansson, heavily clothed, fell out of a boat that was bumping through ice and started to sink rapidly toward the bottom, half a mile below. On the way down he happily spied a weighted rope that was trailing astern and grabbed it. His colleagues pulled him up and hoisted him aboard. He describes this sort of thing in prose so matter-of-fact that the reader, unless he analyzes the facts, accepts the experience as somewhat in the nature of an early-morning plunge. In his eagerness to straighten out the world's conception of the arctic, Stefansson has a tendency to make the region sound like a slightly cooler version of New England. Stefansson has been known to comment with satisfaction that one of his books, *The Standardization of Error,* is classed by libraries as humor. It describes in a light manner how false reasoning can result in the establishment of dangerous fallacies. It is unique among his books, having nothing to do with the North, and is one of his favorites.

It is possible that Stefansson, if he had not become an explorer, would have been a detective. He has long been preoccupied with mystery. In his *Unsolved Mysteries of the Arctic,* published in 1938, he presents interesting conjectures on the fate of several explorers who went into the North and never returned. The stories are written in an absorbing, detective-story style not unlike that of Arthur Conan Doyle, who was a close friend of Stefansson for many years. Sherlock Holmes is Stefansson's pet literary character. He often speaks of Holmes as though he were a real man. "It was about the same thing Holmes had to contend with in *The Adventure of the Missing Three-Quarter,*" he will say, discussing some problem, or "Holmes cleaned up a situation like that beautifully in *The Adventure of the Dancing Men.*" Whenever Stefansson visited England or Doyle visited America, the two men spent considerable time together. They often argued about spiritualism. Doyle kept trying, without success, to convert Stefansson to his belief that the dead can communicate with the living. They attended numerous séances, after each of which Doyle would clap Stefansson on the back and say, "Well, that proves it, hey?" "On the contrary," Stefansson would reply, "it proves just the opposite."

Not many years before his death, Doyle persuaded Stefansson to accompany him to a séance in New York conducted by one Marjorie, a medium who was then having a considerable vogue. A number of their friends came along. The chamber in which the session took place was fitted out with purple drapes, gloomy furniture, crystal balls, and dim lights. Doyle was cheerfully optimistic that he might make a convert out of Stefansson at last. When they were all assembled, the lights got even dimmer and Marjorie, swathed in the conventional burnoose of the medium, entered the room and began a low singsong. Contorting her face suddenly, she cried, "I'm in contact with somebody's mother. . . . Her name seems to be . . . Stefansson." "If you mean me," Stefansson shouted, "my mother's still alive and her name is Stephenson!" Marjorie's grimaces became even more awesome. "I mean grandmother . . . somebody's grandmother . . . name of Stephenson." "I never had a grandmother named Stephenson!" shouted the explorer. "Her name was Stefansson." Soon after this the séance broke up. Doyle was peeved, and later, in a statement to the press, said that Marjorie was a fine young woman and a medium of the first order. The reporters took this statement to Stefansson, who said simply, "Marjorie's a fake." The two men were never friendly again. Stefansson says he does not believe, however, that this has anything to do with the fact that Doyle, since his death, hasn't got in touch with him.

Besides his books for adults, Stefansson has written four books for children, in collaboration with two women. In these stories he was not so intent upon removing the bunk from exploring; he has let down the bars to the point of admitting to his youthful readers that the arctic actually is in the North. In *Kak, the Copper Eskimo,* for example, there is a strong suggestion of snow and cold weather. Stefansson's most recent book, his seventeenth, is called *Ultima Thule.* Concerned chiefly with some ancient explorations of Iceland, it was published, with fortunate timeliness, less than a year ago. Stefansson's books have had a steady though unspectacular sale since the appearance of the first one twenty-eight years ago. They have been translated into a dozen or so languages and a few, such as *The Friendly Arctic,* have sold nearly as well abroad as here.

Stefansson, who has never married, today lives alone in three adjoining four-room apartments in a large Greenwich Village apartment house. After he and Akeley and Spinden broke up housekeeping, because all three had to spend so much time out of town on lecture tours, Stefansson moved to the Village, where he lived for a while with his friend Ridgely Torrence, the poet. During his first few years in the Village, Stefansson lived at several addresses, one of which was on Barrow Street. O. O. McIntyre, who was becoming popular as a columnist, discovered where Stefansson was living and began inserting chummy, imaginative items about him in his daily piece in the *American*. "Up betimes," he would write, "and to breakfast with Stefansson in Barrow Street." Stefansson, never much of a newspaper reader, was apprised of these engagements by his clipping service, to which he paid three cents per clipping. "I kept track of McIntyre's rise by my clippings," Stefansson says. "When he got up to eighty papers, I wrote him and said, 'Dear McIntyre: It would be cheaper for me if you would come to breakfast and say nothing about it.'" The columnist never came for breakfast, but he and Stefansson finally turned up at a banquet together. "He didn't know who I was," Stefansson says, "and I didn't tell him."

Stefansson started out where he is now with one apartment, then added the second, and finally the third, to accommodate his growing library. Whenever he gets restless, he ranges the twelve rooms like a caged polar bear. At sixty-one, he is a formidable figure, tall and heavy, with rough features and an abundant, swirling shock of gray hair. He wears tortoiseshell glasses, and behind them his eyes have a constant look of amusement. When he is discussing one of the many fallacious ideas he thinks are abroad in the world today, he wears a patient smile and rather resembles a friendly evangelist. Despite the years he spent in the outdoors, his skin is pale; the undersides of his wrists are almost dead white. "I didn't wear my skin out in the open," he explains. "I had it covered with fur." He usually has it covered with a double-breasted oxford-gray suit these days.

His home is always open to anyone who wants to read up on the arctic and to all lovers of the North. A visitor to Stefansson's apartments is greeted by one of nine girls he employs as assistants. The girls, headed by Mrs. Olive Wilcox, Stefansson's secretary for the last twenty years, put in seven days a week at indexing his library, cataloguing everything printed about the polar regions, taking dictation, running errands, and opening mail. Stefansson is one of the most indefatigable letter writers of this generation. He carries on a brisk correspondence with most of the residents of the arctic, including quite a few Eskimos who can neither read nor write. The Eskimos hold up their end by enlisting the aid of the nearest mounted policeman or trader. By this constant interchange of mail, Stefansson manages to keep up with all the latest developments in the arctic. Whenever he has visitors, he receives them seated behind a desk on a low platform in his small study. A visitor is placed facing him in an aged, overstuffed chair so saggy that the seat touches the floor. "The arrangement gives me a feeling of great superiority," he says. His conversation invariably turns to the arctic, and he frequently jumps up and stalks out of the room to get a book or a magazine with which to verify what he is saying. When walking, either indoors or on the street, he leans forward slightly and thrusts his chin out, as if heading into a polar storm. A trip through Stefansson's apartments is an exploration in itself. Books are stacked solidly along almost every wall. They have even seriously encroached on the kitchen; large, worn volumes appear on the shelves beside baking powder and salt. He has been collecting his library, which now contains about 15,000 books, most of them on the arctic, ever since he gave up exploring, and has spent about fifty thousand dollars on it.

Stefansson takes to the road early in the fall and spends three months lecturing, mostly at schools and colleges. He averages about two hundred dollars an appearance. His platform manner is casual and his delivery free from oratorical effects. His material is only slightly different from that of his books; he generally tells his audience what a fine place the arctic is and how comfortable the people are up there. Danger, he says, is practically nonexistant and a visitor who gets lost in a snowstorm would probably have been run over by a truck back home. He also tells his audiences that the Eskimos were hit harder by the 1929 Wall Street crash than any other people; many of them, he says, had to give up their radios and phonographs because the bottom dropped out of the fur market. Several explorers who awe lecture audiences with the perils of the North have complained that Stefansson makes it tough for them to earn an honest dollar. According to Stefansson, his income is now about twenty-two thousand dollars a year. Of this, three thousand dollars comes from lecturing. The rest is royalties on his books and fees paid him by the army and navy, for which he is preparing reports on northern countries; by the WPA, whose bibliography of polar literature he is directing; and by Pan American Airways, for which he acts as adviser on northern operations. A year ago Pan American sent him on a survey of its Alaskan lines. During the six weeks he was on the job, he looked in on some of his old Eskimo friends and had a lively time.

Stefansson believes that the work he is doing now is more important than his exploring. At the moment he is putting the finishing touches on his army and navy reports, which he started several years ago. After Congress passed a bill authorizing the President to buy information on the North, Stefansson was placed under contract by the army and navy. He worked two years with a staff of five assistants, then turned in two million words. He lost money on the deal. "It was a monumental job," he says, "and I became overenthusiastic." After studying the reports for a year, the army and navy came to the conclusion that Stefansson was a mine of information and was not yet worked out. He was given another contract, this time to expand his reports into five books: a book of general information about the North and guidebooks on Alaska, Canada, Greenland, and the Soviet Union north of sixty-two degrees. One of Stefansson's radical theories on the Atlantic Ocean, placing Iceland in the Western Hemisphere, was studied by President Roosevelt before our recent landing of troops there. Stefansson has spent a good deal of time lately conferring in New York and Washington with government officials who are concerned with the occupation. He is generally considered to be the foremost American authority on Iceland, a country for which he feels he has a special sympathy because his parents were born there.

In his spare time, as a relaxation from his government work, Stefansson is writing a book on diet. This is the outgrowth of a controversy in which he has been the central figure ever since he first went North in 1904. After noting that the Eskimos ate nothing but meat, he began eating nothing but meat himself, and then reported to the world that all the outstanding theories on diet were hokum. He said that man could live by meat alone. "There are *more* than enough vitamins in meat," he said repeatedly in the twenties. "If people get scurvy, their meat isn't fresh or they overcook. They cook all the vitamins out." Doctors then, even more than at present, were massed firmly behind fresh vegetables. They felt that Stefansson's loose talk about meat was an affront. In 1928, some doctors at the Russell Sage Institute of Pathology, acting for what they thought was the welfare of the profession, set out to prove once and for all that Stefansson was a crank. They invited him to subject himself to a test— now known in the medical world as the Stefansson Diet Experiment— which would require him to embark on a solid year of meat eating under their supervision. The prospect of spending a year in such digestive monotony as this might have struck some men as grim, but Stefansson was elated. "Nothing is too much trouble to prove a scientific fact," he said.

The conditions laid down by the doctors were that he would be confined to Bellevue Hospital, together with a young Danish disciple named Karsten Andersen, for the first month but would be free to go wherever he liked for the next eleven months as long as he stuck to the meat diet. The two men were to eat no cereals, vegetables, or fruit, and to drink only water. The doctors insisted on including Andersen, who had accompanied Stefansson on one of his expeditions, for fear that Stefansson might have a freak metabolism that could adapt itself equally well to an unmixed diet of vegetables, meat, grass, bark, or sand. Andersen was considered a peculiarly suitable subject because he had been working for some time in a Florida orange grove, subsisting almost entirely on fruit and vegetables, and was in feeble health. The month's internment in the hospital was stipulated to allow the doctors to make daily metabolism tests during the period of diet adjustment. The Institute of American Meat Packers, recognizing the promotional value of the experiment, agreed to furnish the necessary meat gratis and to send the doctors at Russell Sage, for analysis, duplicates of every piece of meat Stefansson and Andersen ate. There was an understanding between Stefansson and the medical group that the experiment would be conducted secretly. The doctors were somewhat put out, therefore, to learn the night before it was to start that Stefansson and his assistant were being feted by some sixty friends at a monster banquet at the Harvard Club. "We finally got him and the Dane to Bellevue," one of the doctors said recently, "and the damned thing got under way."

It was in January 1928 that Stefansson and Andersen entered Bellevue, where they were assigned to one of the wards. They were smuggled in, but reporters discovered their names on the register the second day and went into action. The doctors were dismayed, but Stefansson, as usual, was unruffled. He called a group of reporters together and addressed them at some length, explaining what was taking place. "The whole time he was out here," one of the Bellevue doctors has said, "he seemed to wear a halo of reporters." It had been the plan to start the two men on a diet that was 80 per cent fat meat and 20 per cent lean, since Stefansson had said he had always eaten about that proportion of fat and lean while in the arctic. However, he declared that he would go the whole way and eat nothing but lean. Andersen was allowed both. On the third day, the doctors found Stefansson propped up against the wall in a corridor, looking peaked. There was a consultation and some talk of calling the experiment off. Mustering his fading strength, Stefansson cried, "Give me some fat! Fat will fix me up!" His diet was changed to correspond to that of Andersen, who was flourishing, and he soon regained his strength. He grew more active as he got stronger, and some of the patients in his ward began to curse the day they were born. The ward was overrun by visitors most of the time. Only one of the patients there, a riveter who was used to noise, said he enjoyed Stefansson's stay. "It was like going to a newsreel," he said.

Stefansson and Andersen, in good appetite, took to ordering the choicest cuts of meat. "They would call loudly for the shinbones of a steer," one of the doctors recalls, "and crack them open down in the machine shop. Then they would walk around the hall eating pieces of marrow that looked like plumbers' candles." They also ate quantities of steaks, chops, brains fried in bacon fat, boiled short ribs, chicken, fish, and liver. The Institute of American Meat Packers began to grumble about the expense. "They're eating us out of house and home," one of its officials said. The reporters proved a persistent source of annoyance to the doctors. At intervals, Stefansson and

Andersen were placed in a calorimeter, a large, coffin-like box, so that the doctors could check their metabolism. The reporters would get hold of hospital ladders and try to climb into the calorimeter room through the transom. "We had to hide the ladders," one of the doctors has said. "We were afraid the reporters were going to get in the calorimeter with Stefansson."

After a couple of weeks, Stefansson became restless and was permitted, contrary to the terms of the experiment, to take walks in the park. An orderly was assigned to pad around after him to see that he did not eat anything. The orderly reported that Stefansson never attempted to devour as much as a blade of grass. He was also allowed to accept engagements to speak before women's clubs. He would place two broiled lamb chops in the pocket of his jacket before leaving the hospital and startle the ladies by whipping a chop out in the middle of a lecture. He would eat it while discussing the general superiority of meat to other foods and then polish off the other chop after his speech. Occasionally Stefansson sat at lunch with the Bellevue doctors. As they busied themselves with their customary noonday fare of green vegetables and a dash of protein, Stefansson gnawed on a joint of meat and held forth on various pet topics. They found him vigorously argumentative. "I suppose it's very true," one of the doctors might say meekly, "that the peoples of the cold countries do eat a great deal more meat than anything else. I wonder why it is that meat eating has always seemed to go with the cold countries." Stefansson would reach for a casserole of sweetbreads and reply, "Your remark is of interest to me, for I've always been curious as to how these fallacies develop. The heaviest meat eating in the world today goes on among the Australians and the Argentinians. The cowboys in these localities live on beef and will quit work immediately if handed cereals, greens, or fruits. No, I can't say that I agree with you, either in whole or in part." "He blew up about two dozen scientific theories at each meal," one of the doctors recently recalled. "He even took the trouble to tell us it was nonsense about the ostrich sticking its head in the sand."

At the end of three weeks, Stefansson, giving his word that he would eat nothing but meat, left the hospital to go on a lecture tour. Andersen also left a little later, under oath. Throughout the year they reported back regularly for tests, which occasionally took odd forms. Paced by Dr. Eugene F. DuBois, head physician of the experiment group, Stefansson and Andersen were asked to trot from the hospital to Central Park and then around the reservoir. Park visitors were bewildered by the sight of the scholarly-looking DuBois puffing and blowing along in the lead, Stefansson close behind, his thick gray hair tossing in the wind, and Andersen, looking bored and uncomfortable, shuffling along in the rear. Leaving the reservoir, DuBois would make a sprint for his office, followed by Stefansson and Andersen. The two meat eaters would then plop down on cots and DuBois would quickly check their breathing, pulse rate, and other reactions. These tests, the doctors were puzzled to note, indicated that both men's stamina increased with the passage of time. At the end of the year, Stefansson and Andersen re-entered the hospital once more. The doctors gave them a thorough examination and, still incredulous, announced that seemingly the men had suffered no ill effects. "I never felt better in my life," Stefansson told them afterward. In a final magnanimous gesture, he offered to go out and run around the Central Park reservoir for several hours. They told him not to bother. Shortly after Andersen gave up the meat diet he came down with pneumonia; Stefansson and the doctors agreed it was a coincidence. On the whole Andersen's health had improved greatly during the year. He had no more bad colds and his hair, which had been thinning, stopped falling out. Still vigorous, he is employed today as superintendent of the Jekyll Island Club, a sanctuary for retired millionaires off the coast of Georgia.

The doctors reluctantly but dutifully recorded for posterity their conclusion that meat apparently contains all the elements necessary to sustain human life. One of them said recently, "Most medical books tell us meat lacks vitamins, but practically it doesn't seem to work out that way." Stefansson is sometimes able to blot out his awful awareness that the nation is still in the clutches of greens by reflecting that medical colleges are beginning to recognize his dietetic triumph. "They usually get it all wrong, though," he says moodily. He is convinced that sooner or later medicine will allow meat to come into its own. "I seem to recall," he says, "that the brotherhood had a little trouble swallowing the business about germs." One eminent and enlightened dietitian has said of Stefansson, "He made an enormous stride toward liberalizing our ideas about diet." Not long after the conclusion of the experiment, Stefansson, unimpressed by his own vindication, was unsuccessfully trying to get in touch with a man in the interior of Africa who had reported that a tribe of natives there subsisted solely on milk and blood.

Stefansson, still in the best of health, continues to believe that meat is the ideal food. He eats vegetables sparingly. He includes the teeth among the parts of the body benefited by a meat diet. He has alienated all dentists by saying that people's dental troubles would cease if they would lay off the vegetables and take to meat. He says he has examined hundreds of skeletons of Eskimos who lived on meat alone and has never found a single indication of tooth decay. Stefansson's idea of a banquet is a few pounds of half-raw beef and a pitcher of water. He generally eats a fried-egg sandwich for breakfast, fish and a dessert for lunch, and large quantities of meat and dessert for dinner. When dining out, he will eat anything, including green salads. He has breakfast and dinner at one of the restaurants in his neighborhood and his noon meal at home with his staff of nine. Sometimes he cooks, sometimes one of the girls does. He has an attack of indigestion once every three or four years. "I get right back on the meat," he says, "and it clears up immediately." He takes no exercise whatever. "The need for exercise is a matter of endocrine balance," he says. "I don't require any." He spends most of his time in his apartment, at work on his books, his reports, and his correspondence. He lives modestly, and spends nearly all he makes on his research.

Stefansson never wears a hat and seldom wears a topcoat. When, on a midwinter day, Mrs. Wilcox tells him he is likely to catch cold, he always answers, "The belief that colds can result from exposure or wet feet is a myth. Colds are caused by germs." He catches a good many colds. Stefansson enjoys very few forms of recreation. Occasionally he goes to a movie. He has never fired a rifle since he gave up exploring. "I just hunted for food," he says, "not for sport." He spends several evenings a week at Romany Marie's restaurant, an old-fashioned Village hangout on Grove Street. There he finds a congenial group of men and women with whom he likes to debate topics ranging from aboriginal religions to contemporary politics. He frequently stays until past midnight, dominating the conversation and enjoying himself immensely. Every night, before going to sleep, he reads a book, usually a detective story or something on the commerce between the inhabitants of America and Europe in the pre-Columbus era, which is one of his favorite subjects. He likes to shock people who naïvely think of Columbus as a pioneer by saying, "The Americans were undoubtedly going to Europe in their own ships five thousand years ago."

Stefansson's bedroom is bare, containing only a small bed, an old bureau, and books. One of his friends, an interior decorator, recently designed some curtains figured with large polar bears and hung them over the windows. When the friend was gone, Stefansson took them down. "They made me look affected," he says. In his three apartments the only visible relic of his travels is an inscribed silver tray presented to him by the government of British Columbia. He uses it for cocktails. After holding the presidency of the Explorers Club for two years, he resigned his office in 1940 in order to have more time for other things. Before that, he spent several hours a week at the clubhouse, on West Seventy-second Street, but now he rarely drops in. The members, who call him "Klondike Stef," consider him their most imposing member and speak proudly of the fact that he has been awarded medals by the American, National, Philadelphia, Chicago, Berlin, Paris, and London geographical societies and that he holds five honorary degrees. One of the degrees, an LL.D., was given to him in 1930 by the University of North Dakota, where he was thrown out in 1902 but where he is often referred to these days as an honored son.

Stefansson works nine or ten hours every day of the week, but he finds time, too, for numerous cocktail parties and dinners. He is much in demand socially. An anthropologist who frequently sees him at parties explains his popularity by saying, "He gives liberally of himself." At a party, if he is asked a simple question involving the North, he sometimes gives of himself to such an extent that his listeners feel they have just made a round trip to Point Barrow. When anyone asks him if he ever got clear to the North Pole—and someone usually does—he merely smiles and says, "No. I'm a scientist, not a tourist."

ALEXANDER VON GLEICHEN-RUSSWURM

Lauzun

ৡৢ

Ten years in prison couldn't squelch his tremendous joie de vivre.

When after the Fronde* Louis XIV turned the nobles into surly courtiers, the result was an artistically artificial court, the like of which had never been, a mine of psychological wealth for the student. This court it was that gave to those masters of psychological insight La Bruyère, Racine, and Molière the material for their studies—the most delicate and melancholy ever produced in the science of the soul.

Bowing, embracing, scraping, bob-curtsying, *bon mots,* teasing verses, festivals of unending monotony—that was the exterior of court life; but deep below the surface, passions, intrigues, adventures, cabals with and without love, a wild, almost crazy, chase after fortune and favor; a rage for gambling, and many who cheated at play; a single idolatrous religion and many fetishes.

"The court" was in so far a fairyland that there the poorest might suddenly become rich overnight, the meanest powerful, the most insignificant one of the select inner circle; and vice versa. These possibilities created a tense atmosphere, for the artificial sun of royal power cast deep, sinister shadows, and woe to him on whom one of these shadows fell, who was banished or secretly imprisoned—in the epoch of the Iron Mask.

* The Fronde (literally "sling") was the name of the political party that stirred up the nobility during the minority of Louis XIV to resist the absolute power of the Crown 1649–52).

Without this secret and tragic tension, without the sense of living in the midst of wizards and black magic in this palace teeming with gold and in these gardens full of swollen pomp and mysterious fountains, the courtier would have died of tedium. His life was one long yawn of endless waiting, generally vain expectation, from the early morning, when, if fortune favored him, he might watch the king put on his boots, to the evening, when he was permitted to see how the same gentleman deigned to remove the same boots.

A horrible inactivity was the order of the day in the Louvre, in Saint-Germain, and at Versailles. The labor that was here required of the French nobility was merely their presence. To be present and alive to every favorable chance was their task, and so arose a self-contradictory state of affairs, in which this multitude of idlers assumed an air of immense industry, put on a mien of imposing importance, and regarded themselves as important.

What opportunities were there for dandyism in this curious court, which followed the royal example in allotting the principal parts in each tragicomedy to women? Were there, indeed, any openings for the development of a self-assured dandyism?

In a certain sense Louis XIV was himself a dandy. He was proud of his handsome legs and liked to show them at the dance. He rightly prided himself on his outward appearance, for it was imposing; and the current fashion, which depended on the king and radiated from his person, emphasized his royal aspect with the pomp of the enormous wig.

If, on the one hand, the king set an example of pompous, baroque dandyism to bewigged Olympian gods, joining in the dance with goddesses parading in crinolines, the tradition had grown up on the other hand that Monsieur, the king's brother, was chief of fops and mashers, puppies and coxcombs; Gaston d'Orléans, the brother of Louis XIII, had enjoyed that reputation and now Monsieur carried on the tradition and was noted and notorious for his affectation, his womanish cosmetics, his retinue of decked-out minions.

For those who followed fashion, therefore, there were two courses marked out, between which a newcomer must choose.

There seemed to be no possibility in court circles of a triumphant, independent, and original dandyism exercising widespread influence; and a type of any significance, worthy of serious notice, seemed the more improbable because, on the one hand, the ladies held the reins of authority—at the moment the energetic Montespan—and, on the other, the venomous swarm of Monsieur's favorites arrogated power.

It seemed to his contemporaries as the most extraordinary improbability that nevertheless a dandy, heroic after his own fashion, did assert himself, a man whom all France honored for a brief space, for whose sake a royal princess languished and the coldhearted king is said to have shed hot tears, a man whose adventures have been made immortal by the most talented woman in the world in her most brilliant letters.

Madame de Sévigné tells of the brief success of the great dandy as of something altogether fabulous, astonishing, and extraordinary. In her heart no doubt she regards it as something altogether absurd and in bad taste. Saint-Simon and La Bruyère think so too; little Lauzun, the impudent Gascon, overleaps all distinctions and defies all attempts to place him. La Bruyère, who describes him under the name of Straton, becomes unusually poetical in depicting his character: "No dream could create such a life as he lived."

A dream life: such might be the description of this strange courtier's destiny; such is the dreamlike confusion of events. They are united imaginatively by the persistence of a determined dandyism, the grace of a careless irony, and self-mockery, which gave the ascendancy to Lauzun even under torment and in death itself.

To be constantly penetrated with a consciousness of his own superiority, and therein to find proud comfort, thereby to become unconquerable: that is the quality of the grandiose dandy.

Lauzun was grandiose after his own manner, and yet he was called "le petit homme," for he was small of stature, and fate mocked him for it from the first. He, who loved so well to look down with condescension, to whom it was natural to tower above others, was physically short, so that it was easy for his opponents to ridicule him as a dwarf and especially to make a joke of the fact that so small a man should come forward as a suitor of the excessively tall princess who was called "la Grande Mademoiselle" just because of her stature.

He came of a noble family, was a younger son of the Marquis de Puygichan, and himself bore the title of Count of Lauzun until he was made a duke. As in the fairy tale Tom Thumb is sent into the enchanted forest and there succeeds by his wits, so this Tom Thumb, this cadet of Gascony, was sent to the enchanted realm of the court to make his fortune, if the little fellow should have wit enough—he was fourteen years old at the time and had no education beyond the common instruction in riding and fencing and a smattering of reading and writing. But like a true Gascon he was well able to swagger. He was gay and quick-witted and made his way everywhere; at one stroke he became indispensable to one personage of importance and another; knowledge of their weaknesses was his strength.

By the very insignificance of his appearance he made himself a person of consequence; from his small stature he evolved greatness; upon his oddity, which created a sensation in the midst of prescribed conventions, he built his power.

Later Barbey d'Aurevilly called him truly "a dandy of dandies" and "an Englishman of France," for in some respects this Tom Thumb outstripped the great dandies who appeared in England at the beginning of the nineteenth century in imperturbable hauteur, in cold self-satisfaction and assurance, and in a certain indescribably imposing manner. He surpassed his successors in his power of walking without dizziness along dangerous, breakneck paths, of remaining cool in situations that would have broken and annihilated men of a later generation, and he carried vanity to such a pitch of arrogance as even to oppose the king, whom men worshipped as a very sun god.

Were later dandies Stoics of the drawing room? It was he who introduced this fashionable Stoicism, paraded it on the dangerously slippery floors of the Louvre, and preserved it during the horrors of captivity. He was supported by an indestructible and grim humor.

His person stands out so sharply among his contemporaries that in her *Memoirs* the Grande Mademoiselle, who loved him ardently, repeats again and again how people were enchanted because they were startled at his behaving quite differently from others and being distinguished by "a million oddities."

La Bruyère made it his lifework to penetrate the most intricate characters, to dissect and explain their internal machinery, yet even he is forced to admit that he cannot make Straton-Lauzun out, and closes his observations on him with the words: "An ambiguous character, confused, involved, an enigma, something of an unanswered query."

The most pertinent thing to be said of him is that his insolence was boundless. His audacity is expressed in the motto that he chose for his coat of arms: "I rise as high as I can," with a rocket above.

In order so to rise the first essential was the king's favor, and that could be won through the favor of his mistress, the Marquise de Montespan. Through her was the prescribed road, and that road, of course, swarmed with courtiers as tall as masts.

But Lauzun not only understood how to make a place for himself in every crowd at court, sometimes by means of cruel insolence— Saint-Simon tells, among other anecdotes, how once he stamped intentionally on a duchess's hand with his pointed cane—he understood also how to outbid everyone in skillful homage, in casting aspersions on his rivals, in creating the impression that he was indispensable, and playing the fool profitably.

For the king and his mistress wanted to be amused, just like the general public in our own times, which now fills the role of the despots of former days. That was their simple, express, and passionate desire. Lauzun amused them by "a million oddities."

In spite of his small stature he could pass for a master of fashion when he deigned to dress carefully. Thus he is portrayed in a painting, in marvelously rich array, with a double puff in his white silk sleeves, from which the most delicate lace falls over his slender hands; a cascade of gorgeous lace falls over the breast and the splendid belt, and a great cluster of orders is attached with ribbons to the shoulder. The wig curls around his delicate, mocking face and falls in rich tresses at the back over an almost kingly velvet cloak. One hand grasps the hilt of his ornamental sword, the other rests carelessly beside a plumed hat of magnificent proportions.

But among his other peculiarities Lauzun sometimes had the audacity to dress quite crazily and grotesquely, perhaps to test his power and prestige and see whether anyone would dare to jeer at him. He was capable of walking to and fro in a dressing gown, with his courtier's cloak as a train, and a peaked nightcap upon his wig under his plumed hat. Just as the dandies of the nineteenth century sometimes sported with paradoxical modes, introducing, perhaps, shabby coats as a mark of fashion and having them laboriously scraped threadbare with sharp glass, so Lauzun sometimes appeared intentionally untidy as a proof that he could take any liberty.

In fact his absurd and wittily malicious sallies so amused the king that he allowed Lauzun to do whatever he pleased. Moreover, he affected the utmost admiration and devotion to both the king and the marquise.

However much Louis XIV, surrounded by highly skilled flatterers, worshiped and pursued with incense to the point of nausea, might have learned from experience, he seemed as ready to rise to the bait of the quick-witted dwarf as Nobel, the king in the story of "Reynard the Fox," rose to that of the cunning Reynard—and Madame de Montespan had just such a weakness for him as the lioness in the fable had for the fox.

The king himself silenced a lampoon against his favorite, and in spite of all counterintrigues, in spite of the weighty protest of Louvois, the king's minister, the young man, who was put in command of a regiment at twenty-four, rose higher and higher in the royal favor. He even had the audacity to aspire to the position of commander-in-chief of the artillery, and the king promised the office to him.

When Louvois heard of this, he stormed with rage, and Lauzun, fearing he might lose the appointment, appealed to Madame de Montespan for her intercession. She promised to help him.

But the cunning Reynard of the court felt no confidence and risked a bold stroke in order to make sure. Saint-Simon tells the tale at length. The pedantic routine of the court even ruled the king's amour. It was his invariable custom to retire to bed with his mistress at a particular hour in the afternoon.

That was the chosen time when Madame de Montespan urged upon him her protégés' wishes.

Lauzun had bribed her waiting woman and was hidden under the gorgeous four-poster, with its golden spiral posts bearing the curtains like a tabernacle and crowned with tufts of ostrich feathers.

He crouched there as an eavesdropper during the lovers' hour, overheard the intimate effusions of the exalted couple, and pricked up his ears when his own name was mentioned.

But instead of urging his suit fervently, as was agreed between them, the lady, who doubtless had been won over in the meantime by his opponents, was at pains to injure his case and to make mock of him and his ambition.

He was compelled to crouch in his uncomfortable hiding place and hear with fury how she turned the king's mind and endangered his interests. When the lovers rose and Louis took leave, Lauzun was still forced to remain under the bed until Madame de Montespan had completed her elaborate toilet in preparation for the evening ballet.

At last he crept out, made use of the labyrinth of small staircases and corridors in order to meet her on the way to the ballroom, and ceremoniously offered his escort. He met her and asked in a low voice whether she had been so good as to remember his suit to the king.

She allowed him to escort her with courtly state and assured him that she had rendered him every assistance in her power.

And now, whilst he led her ceremoniously, he held her in his cruel grip and, soft and smiling as though he were murmuring flowery words of adulation, he repeated every word that she had just spoken about him—among others, that he was better fitted to twist curlpapers than to fire cannon—and gave her names that were anything but flattering. He threatened to slash her fair, false face with his sword.

She trembled, she was half dead with fright. She reached the ballroom in a state of consternation, and there Lauzun led her ceremoniously to her seat.

He was careful not to confess how he had learned every word of the secret conversation, so that the king and Madame de Montespan were overcome with superstitious terrors, believing that some spirit, perhaps the devil himself, had communicated it to Lauzun.

A few days after this comic episode a historically celebrated scene was enacted. Lauzun came into the king's presence in fury—perhaps merely assumed fury—broke his sword in two, and shrieked that he could no longer serve a king who lived in the toils of a harlot.

Louis thereupon opened the window and threw his stick out, remarking that he would regret it if he allowed himself to be provoked into thrashing a nobleman.

Lauzun was sent to the Bastille, and his enemies hoped he would stay there long, for Louis had never before pardoned a lack of respect.

But within a few weeks the king was pining for his irreplaceable favorite and graciously recalled him. Lauzun, however, responded to this unprecedented mercy with unprecedented defiance, played at injured innocence, and refused to terminate his sojourn in prison without adequate atonement. Only after prolonged chaffering between Saint-Germain, where the king was in residence, and the Bastille, and after various marks of distinguished favor, did he consent to leave his prison.

After this victory Lauzun might well believe that nothing was beyond the reach of his ambition.

It had long been rumored of Tom Thumb, who scored the most remarkable successes with women, that he possessed a secret love charm.

He had no need of that to win the heart of the king's cousin, the Grande Mademoiselle, daughter of Gaston d'Orléans. For this haughty princess, who had wished in her youth to play the parts of Corneille's heroines, who had opposed the king in the Fronde, the famous rising of the nobility, who had always assumed the role of tragic Muse, she who was the richest heiress in Europe and thought no king worthy of her hand, she had let the years slip past and had reached a dangerous age. She was past forty and royal wooers began to fail; the heroic years of the Fronde were forgotten, her exalted part was played out, and nothing remained but the court routine, which was bound to weary her romantic spirit unspeakably.

She was suffering boundless tedium, as her *Memoirs* reveal, when Lauzun appeared; at first she occupied her imagination with this unique man; then, as she confesses, her heart became passionately engaged. She asked herself artlessly whether such a thing were permissible for so great a princess. And she questioned an oracle. Corneille was to her the fountain of faith, Corneille, the majestic revealer of all that is majestic. He alone would be able to pronounce once and for all what was seemly for a daughter of France when unexpectedly her heart became clamorous. She sent to Paris for a volume of Corneille and opened it at the lines:

> *Since we're made for each other by Heaven's decree,*
> *Lisa, without scruple we may quickly agree. . . .*
> *Untroubled by numberless trifling fears,*
> *Our swift-footed faith outstrips speech, it appears.*

So Corneille decided in favor of her heart. Without compromising her dignity she could fix her thoughts upon Lauzun and resolve that he should be her husband; the king must consent. She was convinced that the matter was decreed in heaven; she confessed her sentiments to her lover, who held back for a long time, stimulating her passion with all the arts of an experienced seducer, but proceeding cautiously, step by step.

The two became friends, the more intimately on the occasion of one of those curious self-advertising court journeys (in 1670), when Louis XIV proceeded to Flanders with a retinue of some twelve thousand persons—not counting the kitchen staff—in order to display his royal pomp to the lands newly acquired by the Treaty of Aix-la-Chapelle.

The escorting troops were under Lauzun's command, and Mademoiselle betrayed her feelings when she begged the king not to let him stand hatless for hours in drenching rain, because he would catch cold and would look so absurd with soaked hair that people would laugh at him.

For during this journey, which almost amounted to a migration of peoples, it rained terribly, like the very Flood. The queen and the king's mistresses, princes and princesses, were perpetually sinking into swamps in their heavy traveling coaches. There was no opportunity to display the intended pomp with Gobelin tapestries, velvet-covered furniture, gold, and silver.

The journey was a disappointment to the great dandy, whose equipment outshone all others. "It contained the whole rue Saint-Honoré. It was very fine and magnificent," wrote the Grande Mademoiselle of this equipment.

Upon this extraordinary journey rivers in flood had to be crossed on several occasions, the ladies screamed, and Mademoiselle was happy when Lauzun rebuked her timidity. During the return journey the lovers came to an understanding, but the Grande Mademoiselle's wishes were crossed by the death of Henriette, Duchess of Orléans, and the king's scheme of marrying his cousin to his widowed brother. Only one thing tempted the princess to marry that dissolute prince of coxcombs: she confesses that she would be given a seat in the back of the king's coach on all journeys, "which is very much to be desired"; all other seats were miserably uncomfortable. But she remained faithful to her love and refused the king's brother, obstinately persisting in her demand for a marriage with her beloved *petit homme*.

The king gave his official consent and the betrothal took place, after four noblemen of high standing had applied to the king on Lauzun's behalf for the princess's hand and had been graciously received.

The Grande Mademoiselle was awakened from her dream of love by the general amazement at the proposed *mésalliance,* the universal indignation, which swelled at last to such proportions that Louis withdrew his promise, excusing himself on the plea that "kings must consider the public." Madame de Sévigné has described the popular mood with so masterly a pen that I cannot do better than quote her:

I am going to tell you the most astonishing, the most surprising, the most marvellous, the most miraculous, the most triumphant, the most staggering, the most unheard-of, the most singular, the most extraordinary, the most incredible, the most unexpected, the greatest, the smallest, the rarest, the commonest, the most dazzling, the most secret hitherto, the most brilliant, the most enviable thing; something that we in Paris cannot believe [and how should they believe it in Lyons?]. Something which is to happen on Sunday, but which may not have happened on Monday. Guess. Do you give it up? Well, I must tell you: Monsieur de Lauzun is to be married on Sunday at the Louvre, with the King's consent—guess to whom. [Here Madame de Sévigné interposes all manner of suggestions.] He is to marry, upon my word, my word of honour, the Grande Mademoiselle, grand-daughter of Henri IV, the King's first cousin, who was destined for the throne.

To scorn rank and dignity in order to crave simple happiness in love like any common girl, such a thing seemed lunacy, and not even probable. It was whispered that the king was sacrificing his cousin and her immense wealth to his favorite.

The lawful queen and the unlawful, Madame de Montespan, were alike enraged at this, for each coveted the inheritance for her own children. How dared Tom Thumb cross their hopes? The two women hastily united to induce the king to withdraw his consent. The court opposed the match, the city opposed it, and even popular opinion, of which little notice was taken as a rule, rose in revolt.

So unusual a marriage outraged contemporary sentiment, and even a strong swimmer like Lauzun was unable to make way against the stream in which he had struck out so boldly. He was compelled to scramble onto the nearest bank, a comical and dripping figure. Madame de Sévigné tells how the king suddenly changed his mind, in her next letter to her eager and curious friends in the provinces:

We had a surprise at the Tuileries today which might be described as a bolt from the blue. You are still occupied with the joy, the transports, the rapture of the Princess and her happy lover. Well, it was on Monday that the affair was made known, as you are aware. Tuesday was spent in talk, amazement, and congratulations. On Wednesday Mademoiselle made gifts to Monsieur de Lauzun, conferring upon him the requisite titles, dignities, and honours for inclusion in the marriage contract, which was drawn up on that very day. . . . The contract was made, and in it he bore the newly-acquired title of Montpensier. On Thursday morning— that is, yesterday—Mademoiselle was in hopes that the King would sign, as he had said he would; but towards seven o'clock that evening His Majesty, being persuaded by the Queen, and Monsieur, and several grey-beards that the affair was damaging his reputation, resolved to break it off, and, having sent for the bridal couple, he declared in the presence of the Prince [de Condé] that he forbade them to think further of the marriage. Monsieur de Lauzun received the command with all the respect, the submission, the resolution, and the despair called for by so great a fall. As for Mademoiselle, she burst into tears and broke into loud laments, and kept her bed all day.

Other memoirs relate that the unhappy woman was like a fury, with disheveled hair, tragically flinging up her arms and screaming as she rushed through the apartments; she was particularly wounded by the self-control that Lauzun maintained. But in the moment of defeat he wanted to impress his enemies as a *beau joueur,* and therein he succeeded.

La Fare adds in his *Memoirs* that the king was urgently pressed by those enemies of Lauzun and that Condé even went so far as to threaten that he would, indeed, attend the wedding of the "cadet" Lauzun, but that after the ceremony he would shoot him dead with a pistol.

That there was reason to fear a scandal and that there was much gossip about it are likewise clear from a letter in which Madame de Sévigné told Coulanges of her visit to the Grande Mademoiselle on the day before the catastrophe. She could not resist warning the too confident and blissful princess, saying: "Good heavens, Mademoiselle, you are very happy, but why did you not conclude the affair rapidly on Monday? Do you not know that so long a delay gives all the kingdom time to talk, and that your desire to carry so extraordinary an undertaking so far must tempt God and the king?"

The unhappy lady remembered the warning, for when Madame de Sévigné, having paid a visit of congratulation the day before, now paid a visit of condolence, the princess fell on her neck and burst into tears.

The marquise says of Lauzun that he played his part to perfection. She felt kindly sympathy with the disappointed bride, though she confessed this to none but her friend, for society would have thought it absurd, so great was the irritation at Lauzun's elevation and his presumption, and the exultation over his humiliation.

Mademoiselle received alike condolence and congratulation dramatically. She found comfort in the fact that she was playing a part. She lay in state in her bed, like a widow, and it was said of her that she pointed pathetically to a second pillow beside her own, crying: "He should lie there!"

During the Fronde the princess had hoped, thanks to the popular rising, the barricades, and the artillery, to force her marriage with the king, who was considerably her junior. Now, in her mature age, her heart had renounced ambitious schemes and exposed itself artlessly to Cupid's darts, and she hoped to secure simple happiness by the simple expedients of tears and prayers, to elevate the man of her choice and see him grateful and happy.

But those who grudged Lauzun, if not the middle-aged princess, at least her immense possessions, had moved the king to break his word. He seems to have been ashamed of it. Mademoiselle speaks of tears and caresses with which he sought to comfort her. That was just as absurd as the absurdity of the whole affair of the betrothal.

Lauzun bore this trial with elegant grace. In any case he did not let slip the immense properties made over to him in the deed of gift and we may assume that the couple were soon secretly united. The king apparently hoped to compensate Lauzun by great marks of favor for the humiliation he had suffered; he even offered him a marshal's baton, which, however, was not accepted.

Though he behaved with calm dignity toward the king, his self-control deserted him when he learned by slow degrees who had secretly pulled the wires. Just as on the occasion when he had eavesdropped under her bed, it was the insinuations of Montespan that had been decisive on his enemies' side. Lauzun reproached her in scenes of increasing violence, and the influential woman declared that she went in danger of her life.

She united her own influence with that of the Minister Louvois, in whose heart hatred and envy toward the favorite were accumulating. Less than a year after he reached the climax of fortune and favor, on November 25, 1671, a terrible fate overtook Lauzun at the instigation of these two bitter enemies. He was arrested at Saint-Germain and taken to the fortress of Pinerolo, where another victim of the court clique, Fouquet, had already been pining for seven years.

Mademoiselle had parted from Lauzun the day before with a foreboding of evil and utterly cast down; the terrible news reached her in Paris.

The instructions given to the commander of the fortress are still preserved and they bear witness to extreme cruelty. The commandant said in reply to Louvois that his prisoner "would be like a dead man *in pace.*" He allotted him vaulted rooms with the most heavily grated windows, and as Lauzun entered the gloomy chamber he said in despair: "A tomb."

He had been condemned without trial; there was not even a sham trial, as with Fouquet, and he did actually live buried alive. The period was characterized by refined cruelty toward the man, but it did not fail in respect for the nobleman. Thus state prisoners like Lauzun always retained a servant, and even prison had its etiquette. Even in close confinement a prisoner was not expected to dispense with service; he was allowed good furniture and silver for the table in his intentionally gloomy dungeon; and the commandant of the fortress paid visits of ceremony to inquire for his health.

Lauzun's dandyism stood the test of these visits majestically; he welcomed his guest and escorted him with a mocking and ceremonious superiority, bowing irreproachably.

No less terrible than the solitary languishing existence of her lover was the Grande Mademoiselle's martyrdom. Her proud heart was bursting with rage and hatred of Lauzun's enemies, but she could help him only by amiable means and had to appear at every festival, painted and laced, flattering the king and smiling upon his mistress. For years she begged and prayed indefatigably, but was met with silence and encompassed with scorn.

Years passed by, the last of her youth vanished, and he was far away, buried alive; he was suffering illness and misery in captivity and she had formerly been anxious if he only had a cold in his head.

Attempts to communicate with him ended tragically; the messenger was caught and suffered torture and death.

Perhaps he was angry and offended, perhaps he thought her stupid or faithless—she who spared no pains to help him, whose self-abnegation was boundless in spite of all the malice that sought to alienate her from her unfortunate lover.

In Lauzun's strongbox neatly tabulated love letters were found, locks of hair, and pledges of love; all of this was played into her hands to make mock of her, yet she did not waver.

Years passed by.

The commandant reported to Louvois that his prisoner had become pious and had asked for devotional books; and that he received his visits with a patient smile.

His enemies might now suppose that their victim was harmless, perhaps that he had grown imbecile from grief.

When Lauzun smiled, it was not from imbecility. His greatness, a certain gay impudence in his attitude toward life, and his self-assurance stood the test of his captivity. He attempted a flight that is unique in the annals of attempted escapes. For three years he worked patiently with any tools he could procure—old knives and the like—loosening the stones in the floor of his dungeon. He scratched and scratched till he succeeded in accomplishing his incredible task and had made a hole in the floor large enough to let through his wasted body. In anticipation he had made a rope ladder of serviettes and taken it with him. He landed in a chamber beneath the prison. Its windows were grated, but less strongly, and he succeeded in loosening the grating; with his rope ladder he reached the moat after great exertions.

His efforts were not rewarded, for a sentry saw and betrayed him.

When the affair was reported to the king, it is said that he was moved. Mademoiselle used the opportunity and pleaded her lover's cause with renewed courage. Was Montespan's anger dissipated or did she regard her enemy as harmless—for he professed to be ill, even dying—or did she no longer fear him as a witness now that the scandalous Voisin lawsuit, in which she was involved, had been quashed? The whole affair remains a mystery. Be that as it may, she gradually came to support the Grande Mademoiselle's entreaties, for she wanted money and resolved to extort a ransom from the unhappy lovers.

Mademoiselle was given to understand that Lauzun's liberation, and even an officially recognized marriage, depended upon the presentation to the Duke of Maine, Montespan's bastard son, of the properties promised to Lauzun.

During the unworthy chaffering over this affair the captive's lot was eased, and at last, after ten years' imprisonment, Lauzun was released from Pinerolo in 1681 and sent to recuperate at the baths of Bourbon. There Montespan negotiated with him for the estates of which she meant to swindle him. During the process he was imprisoned once more in order to render him tractable.

It was not till 1682 that he saw Mademoiselle again, and the meeting was a terrible disappointment to the faithful princess.

Not only was he wearing an old-fashioned *just au corps de brevet*, in which he looked pitiful, but his behavior disappointed her as much as his appearance. Fate treats her chosen victims with cynical sadism, and she selects simple, high-spirited creatures like the Grande Mademoiselle to satisfy her cruel humor.

During Lauzun's ten years of captivity she had pined in the midst of the horrible court conventions; she had scratched and scraped as persistently as he in order to secure his liberation, yet now that he was liberated, he paid no heed to it and never thanked her. Or her manner made thanks too burdensome. He almost regarded her as being responsible for the king's disfavor. He was an ambitious man, and now he was free, but still in disgrace and dependent upon Mademoiselle. Such a position embittered him; he was impatient to cast off his fetters and could not even bear the fetters of love with which she romantically bound him.

In Choisy, in a summer palace built on purpose for him, she had caused one chamber to be decorated with painted Cupids. She tried to beautify herself for his pleasure and decked herself with red ribbons. He mocked at her and endeavored to make good the time lost in prison with all manner of amours, which wounded and revolted her.

The married life of the heroic couple went from one castastrophe to another, and it was said that even scences of violence were not wanting. These alternated with dramatic scenes of reconciliation.

While his unfaithfulness drove her to despair, the princess's arrogance wounded him, and she must have had difficulty in parrying the grim jests that Lauzun enjoyed making during such scenes. He called her Henriette de Bourbon and is said to have exclaimed during a quarrel: "Pull off my boots, Henriette de Bourbon!" This was a gibe at her romanticism, for according to the ancient tradition of chivalry it was the wife's privilege to remove her husband's boots after battle.

The haughty princess broke her heart, which had loved and hoped so long and patiently. She refused to be reconciled, withdrew to a life of piety, visited the houses of the poor, and is said to have cried when she saw a humble but happy couple: "Why was I not born in a cottage like this?"

Meanwhile Lauzun's star, which, it seemed, was finally dimmed, rose again in startling brilliance. In 1688 Madame de Sévigné wrote: "I am amazed at Monsieur de Lauzun's star, which elects to guide him once more to brilliant fortune when it seemed that his fame was completely buried."

He went to England, became involved in the disturbances that broke out before the expulsion of the last of the reigning Stuarts, James II, and won high praise by assisting the flight of the queen and her son. By this roundabout method he once more gained high favor, and what the Grande Mademoiselle had formerly exerted all her endeavors to attain now came about, but caused her pain and irritation since Lauzun had become odious to her.

She died in 1693 without seeing him again.

Lauzun mourned ostentatiously. Two years later he married a niece of Count—later Duke—Saint-Simon, a girl of fourteen. He was sixty-three, but his triumph restored his youth. To everybody's astonishment he became once more a dandy in the grandiose style, and in that character played a part at court up to his ninetieth year, famed for wit, fashion, and "a million oddities."

He was a good horseman even in old age and impressed Louis XV by displaying his skill in riding wild horses, which he could break in gracefully. As he subdued these horses, so he had tamed his savage destiny.

His impudent humor remained with him to the last. When he was ninety years old and lay dying, he found amusement in watching several legacy hunters betray themselves in the mirror. He summoned up strength to make game of them; he propped himself up and began to pray to God in a loud voice and beg forgiveness for his sins, vowing to leave all his property to churches and monasteries, to the exclusion of his bodily heirs.

Meanwhile he feasted his eyes on the reflected image of those heirs' horrified gestures and saw Madame de Lauzun signing to them and whispering.

Chuckling at the success of his uncouth jest, this remarkable man closed his eyes.

SIR RABINDRANATH TAGORE

Living or Dead?

The great Indian poet and sage wrote many short stories, all filled with deep philosophical meaning.

The widow in the house of Saradasankar, the Ranihat zemindar, had no kinsmen of her father's family. One after another all had died. Nor had she in her husband's family anyone she could call her own, neither husband nor son. The child of her brother-in-law Saradasankar was her darling. For a long time after his birth, his mother had been very ill, and the widow, his Aunt Kadambini, had fostered him. If a woman fosters another's child, her love for him is all the stronger because she has no claim upon him—no claim of kinship, that is, but simply the claim of love. Love cannot prove its claim by any document which society accepts, and does not wish to prove it; it merely worships with double passion its life's uncertain treasure. Thus all the widow's thwarted love went out toward this little child. One night in *Sraban* Kadambini died suddenly. For some reason her heart stopped beating. Everywhere else the world held on its course; only in this gentle little breast, suffering with love, the watch of time stood still forever.

Lest they should be harassed by the police, four of the zemindar's Brahmin servants took away the body, without ceremony, to be burned. The burning-ground of Ranihat was very far from the village. There was a hut beside a tank, a huge banyan near it, and nothing more. Formerly a river, now completely dried up, ran through the ground, and a part of the watercourse had been dug out to make a tank for the performance of funeral rites. The people considered the tank as part of the river and reverenced it as such.

Taking the body into the hut, the four men sat down to wait for the wood. The time seemed so long that two of the four grew restless and went to see why it did not come. Nitai and Gurucharan being gone, Bidhu and Banamali remained to watch over the body.

It was a dark night of *Sraban*. Heavy clouds hung in a starless sky. The two men sat silent in the dark room. Their matches and lamp were useless. The matches were damp, and would not light for all their efforts, and the lantern went out. After a long silence, one said: "Brother, it would be good if we had a bowl of tobacco. In our hurry we brought none."

The other answered: "I can run and bring all we want."

Understanding why Banamali wanted to go, Bidhu said: "I daresay! Meanwhile, I suppose I am to sit here alone!"

Conversation ceased again. Five minutes seemed like an hour. In their minds they cursed the two who had gone to fetch the wood, and they began to suspect that they sat gossiping in some pleasant nook. There was no sound anywhere, except the incessant noise of frogs and crickets from the tank. Then suddenly they fancied that the bed shook slightly, as if the dead body had turned on its side. Bidhu and Banamali trembled and began muttering "Ram, Ram." A deep sigh was heard in the room. In a moment the watchers leapt out of the hut and raced for the village.

After running about three miles, they met their colleagues coming back with a lantern. As a matter of fact, they *had* gone to smoke, and knew nothing about the wood. But they declared that a tree had been cut down and that, when it was split up, it would be brought along at once. Then Bidhu and Banamali told them what had happened in the hut. Nitai and Gurucharan scoffed at the story and abused Bidhu and Banamali angrily for leaving their duty.

Without delay all four returned to the hut. As they entered they saw at once that the body was gone; nothing but an empty bed remained. They stared at one another. Could a jackal have taken it? But there was no scrap of clothing anywhere. Going outside, they saw that on the mud that had collected at the door of the hut there were a woman's tiny footprints, newly made. Saradasankar was no fool, and they could hardly persuade him to believe in this ghost story. So after much discussion the four decided that it would be best to say that the body had been burnt.

Toward dawn, when the men with the wood arrived they were told that, owing to their delay, the work had been done without them; there had been some wood in the hut after all. No one was likely to question this, since a dead body is not such a valuable property that anyone would steal it.

Everyone knows that even when there is no sign, life is often secretly present and may begin again in an apparently dead body. Kadambini was not dead; only the machine of her life had for some reason suddenly stopped.

When consciousness returned, she saw dense darkness on all sides. It occurred to her that she was not lying in her usual place. She called out "Sister," but no answer came from the darkness. As she sat up, terror-stricken, she remembered her deathbed, the sudden pain at her breast, the beginning of a choking sensation. Her elder sister-in-law was warming some milk for the child, when Kadambini became faint and fell on the bed, saying with a choking voice: "Sister, bring the child here. I am worried." After that everything was black, as when an inkpot is upset over an exercise book. Kadambini's memory and consciousness, all the letters of the world's book, in a moment became formless. The widow could not remember whether the child, in the sweet voice of love, called her "Auntie," as if for the last time, or not; she could not remember whether, as she left the world she knew for death's endless unknown journey, she had received a parting gift of affection, love's passage money for the silent land. At first, I fancy, she thought the lonely dark place was the House of Yama, where there is nothing to see, nothing to hear, nothing to do, only an eternal watch. But when a cold damp wind drove through the open door and she heard the croaking of frogs, she remembered vividly and in a moment all the rains of her short life, and could feel her kinship with the earth. Then came a flash of lightning, and she saw the tank, the banyan, the great plain, the far-off trees. She remembered how at full moon she had sometimes come to bathe in this tank, and how dreadful death had seemed when she saw a corpse on the burning-ground.

Her first thought was to return home. But then she reflected: "I am dead. How can I return home? That would bring disaster on them. I have left the kingdom of the living; I am my own ghost!" If this were not so, she reasoned, how could she have got out of Saradasankar's well-guarded zenana and come to this distant burning-ground at midnight? Also, if her funeral rites had not been finished, where had the men gone who should burn her? Recalling her death moment in Saradasankar's brightly lit house, she now found herself alone in a distant, deserted, dark burning-ground. Surely she was no member of earthly society! Surely she was a creature of horror, of ill omen, her own ghost!

At this thought, all the bonds were snapped which bound her to the world. She felt that she had marvelous strength, endless freedom. She could do what she liked, go where she pleased. Mad with the inspiration of this new idea, she rushed from the hut like a gust of wind and stood upon the burning-ground. All trace of shame or fear had left her.

But as she walked on and on, her feet grew tired, her body weak. The plain stretched on endlessly; here and there were paddy fields; sometimes she found herself standing knee-deep in water.

At the first glimmer of dawn she heard one or two birds cry from the bamboo clumps by the distant houses. Then terror seized her. She could not tell in what new relation she stood to the earth and to living folk. So long as she had been on the plain, on the burning-ground, covered by the dark night of *Sraban,* so long she had been fearless, a denizen of her own kingdom. By daylight the homes of men filled her with fear. Men and ghosts dread each other, for their tribes inhabit different banks of the river of death.

Her clothes were clotted in the mud; strange thoughts and walking by night had given her the aspect of a madwoman; truly, her apparition was such that folk might have been afraid of her, and children might have stoned her or run away. Luckily, the first to catch sight of her was a traveler. He came up, and said: "Mother, you look a respectable woman. Wherever are you going, alone and in this guise?"

Kadambini, unable to collect her thoughts, stared at him in silence. She could not think that she was still in touch with the world, that she looked like a respectable woman, that a traveler was asking her questions.

Again the man said: "Come, mother, I will see you home. Tell me where you live."

Kadambini thought. To return to her father-in-law's house would be absurd, and she had no father's house. Then she remembered the friend of her childhood. She had not seen Jogmaya since the days of her youth, but from time to time they had exchanged letters. Occasionally there had been quarrels between them, as was only right, since Kadambini wished to make it clear that her love for Jogmaya was unbounded, while her friend complained that Kadambini did not return a love equal to her own. They were both sure that if they once met they would be inseparable.

Kadambini said to the traveler: "I will go to Sripati's house at Nisindapur."

As he was going to Calcutta, Nisindapur, though not near, was on his way. So he took Kadambini to Sripati's house, and the friends met again. At first they did not recognize one another, but gradually each recognized the features of the other's childhood.

"What luck!" said Jogmaya. "I never dreamt that I should see you again. But how have you come here, sister? Your father-in-law's folk surely didn't let you go!"

Kadambini remained silent, and at last said: "Sister, do not ask about my father-in-law. Give me a corner and treat me as a servant: I will do your work."

"What?" cried Jogmaya. "Keep you like a servant! Why, you are my closest friend, you are my ——" and so on and so on.

Just then Sripati came in. Kadambini stared at him for some time, and then went out very slowly. She kept her head uncovered and showed not the slightest modesty or respect. Jogmaya, fearing that Sripati would be prejudiced against her friend, began an elaborate explanation. But Sripati, who readily agreed to anything Jogmaya said, cut short her story, and left his wife uneasy in her mind.

Kadambini had come, but she was not at one with her friend: death was between them. She could feel no intimacy for others so long as her existence perplexed her and consciousness remained. Kadambini would look at Jogmaya and brood. She would think: "She has her husband and her work, she lives in a world far away from mine. She shares affection and duty with the people of the world; I am an empty shadow. She is among the living; I am in eternity."

Jogmaya also was uneasy, but could not explain why. Women do not love mystery, because, though uncertainty may be transmuted into poetry, into heroism, into scholarship, it cannot be turned to account in household work. So when a woman cannot understand a thing, she either destroys and forgets it, or she shapes it anew for her own use; if she fails to deal with it in one of these ways, she loses her temper with it. The greater Kadambini's abstraction became, the more impatient was Jogmaya with her, wondering what trouble weighed upon her mind.

Then a new danger arose. Kadambini was afraid of herself; yet she could not flee from herself. Those who fear ghosts fear those who are behind them; wherever they cannot see there is fear. But Kadambini's chief terror lay in herself, for she dreaded nothing external. At the dead of night, when alone in her room, she screamed; in the evening, when she saw her shadow in the lamplight, her whole body shook. Watching her fearfulness, the rest of the house fell into a sort of terror. The servants and Jogmaya herself began to see ghosts.

One midnight Kadambini came out from her bedroom weeping, and wailed at Jogmaya's door: "Sister, sister, let me lie at your feet! Do not put me by myself!"

Jogmaya's anger was no less than her fear. She would have liked to drive Kadambini from the house that very second. The good-natured Sripati, after much effort, succeeded in quieting their guest, and put her in the next room.

Next day Sripati was unexpectedly summoned to his wife's apartments. She began to upbraid him: "You, do you call yourself a man? A woman runs away from her father-in-law and enters your house; a month passes, and you haven't hinted that she should go away, nor have I heard the slightest protest from you. I should take it as a favor if you would explain yourself. You men are all alike."

Men, as a race, have a natural partiality for womankind in general, for which women themselves hold them accountable. Although

Sripati was prepared to touch Jogmaya's body, and swear that his kind feeling toward the helpless but beautiful Kadambini was no whit greater than it should be, he could not prove it by his behavior. He thought that her father-in-law's people must have treated this forlorn widow abominably, if she could bear it no longer and was driven to take refuge with him. As she had neither father nor mother, how could he desert her? So saying, he let the matter drop, for he had no mind to distress Kadambini by asking her unpleasant questions.

His wife, then, tried other means of attack upon her sluggish lord, until at last he saw that for the sake of peace he must send word to Kadambini's father-in-law. The result of a letter, he thought, might not be satisfactory; so he resolved to go to Ranihat, and act on what he learned.

So Sripati went, and Jogmaya on her part said to Kadambini: "Friend, it hardly seems proper for you to stop here any longer. What will people say?"

Kadambini stared solemnly at Jogmaya and said: "What have I to do with people?"

Jogmaya was astounded. Then she said sharply: "If *you* have nothing to do with people, *we* have. How can we explain the detention of a woman belonging to another house?"

Kadambini said: "Where is my father-in-law's house?"

"Confound it!" thought Jogmaya. "What will the wretched woman say next?"

Very slowly Kadambini said: "What have I to do with you? Am I of the earth? You laugh, weep, love; each grips and holds his own; I merely look. You are human, I a shadow. I cannot understand why God has kept me in this world of yours."

So strange were her look and speech that Jogmaya understood something of her drift, though not all. Unable either to dismiss her or to ask her any more questions, she went away, oppressed with thought.

It was nearly ten o'clock at night when Sripati returned from Ranihat. The earth was drowned in torrents of rain. It seemed that the downpour would never stop, that the night would never end.

Jogmaya asked: "Well?"

"I've lots to say, presently."

So saying, Sripati changed his clothes and sat down to supper; then he lay down for a smoke. His mind was perplexed.

His wife stifled her curiosity for a long time; then she came to his couch and demanded: "What did you hear?"

"That you have certainly made a mistake."

Jogmaya was nettled. Women never make mistakes, or, if they do, a sensible man never mentions them; it is better to take them on his own shoulders. Jogmaya snapped: "May I be permitted to hear how?"

Sripati replied: "The woman you have taken into your house is not your Kadambini."

Hearing this, she was greatly annoyed, especially since it was her husband who said it. "What! I don't know my own friend? I must come to you to recognize her! You are clever, indeed!"

Sripati explained that there was no need to quarrel about his cleverness. He could prove what he said. There was no doubt that Jogmaya's Kadambini was dead.

Jogmaya replied: "Listen! You've certainly made some huge mistake. You've been to the wrong house, or are confused as to what you have heard. Who told you to go yourself? Write a letter, and everything will be cleared up."

Sripati was hurt by his wife's lack of faith in his executive ability; he produced all sorts of proof, without result. Midnight found them still asserting and contradicting. Although they were both agreed now that Kadambini should be got out of the house, although Sripati believed that their guest had deceived his wife all the time by a pretended acquaintance, and Jogmaya that she was a prostitute, yet in the present discussion neither would acknowledge defeat. By degrees their voices became so loud that they forgot that Kadambini was sleeping in the next room.

The one said: "We're in a nice fix! I tell you, I heard it with my own ears!" And the other answered angrily: "What do I care about that? I can see with my own eyes, surely."

At length Jogmaya said: "Very well. Tell me when Kadambini

died." She thought that if she could find a discrepancy between the day of death and the date of some letter from Kadambini, she could prove that Sripati erred.

He told her the date of Kadambini's death, and they both saw that it fell on the very day before she came to their house. Jogmaya's heart trembled, and even Sripati was not unmoved.

Just then the door flew open; a damp wind swept in and blew the lamp out. The darkness rushed after it and filled the whole house. Kadambini stood in the room. It was nearly one o'clock, and the rain was pelting outside.

Kadambini spoke: "Friend, I am your Kadambini, but I am no longer living. I am dead."

Jogmaya screamed with terror; Sripati could not speak.

"But, save in being dead, I have done you no wrong. If I have no place among the living, I have none among the dead. Oh! whither shall I go?" Crying as if to wake the sleeping Creator in the dense night of rain, she asked again: "Oh! whither shall I go?"

So saying, Kadambini left her friend fainting in the dark house, and went out into the world, seeking her own place.

It is hard to say how Kadambini reached Ranihat. At first she showed herself to no one, but spent the whole day in a ruined temple, starving. When the untimely afternoon of the rains was pitch-black, and people huddled into their houses for fear of the impending storm, then Kadambini came forth. Her heart trembled as she reached her father-in-law's house; and when, drawing a thick veil over her face, she entered, none of the doorkeepers objected, since they took her for a servant. And the rain was pouring down, and the wind howled.

The mistress, Saradasankar's wife, was playing cards with her widowed sister. A servant was in the kitchen, the sick child was sleeping in the bedroom. Kadambini, escaping everyone's notice, entered this room. I do not know why she had come to her father-in-law's house; she herself did not know; she felt only that she wanted to see her child again. She had no thought where to go next or what to do.

In the lighted room she saw the child sleeping, his fists clenched, his body wasted with fever. At sight of him, her heart became parched and thirsty. If only she could press that tortured body to her breast! Immediately the thought followed: "I do not exist. Who would see it? His mother loves company, loves gossip and cards. All the time that she left me in charge, she was herself free from anxiety, nor was she troubled about him in the least. Who will look after him now as I did?"

The child turned on his side, and cried, half asleep: "Auntie, give me water." Her darling had not yet forgotten his auntie! In a fever of excitement, she poured out some water, and taking him to her breast, she gave it him.

As long as he was asleep, the child felt no strangeness in taking water from the accustomed hand. But when Kadambini satisfied her long-starved longing and kissed him, and began rocking him asleep again, he awoke and embraced her. "Did you die, Auntie?" he asked.

"Yes, darling."

"And you have come back? Do not die again."

Before she could answer, disaster overtook her. One of the maidservants coming in with a cup of sago dropped it and fell down. At the crash the mistress left her cards and entered the room. She stood like a pillar of wood, unable to flee or speak. Seeing all this, the child, too, became terrified, and burst out weeping. "Go away, Auntie," he said, "go away!"

Now at last Kadambini understood that she had not died. The old room, the old things, the same child, the same love, all returned to their living state, without change or difference between her and them. In her friend's house she had felt that her childhood's companion was dead. In her child's room she knew that the boy's "Auntie" was not dead at all. In anguished tones she said: "Sister, why do you dread me? See, I am as you knew me."

Her sister-in-law could endure no longer and fell into a faint. Saradasankar himself entered the zenana. With folded hands, he said piteously: "Is this right? Satis is my only son. Why do you show yourself to him? Are we not your own kin? Since you went, he has wasted away daily; his fever has been incessant; day and night he cries 'Auntie, Auntie.' You have left the world; break these bonds of *maya*.* We will perform all funeral honors."

* Illusory affection binding a soul to the world.

Kadambini could bear no more. She said: "Oh, I am not dead, I am not dead. Oh, *how* can I persuade you that I am not dead? I am living, living!" She lifted a brass pot from the ground and dashed it against her forehead. The blood ran from her brow. "Look!" she cried, "I am *living!*" Saradasankar stood like an image; the child screamed with fear, the two fainting women lay still.

Then Kadambini, shouting "I am not dead, I am not dead," went down the steps to the zenana well and plunged in. From the upper story Saradasankar heard the splash.

All night the rain poured; it poured next day at dawn, was pouring still at noon. By dying, Kadambini had given proof that she was not dead.

STENDHAL

Love at First Sight

ᖜ

A brief chapter from On Love, *one of the great classics on the subject.*

The thing actually exists. I have seen the charming and noble Wilhelmina, the despair of all the fashionable young men of Berlin, scoff at love and ridicule it follies. She was magnificent in her youth, her wit, her beauty, and gifts of every kind; a huge fortune, in giving her the opportunity of developing all her qualities, seemed to conspire with nature to show the world a rare example of perfect happiness granted to a person who was supremely worthy of it. She was twenty-three years old; she had already been some time at court and had declined the homage of men of the very noblest birth; her modesty and impregnable virtue were held up as an example, and even the most charming men after a time despaired of attracting her and only aspired to her friendship. One evening she went to a ball at Prince Ferdinand's and danced for ten minutes with a young captain.

From that moment [she afterward wrote to a friend] he was master of my heart and of myself, to such an extent that I should have been panic-stricken about it if the joy of feasting my eyes on Herman had left me time to think of anything else. My only thought was to try to find out if he was paying any attention to me.

Today, the only consolation I can find for my faults is to nurse the illusion that some superior power bereft me of my personality and of my reason. I can think of no words with which to describe in any way approaching reality, the degree of confusion into which the mere sight of him threw my whole being. I blush with shame when I think of the haste and violence with which I was drawn toward him. If his first words when at last he spoke to me, had been "Do you adore me?" I really believe that I should have lacked the strength not to reply "Yes." I never dreamt that the effects of an emotion could be at once so sudden and so unforeseen. So much so that for a moment I thought I had been drugged.

Unfortunately, my dear friend, you and the rest of the world know how much I loved Herman: well, he was so dear to me after a quarter of an hour that he has never been able to become dearer to me since. I saw all his faults, but I was prepared to forgive him them all, if only he would love me.

Shortly after I had danced with him the king left; Herman, who was in attendance, was compelled to accompany him. With his departure everything in nature disappeared for me. It would be useless for me to try to depict to you the terrible boredom which seemed to come over me as soon as I no longer saw him. It was only equaled by the intensity with which I longed to be alone with myself.

At last I was able to leave. As soon as I had double locked myself into my room I tried to master my passion. I imagined that I had succeeded. Ah! my dear friend, how dearly that evening and during the days that followed did I pay for the pleasure of being able to preen myself on my virtue!

The foregoing passage is an exact account of an incident which was the talk of the day, for at the end of a month or two poor Wilhelmina was unhappy enough for her feelings to be revealed. Such was the beginning of that long series of misfortunes which ended in her dying so young and in so tragic a manner, poisoned either by herself or by her lover. The only thing that we ourselves could see in this young captain was that he danced very well; he was full of high spirits and even more self-assurance, had a pleasant face and liked the society of strumpets; moreover, he was barely of noble birth, very poor, and did not go to court.

It is not sufficient for a woman not to be diffident, she must be tired of being diffident, and she must have become, as it were, impatient of facing the accidents of life courageously. Her mind is, unknown to her, weary of living without love; she is convinced in spite of herself by the example of other women; having surmounted all the anxieties of life she is discontented with the dreary joys of her own pride; and she has in consequence, without realizing it, set up an ideal for herself. One day she meets a man who closely resembles this ideal, crystallization recognizes an object for its action by the turmoil it inspires, and consecrates forever to the master of her destiny all that she has been dreaming of for so long.

Women who are subject to such misfortunes have too much nobility of mind to love other than passionately. They would be saved if they could only lower themselves to intrigue.

As love at first sight arises from a latent lassitude with what the catechism calls virtue, and from the tedium caused by uniform perfection, I should imagine that it must be inspired most often by dissolute people. I doubt very much if a Catonian bearing has ever inspired love at first sight.

A woman whom unhappiness has made distrustful is not susceptible to this upheaval of the soul.

Nothing is so conducive to love at first sight as praise given beforehand by women to the person who is destined to be the object of it.

One of the most ludicrous sources of love affairs is spurious love at first sight. A woman who is bored but not very sensitive imagines for a whole evening that she has fallen in love for the rest of her life. She is proud of having at last experienced one of those great upheavals of the soul for which she has always longed in her imagination. The next day, she does not know where to hide herself and still more how to avoid the wretched object she adored the day before.

Clever men know how to recognize, that is to say, to take advantage of this kind of love at first sight.

There is also purely sensual love at first sight. The other day we saw the prettiest and most wanton woman in Berlin blush suddenly as we sat with her in her carriage. The handsome Lieutenant Findorff had just passed by. She became absentminded and uneasy. That evening at the theatre she admitted to me that she was distracted and light-headed and could think of nothing but of Findorff, whom she had never met. Had she dared, she told me, she would have sent for him: her pretty features bore all the signs of the most violent passion. The next day it was the same; at the end of three days, Findorff having proved a nincompoop, she thought no more of him. A month later she could not bear him.

PHILIP GUEDALLA

Mary Anne Disraeli

ᏸ᎙

"Dizzy married me for my money, but if he had the chance again he would marry me for love."

But I knaw'd a Quaäker feller as often 'as towd ma this: "Doänt thou *marry for munny, but goä wheer munny is!*"
NORTHERN FARMER—NEW STYLE.

Whispering from its towers the last enchantments of baroque (or is it Chinese Chippendale?), the career of Benjamin Disraeli stands like a fantastic summerhouse in the trim garden of Victorian England, casting the oddest shadows on those neatly graveled walks. One sees it always as an annex, as an outbuilding, as something separate from the grave outline of the main edifice and in a widely different style. Sometimes, indeed, it almost seems to be a folly, one of those oddities of architecture that never find a second tenant but survive, wistful memorials of a vanished eccentricity, appealing faintly by the tortured outline and their unlikely ornament. No, the best image is a summerhouse; for one can mix more styles in summerhouses. So there it stands in the clear light of eighty years ago—the strange career of a young Jew who, articled to a solicitor, wrote novels, yet lived a stranger novel than he ever wrote. For the Byronic youth lived to be a Victorian prime minister, and "his Corinthian style" (as he wrote of someone else's), "in which the maenad of Mr. Burke was habited in the last mode of Almack's," survived to write state papers. Life was indeed a novel—almost a novelette; and he ornamented it at every corner with romance—with chibouques and scimitars, with somber broodings on the Mount of Olives, with the oddest politics, with dreams of an aristocracy restored and a church resurgent, with peacocks screaming under his windows on the parterres of Hughenden, with Palmerstonian *coups de théâtre* that sent British battleships to Besika Bay and Sikh infantry to Malta, with a demure flirtation with his unprepossessing sovereign, with an earldom, with peace, with honor, with the Crown regilded, with the Garter. It was all a little like some rococo landscape-gardener's pagoda, hung at every corner with bells and Chinese lanterns, but breaking out occasionally in Gothic ornament; Greek pediments appeared in unexpected places, and horseshoe arches hinted at the Alhambra.

But which of all the decorations of his strange career was stranger than his wife who, voluble and odd, caught something of his eccentricity in clothing, and startled his colleagues with her sudden speeches, until the most sedate of them considered having their leader's wife to stay in order to "complete the astonishment of our neighbors"? And yet she mothered him for thirty years, till he could write of her that "there was no care which she could not mitigate and no difficulty which she could not face," and died, a viscountess of his creation, at eighty. As the impassive figure by her side progressed indomitably toward the chilly summits of public life, she babbled gaily on. Lady Beaconsfield may surely be counted a bell on that queer pagoda, which its architect had hung with care and mourned when it fell silent. So she smiled up at Dizzy and Dizzy smiled down at her, as they grew old together. But who can tell what she made of it, or he of her?

She was not beautiful; but she was bright. Even the dark young gentleman they met at Bulwer's admitted as much. Did he not write off a full account of his encounter with "a pretty little woman, a flirt, and a rattle"? It was surprising that he remembered her at all, because the evening had been crowded. There were so many peers for him to talk to. To say nothing of "L. E. L.," the Muse of Brompton (on really met everyone at Bulwer's in 1832). Besides, he had to watch his moment for a word with Tom Moore, who was extremely civil and showed signs of having read his latest novel. So it was wonderful that he remembered. But then he always had a memory for pretty little women to whom he was presented "by particular desire." He made his bow; she shook her ringlets at him and confessed that she "liked silent, melancholy men." He might, by way of repartee, have shaken his. For those were the days when his distinguished pallor was set off by a generous *coiffure* of gleaming curls that almost reached his shoulders, and he was a little apt to startle evening parties with a velvet coat, lace ruffles, and a spirited waistcoat in delicious conflict with a pair of purple trousers striped with gold. She made her arch avowal. But he only answered, in his dreadfully sarcastic manner, that he "had no doubt of it." Her volubility, it seemed, had scarcely ruffled his Byronic gloom. Still, he remembered it.

Her feminine fluency impressed him at their first meeting; and he was not easily impressed. She was a sailor's daughter, married to a man of means who sat for Maidstone in the House of Commons. He was a strange young man with enigmatic airs, two novels to his credit, and an unholy taste for the society of his betters. He knew all that could be learnt of life in his father's library, a kindergarten and two private schools, a journey up the Rhine, a little unsuccessful speculation, and a grand tour in the East. Like his *beau idéal* in fiction, he had seen through everything—"On all subjects his mind seemed to be instructed, and his opinions formed. He flung out a result in a few words; he solved with a phrase some deep problem that men muse over for years." For he was nearly twenty-eight. But she (if biography must be unchivalrous) was forty. Yet her volubility stayed in his memory. When he tried to describe it to his sister, words failed him. Indeed, her power of rapid and continuous speech was very like a force of nature; for it had something of the flow, all the continuity, and more than all the sparkle of Niagara.

Besides, she had a husband in the House of Commons; and the young writer's fancy was beginning to stray in the direction of politics. True, his political convictions were slightly lacking in precision. Had he not written gaily, "Am I a Whig or a Tory? I forget. As for the Tories, I admire antiquity, particularly a ruin; even the ruins of the Temple of Intolerance have a charm. I think I am a Tory. But then the Whigs give such good dinners, and are the most amusing. I think I am a Whig; but then the Tories are so moral, and morality is my forte; I must be a Tory. But the Whigs dress so much better; and an ill-dressed party, like an ill-dressed man, must be wrong. Yes! I am a decided Whig. And yet . . ." there were obvious attractions in the *entrée* to a political house, even though his host was a Tory member and the dinner parties were sometimes a little dull. Besides, his lady sparkled endlessly and liked silent, melancholy men. They overlooked the park, and he was soon lunching there to see a review. He met Joseph Bonaparte as well, and houses where one could encounter ex-kings of Spain were not to be despised. So his frilled shirts, Byronic collars, and embroidered waistcoats were seen in Mrs. Wyndham Lewis' drawing room in the gay years when he was poet, novelist, and politician by turns. His epic poem failed; he lost several elections; but he was mounting in the scale. Was he not taken up by Lady Blessington and the incomparable d'Orsay? The dandies liked him; Mrs. Norton took him to the play; even the Tories melted. For Lord Lyndhurst seemed to fancy his politics; the duke was credibly reported to have called him manly; and he was positively elected to the Carlton. He was a Tory now, though of slightly nebulous principles, wrote slashing articles for them, and was generally expected to come into Parliament. So no one was surprised when the Whips sent him down to fight the second seat at Maidstone.

The sitting member was the husband of his talkative acquaintance, and they drove down together. The crowd before the hustings showed an unpleasant tendency to greet the new candidate with cheerful cries of "Old clo' " as well as with allusions (of an unexpected literary character) to "Shylock." But the combination was successful; a solitary Whig was routed; and young Disraeli drove back to London as an elected member of the first Parliament of Queen Victoria. The

Wyndham Lewises had brought him in—for the local prestige of the sitting member had been of inestimable electioneering value to a strange candidate—and Mrs. Lewis would have been less than human if she had not gloried in the achievement. But she was never less than human—sometimes, indeed, a little more; and now she wrote with unaccustomed solemnity to a relation,

Mark what I say—mark what I prophesy: Mr. Disraeli will in a very few years be one of the greatest men of his day. His great talents, backed by his friends Lord Lyndhurst and Lord Chandos, with Wyndham's power to keep him in Parliament, will insure his success. They call him my Parliamentary *protégé*.

For her silent, melancholy man was launched and, better still, was launched under her colors.

There was a pleasant interlude, in which they went to stay with his bookish father "among our beechen groves" at Bradenham, admired the dogs, the folios, the adoring sister, and the younger brothers; and once more a relative of Mrs. Lewis received the news that "Our political pet, the eldest, commonly called Dizzy, you will see a great deal of; you know Wyndham brought him in for Maidstone with himself." For it was pleasing to make careers for dark young men with melancholy manners, and more pleasing still to learn from them how "dull and *triste*" it was after she left their homes, with dutiful messages that "all unite here in love an affection and compliments to you and Wyndham" and the shy addition, "I send my quota." She was at Bradenham again a few months later and learned once more on her departure how greatly she was missed and how flat and dull she had left her hosts—"almost as dull and dispirited as you think me." But life was a little dull for her that winter. Her husband was not well; and the very day before his youthful colleague made a maiden speech of some celebrity, he died; and Mrs. Lewis was a widow.

She was, to be ungallant, a widow of forty-five with a bright eye, a restless tongue, and an abundance of dark curls. At first bereavement overwhelmed her; for the shock had been extremely sudden. Her young friend, assiduous in consolation, was among the first callers at the darkened house; and he was soon writing to her in a mood of gentle reminiscence about political engagements at "Maidstone—that Maidstone where we have been so happy!" His tone, in her early weeks of widowhood, was grave and friendly. He proffered advice; he multiplied assurances of a warm place for her in the affections of his family circle; he wrote gay chronicles of life in London to solace her exile; he assured her with a new note of devotion that "the severe afflictions which you have undergone, and the excellent, and to me unexpected qualities with which you have met them, the talent, firmness and sweet temper, will always make me your faithful friend," and generally caught the guardian's tone in a manner that was highly creditable to a young gentleman of thirty-three comporting himself as an old family friend. The role was self-allotted, and young Disraeli became the sympathetic *raisonneur* of Mrs. Wyndham Lewis' comedy. For her silent, melancholy man was growing up.

There was a gradual alteration in the tone of his communications. His letters, which had been subscribed in March "God bless you, dear friend. D.," progressed in April to "Ever your affectionate friend, D." But before May was out, her youthful correspondent was "Your affectionate D." Slightly cheered by these endearments, her drooping spirits rose so far as to make him a little gift of one of those elaborate (and occasionally disastrous) watch chains, of which he was particularly fond. His acknowledgment was almost lover-like—"I assure you that with unaffected delight I felt that for the first time in public I wore your *chains*. I hope you are not ashamed of your slave. . . . Farewell! I am happy if you are." A note of romance seemed to be creeping into the more austere tone of her youthful guardian. June went by, and the young queen was crowned. But even the joys of pageantry failed to distract him; and in July he scrawled a note to her among the glasses on the table of a coaching inn to acquaint her that "you have not been the whole day a moment absent from my thoughts," followed a morning later by the more ardent line, "Let me avail myself of this moment, which I seize in a room full of bustle and chatter, to tell you how much I love you." For it is plain from all the signs that month that he had offered marriage.

His views on marriage were, perhaps, slightly less romantic than his opinions upon other subjects. It was not many years since he had written to his sister:

By the bye, would you like Lady Z—— for a sister-in-law, very clever, £25,000 and domestic? As for "love," all my friends who married for love and beauty either beat their wives or live apart from them. This is literally the case. I may commit many follies in life, but I never intend to marry for "love," which I am sure is a guarantee of infelicity.

That page from an old letter may be a momentary pose, an airy fling, a young man's facile and all-knowing cynicism, or just a clever aside escaped from an unwritten novel and dashed off to impress a round-eyed sister in the country. But the long record of Disraeli's friendships with women scarcely marks him as one of the world's lovers. For his last novel was a sustained paean in praise of female friends, regarded solely from the point of view of their utility to rising young men; his first (and by far his strongest) feminine attachment was to his sister; and the ladies whom he distinguished with his friendship were, with one shadowy exception, advanced in years and almost uniformly unattractive. Indeed, the amorous episodes in his novels were of the wildest unreality. For romance in her most ardent forms seemed somehow to elude the incurable romantic.

Romance and courtesy alike dictated his first attentions to his late colleague's widow. It was delicious to assume protective airs, to wipe away her tears, to lean in manly attitudes above a drooping figure posed in graceful proximity to an urn. Besides, she was distinctly eligible. His family was always pressing him to marry, to secure his fortunes, to insure a line of squires for Bradenham; and what more promising *parti* than a vivacious lady with an income and windows overlooking the park? So he abandoned himself to romance. His predecessor died in March; and in July Disraeli offered marriage. His divinity was pardonably coy. For bereavement was something of a duty in 1838; and she required a year in which to wear her weeds and study Mr. Lewis' remarkable successor. His passion rose to heights that autumn. Writing her name "in large characters" on a sheet of paper, he placed it before his desk and, under this inspiration, essayed a tragedy in verse. The inspiration failed. Her name was Mary Anne: the tragedy was far from good. His ecstasies increased, as she prescribed maternally for his passing ailments. But though the new year opened on a lover's frenzy, his pride began to suffer from the long delay. The insistent wooer pleaded; but his goddess was still exasperatingly coy. She played him—sometimes delicately, sometimes with a less felicitous touch. Once her fatal garrulity so far overcame her as to permit an unforgivable allusion to the material advantages of marrying her—she mentioned money. Her lover's pride was touched; he towered into indignation and was desired to leave the house—that eligible house which overlooked the park. That night he poured out all his bitterness on paper. Money? Yes, he had first thought of her for her money, "influenced by no romantic feelings." But even her money was a snare—"much less than I, or the world, imagined . . . as far as I was concerned, a fortune which could not benefit me in the slightest degree; it was merely a jointure not greater than your station required; enough to maintain your establishment and gratify your private tastes." So he had loved her for herself, only to be rewarded by base suspicions of unworthy motives. Profoundly wounded by the imputation, he renounced her in a tempest of romantic eloquence: "Triumph—I seek not to conceal my state . . . my victim head . . . the scoff and jest of that world, to gain whose admiration has been the effort of my life." He closed upon a slightly unchivalrous note—"For a few years you may flutter in some frivolous circle. But the time will come . . ." It was exactly what he had said to the House of Commons, when it, too, refused to hear him—his invariable threat. Less obdurate, his goddess melted instantly, begged him to come to her, denied her imputations, pleaded the embarrassments of her widowhood which imposed delays upon their happiness—"I am devoted to you." She was indeed. The idyll was resumed; and when the House rose, they married at St. George's, Hanover Square, a bride of forty-seven kneeling at that modish altar beside a bridegroom of thirty-four. Yet who could say which of them was the elder?

The overture was odd enough; but a still odder piece ensued. For their melody endured more than thirty years, and she lived to see him

prime minister, he to make her a viscountess. In a Plutarchian moment
she once contrasted them:

Very calm.	Very effervescent.
He is a genius.	She is a dunce.
His whole soul is devoted to politics and ambition.	She has no ambition and hates politics.

She wronged herself. For the long remnant of her days was devoted
to his politics and his ambition, and he remained (as he had been in
the beginning) her "political pet."

They were the oddest couple. The world observed a husband who
distilled his utterance in measured oracles and was gravely attentive
to his babbling partner, while she rioted in a glorious excess of
speech, which varied from a gay confession that she never knew
whether the Greeks came after or before the Romans, or simple *gaffes*
in the spirit (though not quite the idiom) of Mrs. Malaprop, or still
wilder expositions in a manner all her own of the inferiority of Greek
sculpture to her "Dizzy in his bath." Startling to the ear, she was
almost equally bizarre to the eye; for her style of dress appeared to
veer uncertainly between the ship in full sail and the Burmese idol.
This lively, lovable eccentric informed the world with cheerful candor
that "Dizzy married me for my money, but if he had the chance
again he would marry me for love." The world was skeptical. But
then the world was unaware of how she mothered him; it never heard
who supplied his medicines and cut his hair; it knew nothing of little
dinners eaten off two pairs of knees in a waiting brougham between
division bells in Palace Yard; it never stood outside a lighted house
that overlooked the park to watch a carriage drive up after midnight
and release a hungry politician to polish off a bottle and a bird under
a pair of eyes that had waited up for him. It knew so little of her
immense devotion. But her husband knew; and his long memory was
capable of inexhaustible gratitude.

At first she came into his world and was initiated bravely into the
mysteries of Rothschilds and Montefiores. She met the Bonaparte pre-
tender and scolded him loudly for rowing them on to a Thames mud-
bank; and when slightly solemn youths began to cultivate her husband,

she listened brightly to their endless talk about a new political party (it called itself Young England) that was to regenerate church, throne, and people, to say nothing of annoying Sir Robert Peel. They treated her with the grave courtesy reserved for the one married woman in a circle of undergraduates and sent messages of tremendous chivalry, desiring to be laid "at the little feet of Madame." She was at Deepdene playing, as someone wrote, Proserpine to her "gloomy Dis.", when he got the notion of embodying their new ideas in a trilogy of novels. Indeed, he dedicated the second installment of it "to one whose noble spirit and gentle nature ever prompt her to sympathize with the suffering; to one whose sweet voice has often encouraged, and whose taste and judgment have ever guided, its pages: the most severe of critics, but—a perfect wife!" But though she was the smiling *vivandière* of Young England, she made no other contribution. It was quite enough for her that Dizzy was to be leader. Those were her politics.

Once, at least, this principle inspired her to a disastrous initiative, when she wrote to Peel, pressing upon that frigid man her Dizzy's unanswerable claims to office. The charm failed to work. But she was a skillful partner in his electioneering; and respectful tradesmen told their Member that she was "such a gay lady, sir! You can never have a dull moment, sir!" She even managed to maintain a friendship with Mr. Gladstone through the most heated years of his rivalry with her adored champion. Yet her normal role was more passive. For she gathered his praises to fill budgets for the proud relatives at Bradenham or for the strange old woman at Torquay who took such an interest in him. It was her ear that almost caught the queen herself saying to someone, "There's Mr. Disraeli." When he went up to Oxford to be capped for his honorary degree, her eye smiled down at him from the Sheldonian gallery; and he put in his eyeglass, ranged along the line of watching ladies, found her, and kissed his hand with exquisite *sang-froid*. She was in Paris with him when they dined with the new emperor at the Tuileries; and, quite unperturbed by gold-braided chamberlains and watchful ministers and tall *Centgardes* in blue and silver, she told his lovely empress all about her imperial master's incompetence in rowing-boats. She even followed him to Windsor, whose grim portals were rarely opened to ministers' wives;

and she was positively honored with a place at the Prince of Wales's wedding named by Majesty herself.

So as her political pet mounted the long ascent, she mounted with him. But her work was done behind the shifting scenes of that astonishing pageant. For she was his unfailing nurse. It was years since she had prescribed the drastic remedies of cayenne and stout for his youthful ailments; but a middle-aged Chancellor of the Exchequer could still attribute his final skirmish in defense of a falling Tory government "to your getting up so often, and especially to the laudanum, for, though I did not sleep, it soothed my head." He was fifty-four now, and she sixty-seven. But they aged gracefully together; and once, when both of them were ill at the same time, there was a charming fusillade of little notes between the sickrooms:

You have sent me the most amusing and charming letter I ever had. It beats Horace Walpole and Mme. de Sévigné.

Grosvenor Gate has become a hospital, but a hospital with you is worth a palace with anybody else.

Your own

D.

". . . but if he had the chance again he would marry me for love." Perhaps.

A few years more, and she could share his triumph. For Dizzy was prime minister of England, and one gusty night in 1867 she stood by his side in Downing Street receiving everybody, from the Princess of Wales to Mr. Gladstone, at the great party in the new Foreign Office. There was a dreadful storm that evening, and she was very far from well. But Dizzy was prime minister, and she was seventy-six and happy. She had quite caught his tone now. When she thanked the queen for flowers, she intimated in the rich Disraelian manner that "their luster and perfume were enchanced by the condescending hand which had showered upon him all the treasures of spring." And when she redecorated the house at Hughenden, it was her taste that Gothicized that unpretending mansion into a rococo casket worthy to enclose the great romantic.

But the years were growing shorter. Soon she was nearly eighty, and even her political pet was sixty-seven. She could still lend French

novels to young guests (the guest was Harcourt, but the novel remains nameless); Disraeli's lunch basket, when he set out for Bal-
moral, was still provided with "a partridge breakfast, and a chicken
and tongue dinner; and plenty of good wine," eliciting affectionate
thanks "with a thousand embraces, my dearest, dearest wife." But
"Miladi" failed a little, and her husband walked beside her carriage
on the walks of Hughenden—those walks which she had planned.
Illness kept her in town one summer, and they drove for miles together, exploring London and its startling environs with a map. Then
she saw the trees of Hughenden again, and Disraeli reported a successful "hegira from Grosvenor Gate." But she failed once more; and
he was left to stare with a tormented face at the dreadful prospect,
"if anything happens. *I am totally unable to meet the catastrophe.*" It
came, though. But her long devotion was not ended. He found a
tender line from her—". . . and now, farewell, my dear Dizzy. Do
not live alone, dearest. Some one I earnestly hope you may find as
attached to you as your own devoted MARY ANNE." For he was still,
was always, her political pet.

JOHN GALSWORTHY

The Mother Stone

❧

This story was written in 1914. Makes you think, doesn't it?

It was after dinner, and five elderly Englishmen were discussing the
causes of the war.

"Well," said Travers, a big, fresh-colored graybeard, with little
twinkling eyes and very slow speech, "you gentlemen know more
about it than I do, but I bet you I can lay my finger on the cause
of the war at any minute."

There was an instant clamor of jeering. But a man called Askew, who knew Travers well, laughed and said: "Come, let's have it!" Travers turned those twinkling little eyes of his slowly round the circle, and with heavy, hesitating modesty began:

"Well, Mr. Askew, it was in '67 or '68 that this happened to a great big feller of my acquaintance named Ray—one of those fellers, you know, that are always on the lookout to make their fortunes and never do. This Ray was coming back south one day after a huntin' trip he'd been in what's now called Bechuanaland, and he was in a pretty bad way when he walked one evenin' into the camp of one of those wanderin' Boers. That class of Boer has disappeared now. They had no farms of their own, but just moved on with their stock and their boys; and when they came to good pasture they'd outspan and stay there till they'd cleared it out—and then trek on again. Well, this old Boer told Ray to come right in and take a meal; and heaven knows what it was made of, for those old Boers they'd eat the devil himself without onion sauce, and relish him. After the meal the old Boer and Ray sat smokin' and yarnin' in the door of the tent, because in those days these wanderin' Boers used tents. Right close by in the front the children were playin' in the dust, a game like marbles with three or four round stones, and they'd pitch 'em up to another stone they called the Moer-Klip, or Mother Stone—one, two, and pick up; two, three, and pick up—you know the game of marbles. Well, the sun was settin', and presently Ray noticed this Moer-Klip that they were pitchin' 'em up to shinin'; and he looked at it, and he said to the old Boer: 'What's that stone the children are playin' with?' And the old Boer looked at him and looked at the stone, and said: 'It's just a stone,' and went on smokin'.

"Well, Ray went down on his knees and picked up the stone and weighed it in his hand. About the size of a hazelnut it was and looked—well, it looked like a piece of alum; but the more he looked at it the more he thought: 'By Jove, I believe it's a diamond!'

"So he said to the old Boer: 'Where did the children get this stone?' And the old Boer said: 'Oh! the shepherd picked it up somewhere.' And Ray said: '*Where* did he pick it up?' And the old Boer waved his hand, and said: 'Over the kopje, there, beyond the river. How should I know, brother?—a stone is a stone!' So Ray said: 'You let me take this stone away with me.' And the old Boer went on smokin', and he said: 'One stone's the same as another. Take it, brother.' And Ray said: 'If it's what I think, I'll give you half the price I get for it.'

"The old Boer smiled and said: 'That's all right, brother; take it, take it!'

"The next morning Ray left this old Boer, and, when he was going, he said to him: 'Well,' he said, 'I believe this is a valuable stone!' And the old Boer smiled because he knew one stone was the same as another.

"The first place Ray came to was C——, and he went to the hotel; and in the evenin' he began talkin' about the stone, and they all laughed at him, because in those days nobody had heard of diamonds in South Africa. So presently he lost his temper and pulled out the stone and showed it around; but nobody thought it was a diamond, and they all laughed at him the more. Then one of the fellers said: 'If it's a diamond it ought to cut glass.'

"Ray took the stone, and, by Jove! he cut his name on the window, and there it is—I've seen it—on the bar window of that hotel. Well, next day, you bet, he traveled straight back to where the old Boer told him the shepherd had picked up the stone, and he went to a native chief called Jointje, and said to him: 'Jointje,' he said, 'I go a journey. While I go, you go about and send all your "boys" about, and look for all the stones that shine like this one; and when I come back, if you find me plenty, I give you gun.' And Jointje said: 'That all right, boss.'

"And Ray went down to Cape Town and took the stone to a jeweler, and the jeweler told him it was a diamond of about thirty or forty carats, and gave him five hundred pound for it. So he bought a wagon and a span of oxen to give to the old Boer, and went back to Jointje. The niggers had collected skinfuls of stones of all kinds, and out of all the skinfuls Ray found three or four diamonds. So he went to work and got another feller to back him, and between them they made the government move. The rush began, and they found that place near Kimberley; and after that they found De Beers, and after that Kimberley itself."

Travers stopped and looked around him.

"Ray made his fortune, I suppose?"

"No, Mr. Askew; the unfortunate feller made next to nothin'. He was one of those fellers that never do any good for themselves."

"But what has all this to do with the war?"

Again Travers looked around, and more slowly than ever said: "Without that game of marbles, would there have been a Moer-Klip—without the Moer-Klip, would there have been a Kimberley —without Kimberley, would there have been a Rhodes—without a Rhodes would there have been a raid—without a raid, would the Boers have started armin'—if the Boers hadn't armed, would there have been a Transvaal war? And if there hadn't been the Transvaal war, would there have been the incident of those two German ships we held up, and all the general feelin' in Germany that gave the Kaiser the chance to start his navy program in 1900? And if the Germans hadn't built their navy, would their heads have swelled till they challenged the world, and should we have had this war?"

He slowly drew a hand from his pocket and put it on the table. On the little finger was blazing an enormous diamond.

"My father," he said, "bought it of the jeweler."

The Mother Stone glittered and glowed, and the five Englishmen fixed their eyes on it in silence. Some of them had been in the Boer War, and three of them had sons in this.

At last one of them said: "Well, that's seeing God in a dewdrop with a vengeance. What about the old Boer?"

Travers' little eyes twinkled.

"Well," he said, "Ray told me the old feller just looked at him as if he thought he'd done a damn silly thing to give him a wagon; and he nodded his old head and said, laughin' in his beard: 'Wish you good luck, brother, with your stone.' You couldn't humbug that old Boer; he knew one stone was the same as another."

WILLIAM JAMES

Müller's Prayers

ε∾

In The Varieties of Religious Experience, *James calls this an example of "primitive religious thought." Maybe so.*

As a concrete example of an extreme sort, of the way in which the prayerful life may still be led, let me take a case with which most of you must be acquainted, that of George Müller of Bristol, who died in 1898. Müller's prayers were of the crassest petitional order. Early in life he resolved on taking certain Bible promises in literal sincerity, and on letting himself be fed not by his own worldly foresight but by the Lord's hand. He had an extraordinarily active and successful career, among the fruits of which were the distribution of over 2 million copies of the Scripture text, in different languages; the equipment of several hundred missionaries; the circulation of more than 111 million of scriptural books, pamphlets, and tracts; the building of five large orphanages, and the keeping and educating of thousands of orphans; finally, the establishment of schools in which over 120,000 youthful and adult pupils were taught. In the course of this work Mr. Müller received and administered nearly a million and a half of pounds sterling, and traveled over 200,000 miles of sea and land. During the sixty-eight years of his ministry, he never owned any property except his clothes and furniture, and cash in hand; and he left, at the age of eighty-six, an estate worth only 160 pounds.

His method was to let his general wants be publicly known, but not to acquaint other people with the details of his temporary necessities. For the relief of the latter, he prayed directly to the Lord, believing that sooner or later prayers are always answered if one have trust enough. "When I lose such a thing as a key," he writes, "I ask the Lord to direct me to it, and I look for an answer to my prayer; when a person with whom I have made an appointment does not come, according to the fixed time, and I begin to be inconvenienced by it, I ask the Lord to be pleased to hasten him to me, and I look for an answer; when I do not understand a passage of the Word of God, I lift up my heart to the Lord that he would be pleased by his Holy Spirit to instruct me, and I expect to be taught, though I do not fix the time when, and the manner how it should be; when I am going to minister in the Word, I seek help from the Lord, and . . . am not cast down, but of good cheer because I look for his assistance."

Müller's custom was to never run up bills, not even for a week. "As the Lord deals out to us by the day, . . . the week's payment might become due and we have no money to meet it; and thus those with whom we deal might be inconvenienced by us, and we be found acting against the commandment of the Lord: 'Owe no man anything.' From this day and henceforward whilst the Lord gives to us our supplies by the day, we purpose to pay at once for every article as it is purchased, and never to buy anything except we can pay for it at once, however much it may seem to be needed, and however much those with whom we deal may wish to be paid only by the week."

The articles needed of which Müller speaks were the food, fuel, etc., of his orphanages. Somehow, near as they often came to going without a meal, they hardly ever seem actually to have done so. "Greater and more manifest nearness of the Lord's presence I have never had than when after breakfast there were no means for dinner for more than a hundred persons; or when after dinner there were no means for the tea, and yet the Lord provided the tea; and all this without one single human being having been informed about our need. . . . Through Grace my mind is so fully assured of the faithfulness of the Lord, that in the midst of the greatest need, I am enabled in peace to go about my other work. Indeed, did not the Lord give me this, which is the result of trusting in him, I should scarcely be able to work at all; for it is now comparatively a rare thing that a day comes when I am not in need for one or another part of the work."

In building his orphanages simply by prayer and faith, Müller affirms that his prime motive was "to have something to point to as a visible proof that our God and Father is the same faithful God that he ever was,—as willing as ever to prove himself the living God in our day as formerly, to all that put their trust in him." For this reason he refused to borrow money for any of his enterprises. "How does it work when we thus anticipate God by going our own way? We certainly weaken faith instead of increasing it; and each time we work thus a deliverance of our own we find it more and more difficult to trust in God, till at last we give way entirely to our natural fallen reason and unbelief prevails. How different if one is enabled to wait God's own time, and to look alone to him for help and deliverance! When at last help comes, after many seasons of prayer it may be, how sweet it is, and what a present recompense! Dear Christian reader, if you have never walked in this path of obedience before, do so now, and you will then know experimentally the sweetness of the joy which results from it."

When the supplies came in but slowly, Müller always considered that this was for the trial of his faith and patience. When his faith and patience had been sufficiently tried, the Lord would send more means. "And thus it has proved,"—I quote from his diary,—"for today was given me the sum of 2,050 pounds, of which 2,000 are for the building fund [of a certain house], and 50 for present necessities. It is impossible to describe my joy in God when I received this donation. I was neither excited nor surprised; for I *look out* for answers to my prayers. I *believe that God hears me.* Yet my heart was so full of joy that I could only *sit* before God, and admire him, like David in 2 Samuel vii. At last I cast myself flat down upon my face and burst forth in thanksgiving to God and in surrendering my heart afresh to him for his blessed service."

George Müller's is a case extreme in every respect, and in no respect more so than in the extraordinary narrowness of the man's intellectual horizon. His God was, as he often said, his business partner. He seems to have been for Müller little more than a sort of supernatural clergyman interested in the congregation of trades-men and others in Bristol who were his saints, and in the orphanages and other enterprises, but unpossessed of any of those vaster and wilder and more ideal attributes with which the human imagination elsewhere has invested him. Müller, in short, was absolutely un-philosophical. His intensely private and practical conception of his relations with the Deity continued the traditions of the most primi-tive human thought. When we compare a mind like his with such a mind as, for example, Emerson's or Phillips Brooks's, we see the range which the religious consciousness covers.

There is an immense literature relating to answers to petitional prayer. The evangelical journals are filled with such answers, and books are devoted to the subject, but for us Müller's case will suffice.

ÉMILE COUÉ

Observations on What Autosuggestion Can Do

₰

Émile Coué (1857-1926) got famous with the formula "Day by day, in every way, I am getting better and better," which he taught his patients to repeat twice a day twenty times.

Young B—— thirteen years old, enters the hospital in January 1912. He has a very serious heart complaint characterized by a peculiarity in the respiration; he has such difficulty in breathing that he can only take very slow and short steps. The doctor who attends him, one of our best practitioners, predicts a rapid and fatal issue. The invalid leaves the hospital in February, *no better*. A friend of his family brings him to me, and when I see him I regard him as a hopeless case, but nevertheless I make him pass through the preliminary experiments which are marvelously successful. After having made him a suggestion and advised him to do the same thing for himself, I tell him to come back in two days. When he does so I notice to my astonishment a *remarkable* improvement in his respiration and his walking. I renew the suggestion, and two days afterward, when he returns, the improvement has continued, and so it is at every visit. So rapid is the progress that he makes that, three weeks after the first visit, my little patient is able to go *on foot* with his mother to the plateau of Villers. He can breathe with ease and almost normally, he can walk without getting out of breath, and can mount the stairs, which was impossible for him before. As the improvement is steadily maintained, little B——— asks me if he can go and stay with his grandmother at Carignan. As he seems well I advise him to do so, and he goes off, but sends me news of himself from time to time. His health is becoming better and better, he has a good appetite, digests and assimilates his food well, and the feeling of oppression has entirely disappeared. Not only can he walk like everybody else, but he even runs and chases butterflies.

He returns in October, and I can hardly recognize him, for the bent and puny little fellow who had left me in May has become a tall upright boy, whose face beams with health. He has grown twelve centimeters and gained nineteen pounds in weight. Since then he has lived a perfectly normal life; he runs up and down stairs, rides a bicycle, and plays football with his comrades.

Mlle. X———, of Geneva, aged thirteen. Sore on the temple considered by several doctors as being of tubercular origin; for a year and a half it has refused to yield to the different treatments ordered. She is taken to M. Baudouin, a follower of M. Coué at Geneva, who treats her by suggestion and tells her to return in a week. When she comes back the sore has healed.

Mlle. Z———, also of Geneva. Has had the right leg drawn up for seventeen years, owing to an abscess above the knee which had had to be operated upon. She asks M. Baudouin to treat her by suggestion, and hardly has he begun when the leg can be bent and unbent in a normal manner. (There was, of course, a psychological cause in this case.)

Mme. Urbain Marie, aged fifty-five, at Maxéville. Varicose ulcer, dating from more than a year and a half. First visit in September 1915, and a second one a week later. In a fortnight the cure is complete.

Emile Chenu, ten years old, Grande-Rue, 19 (a refugee from Metz). Some unknown heart complaint with vegetations. Every night loses blood by the mouth. Comes first in July 1915, and after a few visits the loss of blood diminishes, and continues to do so until by the end of November it has ceased completely. The vegetations also seem to be no longer there, and by August 1916 there had been no relapse.

M. Hazot, aged forty-eight, living at Brin. Invalided the fifteenth of January, 1915, with *specific* chronic bronchitis, which is getting worse every day. He comes in to me in October 1915. The improvement is immediate, and has been maintained since. At the present moment, although he is not completely cured, he is very much better.

M. B——, has suffered for twenty-four years from frontal sinus, which had necessitated eleven operations! In spite of all that had been done the sinus persisted, accompanied by intolerable pains. The physical state of the patient was pitiable in the extreme; he had violent and almost continuous pain, extreme weakness; lack of appetite, could neither walk, read, nor sleep, etc. His nerves were in nearly as bad a state as his body, and in spite of the treatment of such men as Bernheim of Nancy, Dèjerine of Paris, Dubois of Bern, X—— of Strasbourg, his ill health not only continued but even grew worse every day. The patient comes to me in September 1915, on the advice of one of my other patients. From that moment he made rapid progress, and at the present time (1921) he is perfectly well. It is a real resurrection.

M. Nagengast, aged eighteen, Rue Sellier, 39. Suffering from Pott's disease. Comes to me in the beginning of 1914, having been encased for six months in a plaster corset. Comes regularly twice a week to the séances, and makes for himself the usual suggestion morning and evening. Improvement soon shows itself, and in a short time the patient is able to do without his plaster casing. I saw him again in April 1916. He was completely cured, and was carrying on his duties as postman, after having been assistant to an ambulance at Nancy, where he had stayed until it was done away with.

M. D——, at Jarville. Paralysis of the left upper eyelid. Goes to the hospital where he receives injection, as a result of which the eyelid is raised. The left eye was, however, deflected outward for more than 45 degrees, and an operation seemed to be necessary. It was at this moment that he came to me: and thanks to autosuggestion the eye went back little by little to its normal position.

Mme. L——, of Nancy. Continuous pain in the right side of the face, which had gone on for ten years. She has consulted many doctors, whose prescriptions seemed of no use, and an operation is judged to be necessary. The patient comes to me on the twenty-fifth of July, 1916, and there is an immediate improvement. In about ten days' time the pain has entirely vanished, and up to the twentieth of December there had been no recurrence.

T—— Maurice, aged eight and a half, at Nancy: club feet. A first operation cures, or nearly so, the left foot, while the right one still remains crippled. Two subsequent operations do no good. The child is brought to me for the first time in February 1915; he walks pretty well, thanks to two contrivances which hold his feet straight. The first visit is followed by an immediate improvement, and after the second the child is able to walk in ordinary boots. The improvement becomes more and more marked, and by the seventeenth of April the child is quite well. The right foot, however, is not now quite so strong as it was, owing to a sprain which he gave it in February 1916.

Mlle. X——, at Blainville. A sore on the left foot, probably of specific origin. A slight sprain has brought about a swelling of the foot, accompanied by acute pains. Different treatments have only had a negative effect, and in a little while a suppurating sore appears which seems to indicate caries of the bone. Walking becomes more and more painful and difficult in spite of the treatment. On the advice of a former patient who had been cured, she comes to me, and there is noticeable relief after the first visits. Little by little the swelling goes down, the pain becomes less intense, the suppuration lessens, and finally the sore heals over. The process has taken a few months. At present the foot is practically normal, but although the pain and swelling have entirely disappeared, the back flexion of the foot is not yet perfect, which makes the patient limp slightly.

Mme. R——, of Chavigny. Metritis dating from ten years back. Comes at the end of July 1916. Improvement is immediate, the pain and loss of blood diminish rapidly, and by the following twenty-ninth of September both have disappeared. The monthly period, which lasted from eight to ten days, is now over in four.

Mme. H——, Rue Guilbert-de-Pivérécourt, at Nancy, aged forty-nine. Suffers from a varicose ulcer dating from September 1914, which has been treated according to her doctor's advice, but without success. The lower part of the leg is enormous (the ulcer, which is as large as a two-franc piece and goes right down to the bone, is situated above the ankle). The inflammation is very intense, the suppuration copious, and the pains extremely violent. The patient comes for the first time in April 1916, and the improvement which is visible after the first treatment continues without interruption. By the eighteenth of February, 1917, the swelling has *entirely subsided,* and the pain and irritation have disappeared. The sore is still there, but it is no larger than a pea, and it is only a few millimeters in depth; it still discharges very slightly. By 1920 the cure has long been complete.

Mlle. D——, at Mirecourt, sixteen years of age. Has suffered from attacks of nerves for three years. The attacks, at first infrequent, have gradually come at closer intervals. When she comes to see me on the first of April, 1917, she has had three attacks in the preceding fortnight. Up to the eighteenth of April she did not have any at all. I may add that this young lady, from the time she began the treatment, was no longer troubled by the bad headaches from which she had suffered almost constantly.

Mme. M——, aged forty-three, Rue d'Amance, 2, Malzéville. Comes at the end of 1916 for violent pains in the head from which she has suffered all her life. After a few visits they vanish completely. Two months afterward she realized that she was also cured of a prolapse of the uterus which she had not mentioned to me, and of which she was not thinking when she made her autosuggestion. (This result is due to the words *"in every way"* contained in the formula used morning and evening.)

Mme. D——, Choisy-le-Roi. Only one general suggestion from me in July 1916, and autosuggestion on her part morning and evening. In October of the same year this lady tells me that she is cured of a prolapse of the uterus from which she had suffered for more than twenty years. Up to April 1920 the cure is still holding good. (Same remark as in the preceding case.)

Mme. Jousselin, aged sixty, Rue des Dominicains, 6. Comes on the twentieth of July, 1917, for a violent pain in the right leg, accompanied by considerable swelling of the whole limb. She can only drag herself along with groans, but after the séance, to her great astonishment, she can walk *normally* without feeling the least pain. When she comes back four days afterward, she has had no return of the pain and the swelling has subsided. This patient tells me that since she has attended the séances she has also been cured of white discharges, and of enteritis from which she had long suffered. (Same remark as above.) In November the cure is still holding good.

Mlle. G. L——, aged fifteen, Rue du Montet, 88. Has stammered from infancy. Comes on the twentieth of July, 1917, and the stammering ceases instantly. A month after I saw her again and she had had no recurrence.

M. Ferry (Eugène), aged sixty, Rue de la Côte, 56. For five years has suffered from rheumatic pains in the shoulders and in the left leg. Walks with difficulty leaning on a stick, and cannot lift the arms higher than the shoulders. Comes on the seventeenth of September, 1917. After the first séance the pains vanish completely and the patient can not only take long strides but even *run*. Still more, he can whirl both arms like a windmill. In November the cure is still holding good.

Mme. Lacour, aged sixty-three, Chemin des Sables. Pains in the face dating from more than twenty years back. All treatments have failed. An operation is advised, but the patient refuses to undergo it. She comes for the first time on July 25, 1916, and four days later the pain ceases. The cure has held good to this day.

Mme. Martin, Grande-Rue (Ville-Vieille), 105. Inflammation of the uterus of thirteen years' standing, accompanied by pains and white and red discharges. The period, which is very painful, recurs every twenty-two or twenty-three days and lasts ten to twelve days. Comes for the first time on the fifteenth of November, 1917, and returns regularly every week. There is visible improvement after the first visit, which continues rapidly until at the beginning of January 1918 the inflammation has entirely disappeared; the period comes at more regular intervals and without the slightest pain. A pain in the knee which the patient had had for thirteen years was also cured.

Mme. Castelli, aged forty-one, living at Einville (M.-et-M.). Has suffered from intermittent rheumatic pains in the right knee for thirteen years. Five years ago she had a more violent attack than usual, the leg swells as well as the knee, then the lower part of the limb atrophies, and the patient is reduced to walking very painfully with the aid of a stick or crutch. She comes for the first time on the fifth of November, 1917. She goes away *without the help of either crutch or stick.* Since then she no longer uses her crutch at all, but occasionally makes use of her stick. The pain in the knee comes back from time to time, but only very slightly.

Mme. Meder, aged fifty-two, at Einville. For six months has suffered from pain in the right knee accompanied by swelling, which makes it impossible to bend the leg. Comes for the first time on December 7, 1917. Returns on January 4, 1918, saying that she has almost ceased to suffer and that she can walk normally. After that visit of the fourth, the pain ceases entirely, and the patient walks like other people.

SAMUEL SMILES

Palissy, the Potter

ॐ

Self-Help was the first great inspirational best seller. No wonder: it's full of stories like this one.

Bernard Palissy is supposed to have been born in the south of France, in the diocese of Agen, about the year 1510. His father was probably a worker in glass, to which trade Bernard was brought up. His parents were poor people—too poor to give him the benefit of any school education. "I had no other books," said he afterward, "than heaven and earth, which are open to all." He learned, however, the art of glass painting, to which he added that of drawing, and afterward reading and writing.

When about eighteen years old, the glass trade becoming decayed, Palissy left his father's house, with his wallet on his back, and went out into the world to search whether there was any place in it for him. He first traveled toward Gascony, working at his trade where he could find employment, and occasionally occupying part of his time in land measuring. Then he traveled northward, sojourning for various periods at different places in France, Flanders, and Lower Germany.

Thus Palissy occupied about ten more years of his life, after which he married, and ceased from his wanderings, settling down to practice glass painting and land measuring at the small town of Saintes, in the Lower Charente. There children were born to him; and not only his responsibilities but his expenses increased, while, do what he could, his earnings remained too small for his needs. It was therefore necessary for him to bestir himself. Probably he felt capable of better things than drudging in an employment so precarious as glass painting; and hence he was induced to turn his attention to the kindred art of painting and enameling earthenware.

Yet on this subject he was wholly ignorant, for he had never seen earth baked before he began his operations. He had therefore every thing to learn by himself, without any helper. But he was full of hope, eager to learn, of unbounded perseverance and inexhaustible patience.

It was the sight of an elegant cup of Italian manufacture—most probably one of Luca della Robbia's make—which first set Palissy thinking about the new art. A circumstance so apparently insignificant would have produced no effect upon an ordinary mind, or even upon Palissy himself at an ordinary time; but occurring as it did when he was meditating a change of calling, he at once became inflamed with the desire of imitating it. The sight of this cup disturbed his whole existence; and the determination to discover the enamel with which it was glazed thenceforward possessed him like a passion. Had he been a single man he might have traveled into Italy in search of the secret; but he was bound to his wife and his children and could not leave them; so he remained by their side groping in the dark, in the hope of finding out the process of making and enameling earthenware.

At first he could merely guess the materials of which the enamel was composed, and he proceeded to try all manner of experiments to ascertain what they really were. He pounded all the substances which he supposed were likely to produce it. Then he bought common earthen pots, broke them into pieces, and, spreading his compounds over them, subjected them to the heat of a furnace which he erected for the purpose of baking them. His experiments failed; and the results were broken pots and a waste of fuel, drugs, time, and labor. Women do not readily sympathize with experiments whose only tangible effect is to dissipate the means of buying clothes and food for their children; and Palissy's wife, however dutiful in other respects, could not be reconciled to the purchase of more earthen pots, which seemed to her to be bought only to be broken. Yet she must needs submit; for Palissy had become thoroughly possessed by the determination to master the secret of the enamel, and would not leave it alone.

For many successive months and years Palissy pursued his experiments. The first furnace having proved a failure, he proceeded to erect another out of doors. There he burned more wood, spoiled more drugs and pots, and lost more time, until poverty stared him and his family in the face. "Thus," said he, "I fooled away several years with sorrow and sighs because I could not at all arrive at my intention." In the intervals of his experiments he occasionally worked at his former callings—painting on glass, drawing portraits, and measuring land; but his earnings from these sources were very small. At length he was no longer able to carry on his experiments in his own furnace because of the heavy cost of fuel; but he bought more potsherds, broke them up as before into three or four hundred pieces, and, covering them with chemicals, carried them to a tile-work a league and a half distant from Saintes, there to be baked in an ordinary furnace. After the operation he went to see the pieces taken out; and, to his dismay, the whole of the experiments were failures. But though disappointed, he was not yet defeated; for he determined on the very spot to "begin afresh."

His business as a land measurer called him away for a brief season from the pursuit of his experiments. In conformity with an edict of the state, it became necessary to survey the salt marshes in the neighborhood of Saintes for the purpose of levying the land tax. Palissy was employed to make this survey and prepare the requisite map. The work occupied him some time, and he was doubtless well paid for it; but no sooner was it completed than he proceeded, with redoubled zeal, to follow up his old investigations "in the track of the enamels." He began by breaking three dozen new earthen pots, the pieces of which he covered with different materials which he had compounded, and then took them to a neighboring glass furnace to be baked. The results gave him a glimmer of hope. The greater heat of the glass furnace had melted some of the compounds; but though Palissy searched diligently for the white enamel, he could find none.

For two more years he went on experimenting without any satisfactory result, until the proceeds of his survey of the salt marshes having become nearly spent, he was reduced to poverty again. But he resolved to make a last great effort; and he began by breaking

more pots than ever. More than three hundred pieces of pottery
covered with his compounds were sent to the glass furnace; and
thither he himself went to watch the results of the baking. Four
hours passed, during which he watched; and then the furnace was
opened. The material on *one* only of the three hundred pieces of
potsherd had melted, and it was taken out to cool. As it hardened,
it grew white—white and polished! The piece of potsherd was
was covered with white enamel, described by Palissy as "singularly
beautiful!" And beautiful it must no doubt have been in his eyes
after all his weary waiting. He ran home with it to his wife, feeling himself, as he expressed it, quite a new creature. But the prize
was not yet won—far from it. The partial success of this intended
last effort merely had the effect of luring him on to a succession of
further experiments and failures.

In order that he might complete the invention, which he now
believed to be at hand, he resolved to build for himself a glass
furnace near his dwelling, where he might carry on his operations
in secret. He proceeded to build the furnace with his own hands,
carrying the bricks from the brick field upon his back. He was
bricklayer, laborer, and all. From seven to eight more months passed.
At last the furnace was built and ready for use. Palissy had in the
meantime fashioned a number of vessels of clay in readiness for the
laying on of the enamel. After being subjected to a preliminary
process of baking, they were covered with the enamel compound,
and again placed in the furnace for the grand crucial experiment.
Although his means were nearly exhausted, Palissy had been for
some time accumulating a great store of fuel for the final effort,
and he thought it was enough. At last the fire was lit, and the operation proceeded. All day he sat by the furnace, feeding it with fuel.
He sat there watching and feeding all through the long night. But
the enamel did not melt. The sun rose upon his labors. His wife
brought him a portion of the scanty morning meal—for he would
not stir from the furnace, into which he continued from time to
time to heave more fuel. The second day passed, and still the
enamel did not melt. The sun set, and another night passed. The
pale, haggard, unshorn, baffled yet not beaten Palissy sat by his

furnace eagerly looking for the melting of the enamel. A third day and night passed—a fourth, a fifth, and even a sixth—yes, for six long days and nights did the unconquerable Palissy watch and toil, fighting against hope; and still the enamel would not melt.

It then occurred to him that there might be some defect in the materials for the enamel—perhaps something wanting in the flux; so he set to work to pound and compound fresh materials for a new experiment. Thus two or three more weeks passed. But how to buy more pots?—for those which he had made with his own hands for the purpose of the first experiment were by long baking irretrievably spoiled for the purposes of a second. His money was now all spent; but he could borrow. His character was still good, though his wife and the neighbors thought him foolishly wasting his means in futile experiments. Nevertheless he succeeded. He borrowed sufficient from a friend to enable him to buy more fuel and more pots, and he was again ready for a further experiment. The pots were covered with the new compound, placed in the furnace, and the fire was again lit.

It was the last and most desperate experiment of the whole. The fire blazed up; the heat became intense; but still the enamel did not melt. The fuel began to run short! How to keep up the fire? There were the garden palings: these would burn. They must be sacrificed rather than that the great experiment should fail. The garden palings were pulled up and cast into the furnace. They were burned in vain! The enamel had not yet melted. Ten minutes more heat might do it. Fuel must be had at whatever cost. There remained the household furniture and shelving. A crashing noise was heard in the house; and amidst the screams of his wife and children, who now feared Palissy's reason was giving way, the tables were seized, broken up, and heaved into the furnace. The enamel had not melted yet! There remained the shelving. Another noise of the wrenching of timber was heard within the house, and the shelves were torn down and hurled after the furniture into the fire. Wife and children then rushed from the house, and went frantically through the town, calling out that poor Palissy had gone mad, and was breaking up his very furniture for firewood!

For an entire month his shirt had not been off his back, and he was utterly worn out—wasted with toil, anxiety, watching, and want of food. He was in debt, and seemed on the verge of ruin. But he had at length mastered the secret; for the last great burst of heat had melted the enamel. The common brown household jars, when taken out of the furnace after it had become cool, were found covered with a white glaze! For this he could endure reproach, contumely, and scorn, and wait patiently for the opportunity of putting his discovery into practice as better days came around.

Palissy next hired a potter to make some earthen vessels after the designs which he furnished; while he himself proceeded to model some medallions in clay for the purpose of enameling them. But how to maintain himself and his family until the wares were made and ready for sale? Fortunately there remained one man in Saintes who still believed in the integrity, if not in the judgment, of Palissy—an innkeeper, who agreed to feed and lodge him for six months while he went on with his manufacture. As for the working potter whom he had hired, Palissy soon found that he could not pay him the stipulated wages. Having already stripped his dwelling, he could but strip himself; and he accordingly parted with some of his clothes to the potter, in part payment of the wages which he owed him.

Palissy next erected an improved furnace, but he was so unfortunate as to build part of the inside with flints. When it was heated these flints cracked and burst, and the spiculæ were scattered over the pieces of pottery, sticking to them. Though the enamel came out right, the work was irretrievably spoiled, and thus six more months' labor was lost. Persons were found willing to buy the articles at a low price, notwithstanding the injury they had sustained; but Palissy would not sell them, considering that to have done so would be to "decry and abase his honor"; and so he broke in pieces the entire batch. "Nevertheless," says he, "hope continued to inspire me, and I held on manfully; sometimes, when visitors called, I entertained them with pleasantry, while I was really sad at heart. . . . Worst of all the sufferings I had to endure were the mockeries and persecutions of those of my own household, who were so unreasonable as to expect me to execute work without the means of doing so. For years my furnaces were without any covering or protection, and while attending them I have been for nights at the mercy of the wind and the rain, without help or consolation, save it might be the wailing of cats on the one side and the howling of dogs on the other. Sometimes the tempest would beat so furiously against the furnaces that I was compelled to leave them and seek shelter within doors. Drenched by rain, and in no better plight than if I had been dragged through mire, I have gone to lie down at midnight or at daybreak, stumbling into the house without a light, and reeling from one side to another as if I had been drunken, but really weary with watching and filled with sorrow at the loss of my labor after such long toiling. But alas! my home proved no refuge; for, drenched and besmeared as I was, I found in my chamber a second persecution worse than the first, which makes me even now marvel that I was not utterly consumed by my many sorrows."

At this stage of his affairs, Palissy became melancholy and almost hopeless, and seems to have all but broken down. He wandered gloomily about the fields near Saintes, his clothes hanging in tatters and himself worn to a skeleton. In a curious passage in his writings he describes how that the calves of his legs had disappeared, and were no longer able with the help of garters to hold up his stockings, which fell about his heels when he walked. The family continued to reproach him for his recklessness, and his neighbors cried shame upon him for his obstinate folly. So he returned for a time to his former calling; and after about a year's diligent labor, during which he earned bread for his household and somewhat recovered his character among his neighbors, he again resumed his darling enterprise. But though he had already spent about ten years in the search for the enamel, it cost him nearly eight more years of experimental plodding before he perfected his invention. He gradually learned dexterity and certainty of result by experience, gathering practical knowledge out of many failures. Every mishap was a fresh lesson to him, teaching him something new about the nature of enamels, the qualities of argillaceous earths, the tempering of clays, and the construction and management of furnaces.

At last, after about sixteen years' labor, Palissy took heart and called himself potter. These sixteen years had been his term of apprenticeship to the art, during which he had wholly to teach himself, beginning at the very beginning. He was now able to sell his wares and thereby maintain his family in comfort. But he never rested satisfied with what he had accomplished. He proceeded from one step of improvement to another; always aiming at the greatest perfection possible. He studied natural objects for patterns, and with such success that the great Buffon spoke of him as "so great a naturalist as nature only can produce." His ornamental pieces are now regarded as rare gems in the cabinets of virtuosi, and sell at almost fabulous prices. The ornaments on them are for the most part accurate models from life, of wild animals, lizards, and plants, found in the fields about Saintes, and tastefully combined as ornaments into the texture of a plate or vase. When Palissy had reached the height of his art he styled himself *Ouvrier de Terre et Inventeur des Rustics Figulines*.

We have not, however, come to an end of the sufferings of Palissy, respecting which a few words remain to be said. Being a Protestant at a time when religious persecution waxed hot in the south of France, and expressing his views without fear, he was regarded as a dangerous heretic. His enemies having informed against him, his house at Saintes was entered by the officers of "justice," and his workshop was thrown open to the rabble, who entered and smashed his pottery, while he himself was hurried off by night and cast into a dungeon at Bordeaux, to wait his turn at the stake or the scaffold. He was condemned to be burned, but a powerful noble, the Constable de Montmorency, interposed to save his life—not because he had any special regard for Palissy or his religion, but because no other artist could be found capable of executing the enameled pavement for his magnificent château then in course of erection at Ecouen, about four leagues from Paris. By his influence an edict was issued appointing Palissy Inventor of Rustic Figulines to the king and to the constable, which had the effect of immediately removing him from the jurisdiction of Bordeaux. He was accordingly liberated, and returned to his home at Saintes only to find it devastated and broken up. His workshop was open to the sky, and his works lay in ruins. Shaking the dust of Saintes from his feet, he left the place never to return to it, and removed to Paris to carry on the works ordered of him by the constable and the queen mother, being lodged in the Tuileries while so occupied.

Besides carrying on the manufacture of pottery, with the aid of his two sons, Palissy, during the latter part of his life, wrote and published several books on the potter's art, with a view to the instruction of his countrymen, and in order that they might avoid the many mistakes which he himself had made. He also wrote on agriculture, on fortification, and natural history, on which latter subject he even delivered lectures to a limited number of persons. He waged war against astrology, alchemy, witchcraft, and like impostures. This stirred up against him many enemies, who pointed the finger at him as a heretic, and he was again arrested for his religion and imprisoned in the Bastille.

He was now an old man of seventy-eight, trembling on the verge of the grave, but his spirit was as brave as ever. He was threatened with death unless he recanted; but he was as obstinate in holding to his religion as he had been in hunting out the secret of the enamel. The king, Henry III, even went to see him in prison to induce him to abjure his faith. "My good man," said the king, "you have now served my mother and myself for forty-five years. We have put up with your adhering to your religion amidst fires and massacres: now I am so pressed by the Guise party, as well as by my own people, that I am constrained to leave you in the hands of your enemies, and tomorrow you will be burned unless you become converted."

"Sire," answered the unconquerable old man, "I am ready to give my life for the glory of God. You have said many times that you have pity on me; and now I have pity on you, who have pronounced the words *I am constrained!* It is not spoken like a king; it is what you, and those who constrain you, the Guisards and all your people, can never effect upon me, for I know how to die."

Palissy did indeed die shortly after, a martyr, though not at the stake. He died in the Bastille, after enduring about a year's imprisonment—there peacefully terminating a life distinguished for heroic labor, extraordinary endurance, inflexible rectitude, and the exhibition of many rare and noble virtues.

OTTO EISENSCHIML and E. B. LONG

A Pleasant Interlude

ह&

From a shad bake to Appomattox Courthouse.

When Thomas Lafayette Rosser was only twenty-eight years old, he had already been a major general in the Confederate Army for over half a year. Six foot two inches tall, he presented an imposing figure which, however, stood in sharp contrast to his exuberant spirit and the slow Texas drawl he had acquired in his boyhood days. J. E. B. Stuart, in an official report, once had called him a "bold cavalier." No one who fought under the Stars and Bars could wish for a more enviable tribute than that.

The last days of March 1865 had come, and the Confederacy was in its death throes. Lee's army was crumbling, but Rosser's youthful enthusiasm kept him from giving up hope. As he inspected the dwindling force which he had just brought from the Shenandoah Valley to the environs of Petersburg, he had a cheerful word for everyone. The next few days would bring hard fighting, but he was full of confidence. Had he been able to read the future, he would have been astounded to learn that of all southern generals he was going to be the only one to cut his way through Grant's army at Appomattox Courthouse. He would have been still more astounded to know that thirty-odd years hence he would command a brigade of northern volunteers in the Spanish-American War.

Rosser's division, shrunk to twelve hundred men and greatly fatigued after the heavy fighting it had undergone, was resting at

Stony Creek, southwest of Petersburg, when it was again ordered to the front. The iron ring which Grant had forged around Richmond and Petersburg was drawing closer and now threatened to crush the two remaining railroads over which flowed the sustenance of the army and the civilian population. How to prevent this calamity in face of an overwhelming enemy superiority, numerical and material, was a problem to which the Confederate leaders had vainly tried to find a solution.

Lee's position had indeed become desperate. So far he had met each new enemy front with one of his own, but now his lines were stretched to the breaking point. In some spots the trenches were manned by scarcely more than pickets. Grant kept harassing the defenders by constant thrusts, lest Lee pull out his troops surreptitiously some night and join General Joseph E. Johnston, who commanded the only other eastern Confederate army still in the field. Johnston was somewhere in North Carolina, and if the two leaders combined their forces, the war would go on. So far Grant had not been able to force the issue for lack of sufficient cavalry, but Philip H. Sheridan had recently arrived from the Shenandoah Valley and filled this want. Something was bound to happen soon.

Lee saw the picture clearly. He reasoned correctly that the Union armies would push westward to break the vital Southside Railroad. If that went, Petersburg and Richmond would go too. There would be left then only the railroad to Danville, over which the government and the troops must be evacuated if they were to avoid capture or starvation. To avert this danger, Lee scraped together his last reserves. Rosser was ordered to report to General George Pickett, of Gettysburg fame, who was to ward off the expected blow. Together with six thousand men on foot and Fitzhugh Lee's cavalry, the total number of this detached force was swelled to ten thousand, about one quarter of Lee's entire army. The decision to deplete the trenches by so many men was a desperate gamble. It meant that the Confederates must leave their fortifications and fight in the open, where the losses on both sides would be more equal; but there was nothing else Lee could do. If Pickett could not halt the Federal advance, all was lost. The prayers of millions were with him.

Rosser immediately set his troops in motion. He had been instructed to join Pickett at Five Forks, an important crossroad a few miles north of Dinwiddie Courthouse, between that settlement and the Southside Railroad. Since the distance he had to traverse was short, he did not hurry. On the way he had to cross the Nottoway River, and it occurred to him that he might take a few hours off and go fishing. Should he be lucky it would help conserve his meager supply of provisions; if not, he would at least spend a peaceful afternoon. Accordingly, he borrowed a seine from a neighboring farmer and set out on his foraging expedition.

The success of his short excursion surpassed all his expectations. The shad he caught were more than could be consumed before they would spoil. He and his officers feasted for a day, and what was left of the fish Rosser loaded into an ambulance. Tomorrow was another day and would bring with it renewed appetites which had to be satisfied.

When Rosser reported to Pickett he was ordered to the rear. There, two miles north of Five Forks and behind a small stream called Hatcher's Run, he was to guard the train and act as a general reserve.

Lee's uncanny ability to read Grant's mind, so successfully displayed in the campaign of the Wilderness, again proved itself. As Lee had anticipated, Sheridan began his march toward Dinwiddie Courthouse, expecting to overlap and turn the southern defense line at Petersburg. From Dinwiddie Courthouse Sheridan struck northward, to gain the Southside Railroad. Up to then he had advanced unhindered, but now he found Pickett across his path, offering not passive but active opposition. Lee, always anxious to keep the initiative, had directed Pickett to take the offensive so as to disrupt the Federal plan. On March 30 the two forces met and Sheridan was thrown back. The victors then lay down at Five Forks for a much-needed night's rest.

The next morning, March 31, General Lee in person watched the onset of his left wing and was satisfied with its early progress. He then left for his headquarters. The troops, however, could not retain their forward position. By sundown the left wing had been pushed back again to the vicinity of its starting point. The right wing under Pickett and Fitzhugh Lee had fared no better. It had come to within a few hundred yards of Dinwiddie Courthouse, then also had been forced to withdraw in the face of vastly superior forces and the concentrated fire of repeating rifles. When Lee was advised of the day's events, he expressed keen disappointment, something he rarely did, but ordered Pickett to "hold Five Forks at all hazards." The fate of Richmond depended on it, for the crossroads protected the White Oak Road and the Southside Railroad. The White Oak Road was the main artery between Five Forks and Petersburg; the Southside Railroad led to Danville, to General Johnston—and to food.

Rosser had not been engaged in the day's fighting. Mindful of his fish supply, he invited Pickett, upon the latter's return in the evening, to join him next day in a shad bake at his camp. Fitzhugh Lee, second in command, was included in the invitation. Pickett's mouth watered, but he hesitated. His position at Five Forks offered no natural advantages, as it lay in a flat, heavily wooded country and had been strengthened only perfunctorily by hastily erected breastworks. Ordinarily the situation would have called for special precautions, but the comparative ease with which Pickett had repulsed Sheridan made him overconfident. In view of his success on the day before, he did not expect to be molested for some time. Perhaps he also did some wishful thinking. At any rate, the prospect of a shad bake was too tempting to be resisted. It would be a pleasant interlude in this eternal business of killing or being killed.

The next morning Pickett sent part of his cavalry out toward Dinwiddie Courthouse. They found everything quiet. Unfortunately they did not extend their scouting to the White Oak Road on the left of their position. If they had, the day might have ended differently.

It was about one o'clock in the afternoon when Pickett and Fitzhugh Lee left Five Forks for the shad bake. Just as they were about to start out, Brigadier General Thomas T. Munford, Fitzhugh Lee's chief lieutenant, was told of a stir among the pickets to the east, on or near the White Oak Road, and so informed his commander. Fitzhugh, impatient to be off, took the matter lightly and ordered Munford to take proper measures if it meant anything more than a slight brush, which he thought unlikely. Together with Pickett he then rode to Rosser's headquarters where the promised meal awaited them.

Hardly had the two generals left when Munford discovered that what was happening to his left was more than a mere brush. His pickets were being driven in, and the White Oak Road was already swarming with Federal cavalry. Heavy groups of infantry were massing in its rear. This road had to be kept clear at all cost, or Pickett's ten thousand men would be cut off from the rest of Lee's army. The Southside Railroad, for the defense of which Lee had detached such a large body of valuable troops, would be periled.

The real cause of the disturbance had been successfully hidden from Munford's outposts. The entire Union 5th Corps, under General G. K. Warren, had arrived overnight and was stealthily executing a wide encircling movement, so wide that it was safe from enemy observation. Yet Munford began to suspect what was going on and knew that something had to be done. Five Forks could not be defended easily, and a retreat at least beyond Hatcher's Run seemed imperative, so as to re-establish contact with Lee. Munford, however, did not dare run counter to Lee's explicit order that Five Forks had to be held at all hazards. Frantically he sent messengers in all directions, trying to locate his commanding officers, who had not advised him of their destination. One of the horsemen finally discovered the generals at Rosser's camp. The three officers were calmly munching shad and made light of Munford's fears. Everything was quiet; they had heard no firing; Munford was too excitable. They refused to interrupt their meal. According to testimony given by one of them at a later hearing, they did not believe that "the enemy was in much of a hurry to find us at Five Forks."

They did not know Sheridan; that dynamic little man always was in much of a hurry. If he had not attacked sooner, it was due to the slowness with which the 5th Army Corps had to work its way through a section of the country in which, as General Horace Porter phrased it, the dust in summer was so thick that an army could not see where it moved, and the mud in winter so deep that it could not move at all. This being spring, there was no dust, but plenty of mud.

The army could move, but not much more than that.

Sheridan had conceived an excellent battle plan. Warren's infantry was to occupy White Oak Road quietly, far east of the crossroads and the enemy pickets. A sudden mass attack was then to be launched on the Confederate left flank and rear. Sheridan's dismounted cavalrymen meanwhile were to creep up in front and coordinate their assault with that of their comrades. When Sheridan found the infantry slowed up by the marshy ground, worsened by recent rains, he fumed and fretted, taking Warren to task for his tardiness and accusing him of apathy. Before the day was over, he would replace him with General Charles Griffin. The redoubtable Warren, whose quick thinking had saved Little Round Top, and with it the second day at Gettysburg, was fated to wait fourteen years before a court of inquiry would hear his side of the story.

At four o'clock every regiment was in position, and the assault hit Pickett's flank like an avalanche. Bursting forth from the woods on both sides of the Whie Oak Road, the Union phalanx hurled itself on the leaderless Confederates. Accompanying the infantry was a band on horseback which played "Nelly Bly" as gaily as at a county fair. This was one of Sheridan's favorite devices to foster the spirit of his troops. Munford's protecting cavalry screen was easily dispersed, but Warren's men found brave resistance where the trenches curved back at an angle to guard the left flank. The defenders were making a mighty good fight of it, when a new attack from another side hit them. The dismounted cavalry had silently approached and was now trying to get a foothold at their front. The gray line had to face two ways, but even that did not dishearten them. They were hardened veterans, and used to fighting against top-heavy odds. In the meantime, however, Federal forces had penetrated to their rear, too. How many more Yanks would they have to take on? Still they battled on valiantly, their backs to one another, and with the courage of desperation. But the weight of numbers told. The combined Union cavalry and infantry were beginning to climb over the ramparts. Guns gave way to bayonets, rocks, and fists. Sheridan himself appeared in the front line. Putting the spurs to his famous black horse Rienzi, he jumped over the breastwork into the midst of

the melee. Surrounded on three sides, the defenders of the angle surrendered. With its left flank crushed, the entire Confederate line became untenable and was rolled up like a scroll. Resistance ceased
shortly; in less than an hour three to four thousand prisoners were
marched off to Dinwiddie Courthouse. The number was to grow to
five thousand before the day was over. The extreme right of the line
still held; but it was only a question of minutes before it, too, dis-
solved.

The heavy firing which, without preliminaries, had begun at 4 P.M.,
acted on the three picnicking generals at Rosser's camp like an electric
shock. They suddenly realized how timely Munford's warning had
been, and that by ignoring it they had blundered disastrously. The
horror of their guilt must have struck them like a physical blow. Two
miles away their troops had been surrounded, while they were feasting.
Pickett was the first to recover. Throwing himself flat on his horse,
he plunged across the bridge over Hatcher's Run and rode the long
gantlet of a furious fusillade by Union troops, but none of the shots
found its mark. The remnants of his broken forces rallied around him,
and he led them in flight. Fitzhugh Lee and Rosser were completely
cut off and only managed to mingle with the few fugitives who
streamed confusedly across Hatcher's Run. On the banks of the little
river Rosser's reserve cavalry stood guard, successfully disputing
further pursuit.

Pickett's defeat was a disaster as unexpected as it was irreparable.
In an hour's time Lee had lost his last reserves and his hope of keeping Grant out of Richmond.

It is improbable that the mere presence of Pickett and Fitzhugh
Lee—Rosser was at his headquarters, where he should have been—
could have staved off the debacle. The Confederates fought well
enough even in the absence of their leaders. Against the overwhelming
odds with which they were confronted, military leadership, even of
the highest type, would not have availed. What Pickett and Fitzhugh
might, and undoubtedly would have done, though, was to retreat
behind Hatcher's Run regardless of orders as soon as Sheridan's
encircling plan became discernible. Both were experienced command-
ers, and if they had remained where duty had placed them, they would

hardly have let themselves be caught in a trap. Lee had issued his directions under the misapprehension that Sheridan's force could be dealt with by ten thousand men; he certainly would have rescinded his dispositions when advised that Sheridan's cavalry had been strengthened by Warren's infantry corps, although he could not have known that the enemy had at least three times his own number of troops in the field. Even had Pickett shied away from disobeying a specific order, he would have had abundant time to inform the general in chief of the changed conditions, for between Munford's first alarm and the final attack three hours had elapsed. Nor was the heartbreaking loss in men the worst consequence of Pickett's and young Lee's aberration. Still worse was their failure to notify their commander promptly of the catastrophe. By nightfall Lee had received only incomplete reports, one from a fugitive captain, the other from his nephew Fitzhugh. Both led him to believe that Pickett had suffered a slight setback. Pickett himself either could not or dared not communicate with Lee, who did not learn the full truth until the morning of April 2. Then it was brought home to him in a forceful manner.

He was sleeping at his headquarters, the Turnbull House on Edge Hill, about three miles out of Petersburg. General A. P. Hill had come over from his nearby headquarters and was resting on the floor. Longstreet, who had been recalled from the northern defenses, arrived about 4 A.M. It was still dark when Colonel Charles S. Venable of Lee's staff happened to stroll out through the gate. A rumbling of wagons driven at breakneck speed reached his ears. A few moments later, frantic teamsters rushed by, whipping up their horses and yelling that the Yankees were right behind them.

Venable immediately rushed into the house to warn Lee, then rode out with A. P. Hill to reconnoiter. Hill was never again seen alive. In the early dawn Venable became terror-stricken upon discovering that a few huts half a mile away were already in possession of Federal troops. They might have captured Lee and his staff had they been aware of their opportunity.

A short period of quiet was restored at the Turnbull House when it was found that the Federals who had occupied the huts were only vedettes. They soon disappeared, evidently having been recalled. Lee's headquarters, although no longer safe, were kept intact for the time being.

Lee now knew what had happened at Five Forks. Had he known it the night before, he undoubtedly would have ordered the immediate evacuation of Richmond. One day sooner would have made a great deal of difference. A true report of the battle at Five Forks reached him at last around ten o'clock in the forenoon, and then immediate action was inadvisable. A retrograde movement of the whole army in broad daylight would have invited a full-scale attack by Grant, and such an attack could not have been successfully resisted. The delusion that the trenches were fully manned had to be kept until nightfall.

Lee realized that Pickett's defeat meant the end. One gate in his defense wall had been smashed in, five thousand of his best infantry were gone, the bulk of his cavalry had been scattered. He hid his despair behind his usual composure, but it was no secret that, contrary to his noble and generous nature, he could not bring himself to forgive Pickett. It was said that Lee never spoke to him again as long as he lived. Perhaps he might have overlooked Pickett's delinquency, which could be partially repaired by a quick evacuation of Petersburg; but he could not forget the catastrophic consequences which followed in its wake and which he could not have foreseen at the time.

At 10:40 A.M. the Secretary of War at Richmond received this telegram:

> Headquarters, via Petersburg,
> April 2, 1865.
>
> General J. C. Breckenridge:
> I see no prospect of doing more than holding our position here till night. I am not certain that I can do that; if I can, I shall withdraw tonight north of the Appomattox. . . . Our only chance . . . of concentrating our forces is to do so near Danville Railroad, which I shall endeavor to do at once. I advise that all preparations be made for leaving Richmond tonight. I shall arrive later according to circumstances.
>
> R. E. Lee

This dispatch, which was handed to Jefferson Davis in St. Paul's Church, made him prepare for immediate flight.

The night from April 1 to April 2, plus a whole precious day, had been wasted because Pickett and Fitzhugh Lee had behaved like little boys afraid to confess that they had started a fire until it was too late to extinguish it.

Soon after the morning dispatch to Richmond had been sent off, the Turnbull House was given up, for it had become the target of Federal artillerists. With it, of course, went the telegraph apparatus by means of which the general in chief had been conversing with the capital. It, too, would have been moved the night before had Lee known the danger in which Sheridan's breakthrough had placed him. The moving of the telegraph did not look important then, but it helped start a sequence of events from which eventually would spring total disaster.

During the night from April 2 to April 3 Lee withdrew, and the race with Grant's pursuing troops began. The goal of both armies was Burkeville, a railroad junction some fifty miles west of Petersburg. If Lee could get there first, he might be able to establish connections with General Johnston in North Carolina; if Grant won, he would prevent their junction. This time both Lee and Grant could read each other's minds. One look at the map was enough to show each which way his opponent intended to go, and over which roads he would move.

A few miles from Burkeville, in a northeasterly direction and on the Danville Railroad, lay the little settlements of Jetersville and Amelia Courthouse. It was to Amelia Courthouse that Lee had ordered supplies sent from Richmond, where 350,000 army rations had been stored against an emergency of this kind. These rations would last his army of 30,000 to 35,000 men a few days; and once back on the railroad, more provisions could easily be procured from interior points.

In his dispatch of April 2, which had been received in Richmond at 10:40 A.M., Lee had announced that he was retreating westward, but had not mentioned the place to which the supplies were to be sent, for at that hour he had not yet prepared his plans in detail. He had not envisioned that, due to Pickett's utter defeat, his retreat would have to be so precipitate. All he could say in his telegram was that he would concentrate near the Danville Railroad. His chief commissary in the capital, General I. M. St. John, was an able officer and immediately wired back for specific instructions. Well did he know the half-starved condition of the Confederate soldiers, to whom food was even more essential than ammunition. St. John's urgent message was not answered, because the headquarters telegraph station was then in the process of being moved. Lee himself, unsolicited, supplied the information as soon as the station had been set up again and he had mapped out his hurried retreat. "The troops will all be directed to Amelia Courthouse," he telegraphed later in the day. He did not need to say more; St. John could be relied on to read this message right and divert the supplies accordingly. That done, Lee turned his attention to the thousand and one other matters which required his personal supervision and which presented an almost super-human task even to his towering genius.

For three days the retreating army stumbled on its way toward Amelia Courthouse. Thousands of pursuers, well-fed and riding on well-fed horses, were constantly harassing them. Lee's men, down to a few grains of corn per day, dropped out by the hundreds. They saw their exhausted horses fall down in their traces, they saw wagons abandoned, turned over, and set on fire to keep them from being captured by the enemy. Throughout the long march the specter of starvation kept in step with them, but always beyond the horizon their lackluster eyes looked forward to the rations which were awaiting them at Amelia Courthouse. The very name of the little hamlet became a charm which prompted them on. Amelia Courthouse!

At last, on the morning of April 4, the advance tottered into the promised land of plenty. They were joyfully greeted: yes, there were all kinds of supplies on hand—ordnance supplies, artillery and infantry caissons, even harnesses. But food? No, nobody had ordered food sent to the village. There was not enough of it around to feed a corporal's guard. Lee's blood turned cold. Someone had again blundered, and this time the blunder could not be retrieved. He had given his orders, and they had not been obeyed. His men, his poor starving men! What could he say to them? Those who saw their beloved leader that day said that he suddenly looked haggard, like a man deprived of all hope.

Although Lee was at a loss to understand why his instructions had not been followed, he took what steps he could to remedy the situation. In a pathetic appeal to the farmers in and around Amelia Courthouse he stated that he had expected to find provisions, which had been ordered placed there several days before. His words expressed "surprise and regret" that he had found not even a pound of subsistence for man or horse. As usual, he kept his inner feelings to himself, but his thoughts must have burned hotly in bitterness against General Pickett's frivolous pleasure excursion. The hasty evacuation of the Petersburg headquarters had unquestionably been Pickett's fault and had brought about the fatal delay in the telegram mentioning Amelia Courthouse. Lee did not know then that it was also the cause of St. John's inability to reach him by telegraph. It had been the last chance to rectify the situation. Even downright treason could not have done worse than Pickett's boyish behavior.

Ugly rumors began to make the rounds among the famished troops. Some said that a string of railroad cars, loaded with edibles, had rolled into Amelia Courthouse from Danville, but had not been unloaded because panic-stricken government officials had ordered them sent to Richmond in order to hasten their own departure and the removal of their personal property. Others had it that Jefferson Davis and his Cabinet, together with other high officials, had requisitioned an empty train which was about to be loaded for Amelia Courthouse and had instead packed them with archives and bullion, using the rest of the space for themselves and their families. The hungry soldiers, cruelly disappointed by the mirage of a full meal, were ready to believe anything.

The facts belied all these malicious rumors. General St. John, anxious to forward the supplies, had been holding a reserve of boxcars in readiness, but had been unable to establish wire connections during the crucial hours while the Petersburg end of the line was being moved. Lee's telegram with specific instructions, due largely to the existing confusion, had not been received in Richmond until 7 P.M. By that time it was too late. The cars with the Confederate treasury and the highest officials had already left and no other cars were available. St. John, realizing the enormity of the catastrophe which he saw developing, and which he was powerless to stop, took possession of all the horse-drawn vehicles he could lay his hands on, loaded them with food, and sent them posthaste after Lee's army. Few of them, if any, reached their destination.

Neither Lee, nor Jefferson Davis, nor the Richmond commissary department could rightfully be blamed for the food crisis at Amelia Courthouse. If Lee's second wire had arrived—or had been sent off— a few hours earlier (which would have been the case if Lee had known the extent of Pickett's defeat) the supplies would have been given priority over anything else. No one, including President Davis, would have interfered. The success or failure of Lee's retreat had hung on this slender thread.

By superhuman efforts Lee had reached the railroad to Danville one day ahead of Sheridan's cavalry, and hoped that the bulk of Grant's army, at least his infantry, was still far behind. If Lee had been able to feed his men and move on at once, he could have chosen between two courses: either use the Danville Railroad in order to join General Johnston, or keep straight ahead to find refuge in the hilly district around Lynchburg. The Danville route was the more hazardous but promised a more worthwhile goal, for the two combined Confederate armies would still present a formidable force which might defeat Sherman; on the other hand, the railroad to Danville might be reached by the pursuers before the whole army had passed. The road to Lynchburg was the safer one, but led nowhere in particular, and would condemn both Lee and Johnston to guerrilla warfare. The lack of provisions at Amelia Courthouse made the choice illusory. It took fully a day for the wagons to gather scanty supplies, barely enough to keep the men and animals from dying on their feet, but the time lost could not be recovered. When, on the following morning, Lee in person reconnoitered along the road toward Jetersville, the next station on the road to Danville, he found that both Grant and Sheridan had caught up with him. The roads to North Carolina were already blocked. The only direction in which Lee still could hope to escape was west, toward Lynchburg, and even then his chances depended on speed. He knew that the odds were nearly impossible, and that the nearly impossible rarely happened. Four days later, on April 9, came the surrender.

The army of Northern Virginia, proud and full of fight to the last, had not been conquered by arms, but by hunger. Its final defeat had not taken place on the field, but at the peaceful but foodless hamlet of Amelia Courthouse.

It cannot be argued that the shad bake near Hatcher's Run influenced the outcome of the war. The Confederacy would have succumbed regardless of Pickett's faulty actions. What the latter did do, however, was to start the chain of events which led to disaster after disaster after the first error had been committed. If Pickett and Fitzhugh Lee had stayed with their troops, instead of partaking of a shad bake, the battle of Five Forks would either not have been fought, or might not have led to annihilation. Petersburg would have held out a little longer. Certainly the telegraph station at Lee's headquarters would have functioned long enough to receive and transmit the vital ration dispatches, thereby assuring supplies for the army at Amelia Courthouse. Or if the two defeated generals had told Lee the full truth at once, evacuation could have started twenty-four hours earlier, with equally satisfactory results. Without the day's delay at Amelia Courthouse, Lee could have marched far beyond Appomattox before being brought to bay, if at all. He had once told Jefferson Davis that with the advantages which the topography of the terrain offered, he could carry on the war for another twenty years against all the troops the federal government could bring to bear on him.

And so, if General Rosser had not been a lucky fisherman, the dramatic ending of the Civil War would have been written differently. On that morning when he put out his seine in the Nottoway River he made Appomattox Courthouse a certainty.

ISAAC D'ISRAELI

The Progress of Old Age in New Studies
ᵹ•

Benjamin Disraeli's father was the author of the best-selling Curiosities of Literature. *Here's a brief sample.*

Of the pleasures derivable from the cultivation of the arts, sciences, and literature, time will not abate the growing passion; for old men still cherish an affection and feel a youthful enthusiasm in those pursuits, when all others have ceased to interest. Dr. Reid, to his last day, retained a most active curiosity in his various studies, and particularly in the revolutions of modern chemistry. In advanced life we may resume our former studies with a new pleasure, and in old age we may enjoy them with the same relish with which more youthful students commence. Adam Smith observed to Dugald Stewart that "of all the amusements of old age, the most grateful and soothing is a renewal of acquaintance with the favorite studies and favorite authors of youth"—a remark, adds Stewart, which, in his own case, seemed to be more particularly exemplified while he was re-perusing, with the enthusiasm of a student, the tragic poets of ancient Greece. "I have heard him repeat the observation more than once, while Sophocles and Euripides lay open on his table."

Socrates learned to play on musical instruments in his old age; Cato, at eighty, thought proper to learn Greek; and Plutarch, almost as late in his life, Latin.

Theophrastus began his admirable work on the characters of men at the extreme age of ninety. He only terminated his literary labors by his death.

Ronsard, one of the fathers of French poetry, applied himself late to study. His acute genius, and ardent application, rivaled those poetic models which he admired; and Boccaccio was thirty-five years of age when he commenced his studies in polite literature.

The great Arnauld retained the vigor of his genius, and the command of his pen, to the age of eighty-two, and was still the great Arnauld.

Sir Henry Spelman neglected the sciences in his youth, but cultivated them at fifty years of age. His early years were chiefly passed in farming, which greatly diverted him from his studies; but a remarkable disappointment respecting a contested estate disgusted him with these rustic occupations: resolved to attach himself to regular studies, and literary society, he sold his farms, and became the most learned antiquary and lawyer.

Colbert, the famous French minister, almost at sixty, returned to his Latin and law studies.

Dr. Johnson applied himself the Dutch language but a few years before his death. The Marquis de Saint Aulaire, at the age of seventy, began to court the Muses, and they crowned him with their freshest flowers. The verses of this French Anacreon are full of fire, delicacy, and sweetness.

Chaucer's *Canterbury Tales* were the composition of his latest years: they were begun in his fifty-fourth year, and finished in his sixty-first.

Ludovico Monaldesco, at the extraordinary age of one hundred and fifteen, wrote the memoirs of his times. A singular exertion, noticed by Voltaire; who himself is one of the most remarkable instances of the progress of age in new studies.

The most delightful of autobiographies for artists is that of Benvenuto Cellini; a work of great originality, which was not begun till "the clock of his age had struck fifty-eight."

Koornhert began at forty to learn the Latin and Greek languages, of which he became a master; several students, who afterward distinguished themselves, have commenced as late in life their literary pursuits. Ogilby, the translator of Homer and Vergil, knew little of Latin or Greek till he was past fifty; and Franklin's philosophical pursuits began when he had nearly reached his fiftieth year.

Accorso, a great lawyer, being asked why he began the study of the law so late, answered, beginning it late, he should master it the sooner.

Dryden's complete works form the largest body of poetry from the pen of a single writer in the English language; yet he gave no public testimony of poetic abilities till his twenty-seventh year. In his sixty-eighth year he proposed to translate the whole *Iliad*: and his most pleasing productions were written in his old age.

Michelangelo preserved his creative genius even in extreme old age: there is a device said to be invented by him, of an old man represented in a go-cart, with an hourglass upon it; the inscription *Ancora imparo!*—Yet i am learning!

GEORGE ORWELL

A Queer Tale

~

A chapter from the autobiographical book Down and Out in Paris and London. *Is the story true? Your guess is as good as mine.*

I heard queer tales in the hotel. There were tales of dope fiends, of old debauchees who frequented hotels in search of pretty page boys, of thefts and blackmail. Mario told me of a hotel in which he had been, where a chambermaid stole a priceless diamond ring from an American lady. For days the staff were searched as they left work, and two detectives searched the hotel from top to bottom, but the ring was never found. The chambermaid had a lover in the bakery, and he had baked the ring into a roll, where it lay unsuspected until the search was over.

Once Valenti, at a slack time, told me a story about himself.

"You know, *mon p'tit,* this hotel life is all very well, but it's the devil when you're out of work. I expect you know what it is to go without eating, eh? *Forcément,* otherwise you wouldn't be scrubbing dishes. Well, I'm not a poor devil of a *plongeur;* I'm a waiter, and *I* went five days without eating, once. Five days without even a crust of bread—Jesus Christ!

"I tell you, those five days were the devil. The only good thing was, I had my rent paid in advance. I was living in a dirty, cheap little hotel in the Rue Sainte Éloise up in the Latin quarter. It was called the Hôtel Suzanne May, after some famous prostitute of the time of the Empire. I was starving, and there was nothing I could do; I couldn't even go to the cafés where the hotel proprietors come to engage waiters, because I hadn't the price of a drink. All I could do was to lie in bed getting weaker and weaker, and watching the bugs running about the ceiling. I don't want to go through that again, I can tell you.

"In the afternoon of the fifth day I went half mad; at least, that's how it seems to me now. There was an old faded print of a woman's head hanging on the wall of my room, and I took to wondering who it could be; and after about an hour realized that it must be Sainte Éloise, who was the patron saint of the quarter. I had never taken any notice of the thing before, but now, as I lay staring at it, a most extraordinary idea came into my head.

" '*Écoute, mon cher*,' I said to myself, 'you'll be starving to death if this goes on much longer. You've got to do something. Why not try a prayer to Saint Éloise? Go down on your knees and ask her to send you some money. After all, it can't do any harm. Try it!'

"Mad, eh? Still, a man will do anything when he's hungry. Besides, as I said, it couldn't do any harm. I got out of bed and began praying. I said:

" 'Dear Sainte Éloise, if you exist, please send me some money. I don't ask for much—just enough to buy some bread and a bottle of wine and get my strength back. Three or four francs would do. You don't know how grateful I'll be, Sainte Éloise, if you help me this once. And be sure, if you send me anything, the first thing I'll do will be to go and burn a candle for you, at your church down the street. Amen.'

"I put in that about the candle, because I had heard that saints like having candles burnt in their honor. I meant to keep my promise, of course. But I am an atheist and I didn't really believe that anything would come of it.

"Well, I got into bed again, and five minutes later there came a bang at the door. It was a girl called Maria, a big fat peasant girl who lived at our hotel. She was a very stupid girl, but a good sort, and I didn't much care for her to see me in the state I was in.

"She cried out at the sight of me. '*Nom de Dieu!*' she said, 'what's the matter with you? What are you doing in bed at this time of day? *Quelle mine que tu as!* You look more like a corpse than a man.'

"Probably I did look a sight. I had been five days without food, most of the time in bed, and it was three days since I had had a wash or a shave. The room was a regular pigsty, too.

" 'What's the matter?' said Maria again.

" 'The matter!' I said; 'Jesus Christ! I'm starving. I haven't eaten for five days. That's what's the matter.'

"Maria was horrified. 'Not eaten for five days?' she said. 'But why? Haven't you any money, then?'

" 'Money!' I said. 'Do you suppose I should be starving if I had money? I've got just five sous in the world, and I've pawned everything. Look around the room and see if there's anything more I can sell or pawn. If you can find anything that will fetch fifty centimes, you're cleverer than I am.'

"Maria began looking around the room. She poked here and there among a lot of rubbish that was lying about, and then suddenly she got quite excited. Her great thick mouth fell open with astonishment.

" 'You idiot!' she cried out. 'Imbecile! What's *this,* then?'

"I saw that she had picked up an empty oil *bidon* that had been lying in the corner. I had bought it weeks before, for an oil lamp I had before I sold my things.

" 'That?' I said. 'That's an oil *bidon.* What about it?'

" 'Imbecile! Didn't you pay three francs fifty deposit on it?'

"Now, of course I had paid the three francs fifty. They always make you pay a deposit on the *bidon,* and you get it back when the *bidon* is returned. But I'd forgotten all about it.

" 'Yes—' I began.

" 'Idiot!' shouted Maria again. She got so excited that she began to dance about until I thought her sabots would go through the floor. 'Idiot! *T'es fou! T'es fou!* What have you got to do but take it back to the shop and get your deposit back? Starving, with three francs fifty staring you in the face! Imbecile!'

"I can hardly believe now that in all those five days I had never once thought of taking the *bidon* back to the shop. As good as three francs fifty in hard cash, and it had never occurred to me! I sat up in bed. 'Quick!' I shouted to Maria, 'you take it for me. Take it to the grocer's at the corner—run like the devil. And bring back food!'

"Maria didn't need to be told. She grabbed the *bidon* and went clattering down the stairs like a herd of elephants, and in three minutes she was back with two pounds of bread under one arm and a half-liter bottle of wine under the other. I didn't stop to thank her; I just seized the bread and sank my teeth in it. Have you noticed how bread tastes when you have been hungry for a long time? Cold, wet, doughy—like putty almost. But, Jesus Christ, how good it was! As for the wine, I sucked it all down in one draught, and it seemed to go straight into my veins and flow around my body like new blood. Ah, that made a difference!

"I wolfed the whole two pounds of bread without stopping to take breath. Maria stood with her hands on her hips, watching me eat. 'Well, you feel better, eh?' she said when I had finished.

" 'Better!' I said. 'I feel perfect! I'm not the same man as I was five minutes ago. There's only one thing in the world I need now—a cigarette.'

"Maria put her hand in her apron pocket. 'You can't have it,' she said. 'I've no money. This is all I had left out of your three francs fifty—seven sous. It's no good; the cheapest cigarettes are twelve sous a packet.'

" 'Then I can have them!' I said. 'Jesus Christ, what a piece of luck! I've got five sous—it's just enough.'

"Maria took the twelve sous and was starting out to the tobacconist's. And then something I had forgotten all this time came into my head. There was that cursed Sainte Éloise! I had promised her a candle if she sent me money; and really, who could say that the prayer hadn't come true? 'Three or four francs,' I had said; and the next moment along came three francs fifty. There was no getting away from it. I should have to spend my twelve sous on a candle.

"I called Maria back. 'It's no use,' I said; 'there is Sainte Éloise —I have promised her a candle. The twelve sous will have to go on that. Silly, isn't it? I can't have my cigarettes after all.'

" 'Sainte Eloise?' said Maria. 'What about Sainte Éloise?'

" 'I prayed to her for money and promised her a candle,' I said. 'She answered the prayer—at any rate, the money turned up. I shall have to buy that candle. It's a nuisance, but it seems to me I must keep my promise.'

" 'But what put Sainte Éloise into your head?' said Maria.

" 'It was her picture,' I said, and I explained the whole thing. 'There she is, you see,' I said, and I pointed to the picture on the wall.

"Maria looked at the picture, and then to my surprise she burst into shouts of laughter. She laughed more and more, stamping about the room and holding her fat sides as though they would burst. I thought she had gone mad. It was two minutes before she could speak.

" 'Idiot!' she cried at last. *'T'es fou! T'es fou!* Do you mean to tell me you really knelt down and prayed to that picture? Who told you it was Sainte Éloise?'

" 'But I made sure it was Sainte Éloise!' I said.

" 'Imbecile! It isn't Sainte Éloise at all. Who do you think it is?'

" 'Who?' I said.

" 'It is Suzanne May, the woman this hotel is called after.'

"I had been praying to Suzanne May, the famous prostitute of the Empire. . . .

"But, after all, I wasn't sorry. Maria and I had a good laugh, and then we talked it over, and we made out that I didn't owe Saint Éloise anything. Clearly it wasn't she who had answered the prayer, and there was no need to buy her a candle. So I had my packet of cigarettes after all."

JEWISH FOLK TALE

Rabbi Akiba

ট

A proverbial story about divine Providence, told and retold for over a thousand years.

Compelled by violent persecution to quit his native land, Rabbi Akiba wandered over barren wastes and dreary deserts: his whole equipage consisting of a lamp, which he used to light at night in order to study the law; a cock which served him instead of a watch to announce to him the rising dawn; and an ass on which he rode.

The sun was gradually sinking beneath the horizon, night was fast approaching, and the poor wanderer knew not where to shelter his head or where to rest his weary limbs. Fatigued, and almost exhausted, he came at last near a village. He was glad to find it inhabited, thinking where human beings dwelt there dwelt also humanity and compassion; but he was mistaken. He asked for a night's lodging; it was refused, not one of the inhospitable inhabitants would accommodate him. He was therefore obliged to seek shelter in a neighboring wood. "It is hard, very hard," said he, "not to find a hospitable roof to protect me against the inclemency of the weather; *but God is just, and whatever He does is for the best.*"

He seated himself beneath a tree, lighted his lamp, and began to read the *law;* he had scarcely read a chapter, when a violent storm extinguished the light. "What," exclaimed he, "must I not be permitted even to pursue my favorite study? *but God is just, and whatever He does is for the best.*"

He stretched himself on the bare earth, willing, if possible, to have a few hours' sleep. He had hardly closed his eyes, when a fierce wolf came and killed his cock. "What new misfortune is this?" ejaculated the astonished Akiba; "my vigilant companion is gone; who then will henceforth awaken me to the study of the law? but God is just, He knows best what is good for us poor mortals."

Scarcely had he finished the sentence, when a terrible lion came and devoured the ass. "What is to be done now?" exclaimed the lonely wanderer; "my lamp and my cock are gone, my poor ass too is gone —all is gone! *But praised be the Lord, whatever He does is for the best.*"

He passed a sleepless night, and early in the morning went to the village, to see whether he could procure a horse or any other beast of burden, to enable him to pursue his journey. But what was his surprise not to find a single individual alive! It appears that a band of robbers had entered the village during the night, and killed its inhabitants, and plundered their houses.

As soon as Akiba had sufficiently recovered from the amazement into which this wonderful occurrence had thrown him, he lifted up his voice and exclaimed, "Thou great God, the God of Abraham, Isaac, and Jacob! now I know by experience that poor mortal men are shortsighted and blind; often considering as evils what is intended for their preservation. But Thou alone art just, and kind, and merciful. Had not the hardhearted people driven me by their inhospitality from the village, I should assuredly have shared their fate; had not the wind extinguished my lamp, the robbers would have been drawn to the spot and have murdered me. I preceive also that it was Thy mercy which deprived me of my two companions, that they might not by their noise give notice to the bandits where I was. Praised then be Thy name, for ever and ever!"

ARABIAN NIGHTS

The Ruined Man Who Became Rich Again Through a Dream

❧

One of the many versions of the famous folktale Acres of Diamonds.

There lived once in Baghdad a very wealthy man who lost all his substance and became so poor that he could only earn his living by excessive labor. One night, he lay down to sleep, dejected and sick at heart, and saw in a dream one who said to him, "Thy fortune is at Cairo; go thither and seek it." So he set out for Cairo; but, when he arrived there, night overtook him and he lay down to sleep in a mosque.

Presently, as fate would have it, a company of thieves entered the mosque and made their way thence into an adjoining house; but the people of the house, being aroused by the noise, awoke and cried out; whereupon the chief of the police came to their aid with his officers. The robbers made off; but the police entered the mosque and finding the man from Baghdad asleep there, laid hold of him and beat him with palmrods, till he was well-nigh dead.

Then they cast him into prison, where he abode three days, after which the chief of the police sent for him and said to him, "Whence art thou?" "From Baghdad," answered he. "And what brought thee to Cairo?" asked the magistrate. Quoth the Baghdadi, "I saw in a dream one who said to me, 'Thy fortune is at Cairo; go thither to it.' But when I came hither, the fortune that he promised me proved to be the beating I had of thee."

The chief of the police laughed till he showed his jawteeth, and said, "O man of little wit, thrice have I seen in a dream one who said to me, 'There is in Baghdad a house of such a fashion and situated

so-and-so, in the garden whereof is a fountain and thereunder a great
sum of money buried. Go thither and take it.' Yet I went not; but
thou, of thy little wit, hast journeyed from place to place, on the faith
of a dream, which was but an illusion of sleep." Then he gave him
money, saying, 'This is to help thee back to thy native land.'"

Now the house he had described was the man's own house in
Baghdad; so the latter returned thither, and digging underneath the
fountain in his garden, discovered a great treasure; and thus God
gave him abundant fortune.

MEYER BERGER

School Bus

&>

*On April 16, 1954, the great reporter wrote one of his regular
"About New York" columns—and came up with a small masterpiece of journalism.*

Every school morning Sam picks up Veronica, Mary-Jo, Debbie,
Davey, Jackie, and Julio in a limousine owned by the Parochial Bus
System, Inc. He drives Mary-Jo and Debbie to 59 East Fifty-seventh
Street, between Second and Third Avenues. The others he put down
at Public School 135 on First Avenue at Fifty-first Street.

At 2:30 P.M. Sam calls for the children at the two schools and
takes them home again. His boss, F. E. Arrigoni, has a contract with
the Board of Education for the service. He runs limousines in other
parts of Manhattan and in Brooklyn, the Bronx, and Queens. The
riders are youngsters with cerebral palsy, like Veronica, Davey, Julio,
and Jackie, or blind children, like Mary-Jo and Debbie.

The other day Sam called for his group at P. S. 135. The teachers
dressed the children while they occupied their wheelchairs, which
are their school seats, too. It is difficult to put coats and sweaters and

hats on cerebral palsy sufferers, because their limbs and their heads keep convulsively pulling away all the time. But they laugh, like any other kids, and Big Sam and the teachers unlock their foot braces and lift them into the cars.

Curly-haired Veronica went in first to a corner back seat. Seven-year-old Jackie was put next to her, and dark-eyed Julio sat in his mother's lap. Davey got a jump seat. Sam looked them over to see that they were as comfortable as they can ever get to be and drove to the Fifty-seventh Street school. Two bright-faced little girls with sparkling eyes waited at the curb. You didn't know until they felt their way into the front seat next to Sam that they were blind.

All the children had Easter baskets in brown paper bags. They had decorated them with crayons in all manner of scrawls and eccentric patterns, but the colors were cheerful and good to look upon. Mary-Jo stared straight ahead, unseeing, through the windshield, a pretty blonde thing in a light-blue leather jacket and dark-blue beret. She said, "Jackie, let me feel your Easter basket." Jackie fumbled for it, so Big Sam reached back for it and gave it to Mary-Jo.

Her fingers probed inside the bag, over the candy eggs and the rough sides of the basket. She passed it awkwardly back to Sam. "Jackie," she said, "that's the prettiest Easter basket I have ever seen." Jackie grunted and clutched his property again.

All the kids were quiet as the car pushed into Fifty-first Street, just below Ninth Avenue. A man came to the car, lifted Davey out, and carried him up a tenement stoop. The other youngsters shrilled good-by. Davey, limp in his father's arms, waved back and vanished in a dark hallway.

Sam drove down Ninth Avenue and into Twenty-fourth Street, eastward. A tired-looking woman came to help Debbie to the curb. The child turned sightless eyes on the group. She fingered her Braille wrist watch and said: "It's just exactly three o'clock, Sam. You're right on time." "Get going, Chatterbox," the good-natured driver told her. Debbie giggled. Her mother led her into a big apartment house.

Sam got onto the West Side Highway and headed for South Ferry. You wanted to tell the kids to see the big liner pulling out, and the gulls floating against spring's sky, but you remembered Mary-Jo and kept silent.

A gray-haired lady waited for Veronica at the Staten Island Ferry gate. It was difficult getting the little girl out and onto the ferry. Sam said: "That poor kid's got no more stand-up than a bag of pertaters." Veronica smiled. Her head pulled away, uncontrolled, but came right again, and a palsied little hand waved good-by.

Jackie's mother waited for him at the Alfred E. Smith Houses. He all but tumbled out, a wee thing. He caught the handles of a perambulator his mother pushed, got his sea legs, more or less, and hanging on, made slow progress up the walk.

Mary-Jo go off in crowded Elizabeth Street. Her mother, a young woman, was waiting for her with Francine, another blonde daughter, but younger, dressed in blue like Mary-Jo. Standing off a little from the limousine, eyes wide and clear gray, Mary-Jo said: "I go to the Lighthouse on Saturday, Sam. I dance with boys." Sam pretended gruffness. He said, gravel-voiced, "You got too many boy friends, Mary-Jo. You knock them dead," and the car parted a group of shrill children in the street. Mary-Jo and her sister waved after the car.

The extra rider cleared his throat. He said: "It's a heartbreaker, isn't it, Sam? Those poor kids."

"You didn't look right for the story, mister," Sam suggested. "You got to look at those mothers' faces; that's the story."

JOHN SACK

The S.M.O.M.

ই৺

The smallest country in the world—and possibly the most interesting.

The smallest country in the world is half as big, approximately, as a football field and is located in downtown Rome two or three blocks from American Express, and next door to Cucci's, the haberdasher. Its flag is red and white, a lot like Denmark's, and its name is rather immoderate, I think: the Sovereign and Military Order of St. John of Jerusalem, Rhodes, and Malta, which is abbreviated at all but the most ceremonious of state occasions to the Sovereign and Military Order of Malta, or the S.M.O.M. That the Sovereign and Military Order of Malta, or S.M.O.M., is truly sovereign is shown by its being recognized by Italy, the Vatican, San Marino, Austria, Spain, Portugal, the Dominican Republic, Haiti, Panama, Costa Rica, Nicaragua, El Salvador, Ecuador, Colombia, Paraguay, Argentina, Chile, Peru, Brazil, and Lebanon, and that it's truly military is shown by an air force bigger than most of these places—one hundred and twenty planes, of which three, at the very least, are said to be in sufficient repair to permit them to leave the ground. The S.M.O.M. has a minister in each of the twenty countries that recognize it, and vice versa, and while it would be nonsense for me to suggest that he has anything to do, I can suggest how he sometime *might*. Put the case that Signor Cucci, the haberdasher, is murdered today by a disgruntled client, who flees across the border into the S.M.O.M.: the only recourse now for the Italian police is to extradite the man, something that would be done, of necessity, through the Italian minister to the S.M.O.M., and the S.M.O.M.ian minister to Italy.

What the Sovereign and Military Order of St. John of Jerusalem, Rhodes, and Malta lacks in territory, it also lacks in population, being inhabited at the last census by two people, Brother Paternó and Baron Apor. (There used to be a third—Prince Chigi, who was the grand master, or sovereign, of the S.M.O.M., but who died in 1951 and hasn't been replaced yet.) Brother Paternó is the lieutenant grand master, and, as such, is kept so awfully busy with matters of state that I couldn't see him, while Baron Apor, whom I did see and chatted with for quite a while, in fact, is the chancellor—a small, animated, merry old gaffer who wears a black homburg and carries a black umbrella, and is ever losing himself in old jokes and reminiscences, a characteristic one being of the fellow who learned, from his doctor, that wine, women, and song were killing him, and who replied, *"Allora, smetto di cantare"*—"Okay, I'll give up singing." Between such jokes as these, the baron told me he doesn't pay taxes to Italy, being a citizen of the S.M.O.M., and that he brings in cigarettes, liquor, and suchlike free of duty; and he offered me a free-of-duty Chesterfield. He travels, said the baron, on a passport of the S.M.O.M., and he graciously let me see the thing: it was red and white and very natty, and the page that is signed by Mr. Dulles on *my* passport was signed by Baron Apor, himself, on his, and carried the words, "His Eminent Highness, Fra Ludovico Chigi Albani Della Rovere, Prince and Grand Master of the Sovereign Military Order of Malta, request all to whom it may concern to allow the bearer, Baron Gabriel Apor, to pass freely and to afford him such assistance and protection of which he may stand in need." The next several pages were full of visas. Hereupon, the baron observed that nothing except the discovery of bootleg gold will cause such a to-do at the international borders of Europe as the arrival there of himself or Brother Paternó with an S.M.O.M.ian passport, it being treated by the customs people as if it were practically radioactive. That the passport is allowed, eventually, at all of these borders, the baron said, is a proof positive of the sovereignty of the S.M.O.M. He added that the S.M.O.M. doesn't give any visas of its own, but can; that it doesn't mint any money of its own, but did; and that it doesn't print any stamps of its own, but will—at some as yet undetermined time in the future, after the proper arrangements are made with the International Postal Union and an adequate place, if any, is found for a mailbox on the S.M.O.M.'s soil.

Well, I think this is very unusual. How it managed to come about is a long story, and, with the reader's indulgence, I'd like to make it as long as possible, as there's so very little I can say about the S.M.O.M. of today. The fact is that the S.M.O.M. has been a country ever since 1048, but, unlike such countries of those days as Slavonia, Catalonia, Lower Lorraine, and the caliphate of Cordova, it manages to be with us in the twentieth century by having put its lock, stock, and population on a dozen or so ships whenever it was conquered, and popping up somewhere else in Europe or Asia. Six hundred and twenty-six years of this peripateticism are noted, in chronological order, in the very name of the S.M.O.M.—the Sovereign and Military Order of St. John of Jerusalem (143 years), Rhodes (214 years), and Malta (269 years)—the omissions being 100 years at Acre, 18 years on Cyprus, 42 years getting from one of these places to another, and, of course, all of this century and most of the last in Rome. I suppose there's no reason why a nation shouldn't behave this way—my dictionary says a nation should have "a more or less compact territory," and in the case of the S.M.O.M. it's less—but, I think, it's altogether too trying on the rest of us, and sometimes the S.M.O.M. was gadding about so much that even its citizens didn't know where it was: at the turn of the nineteenth century they thought it was in Leningrad, of all places, and elected the czar as grand master. In spite of its aberrations, the S.M.O.M. was one of the great countries of Europe for much of the millennium, owning a half dozen forts along the Mediterranean, 140 estates in Palestine, and 19,000 in Europe, and in protocol always coming the first.

In those days, the S.M.O.M.ians were known as the Hospitalers, for as a hospital the S.M.O.M. had begun—in 1048 or thereabouts, in Jerusalem, to care for the pilgrims. The Hospital of St. John the Baptist was given a kind of extraterritoriality by the Moslems, making it a kind of Vatican City, and it stayed so after the Moslems left and the Crusaders came, in 1087. On that day, ten thousand people were killed in the Mosque of Omar alone, and their bodies floated out in the blood; the hospital had much to do; and later it was given money by many of the Crusaders it cared for, growing in power and population. Its first grand master was the Blessed Raymond du Puy, who made the S.M.O.M. a military, as well as a sovereign, state, and sent it into the Crusades, and who prescribed for it the religious rule it still uses: "Firstly, I ordain that all the brethren, engaging in the service of the poor and the defense of the Catholic faith, should keep the three things with the aid of God that they have promised to God: that is to say, chastity and obedience, which means whatever thing is commanded to them by their masters, and to live without property of their own: because God will require these three things of them at the Last Judgment. And let them not claim more as their due than bread and water, and raiment, which things are promised to them. And their clothing should be humble, because Our Lord's poor, whose servants we confess ourselves to be, go naked and miserably clad. And it is a wrong thing for a servant that he should be proud, and his Lord should be humble." The grand masters after the Blessed Raymond du Puy realized, though, that a nation founded on chastity would be rather a flash-in-the-pan, so just a few of the citizens took the vows. Those who did were Knights of Justice, and those who didn't were Knights of Honor and Devotion or Knights of Magistral Grace, and this differentiation obtains in the S.M.O.M. today. Baron Apor is a Knight of Honor and Devotion, and Brother Paternó is a Knight of Justice.

Jerusalem fell again to the Moslems in 1271, and, it's written, the nuns of the S.M.O.M. chose death to dishonor: they couldn't commit suicide, but they could cut their noses off, and they made themselves so hideous doing so that they were killed, and weren't raped, by the Moslems. The rest of the S.M.O.M. had already taken its kit and caboodle, as it would often in the future, and had relocated to the north of Jerusalem, at Acre; it was run out of there in 1291, and it wasn't seen in the Holy Land again until 1954, when it opened the legation in Lebanon. From Jerusalem to Acre; from Acre to Cyprus; from Cyprus to Rhodes, by which time even the grand master was so bewildered as to where, if anywhere, the S.M.O.M. would materialize next that he was thirteen years in catching up. Presently, the grand master was Deodato de Gozon. It's said in many histories of the S.M.O.M.—almost all of which, incidentally, are called *A Short History of the Order* (or *Knights*) *of St. John of Jerusalem*—that Deodato de Gozon nominated himself and voted for himself and was, even so, spoken of as a modest man—and little wonder, for Deodato de Gozon had been the first S.M.O.M.ian to slay a dragon. According to the many *Short Histories,* the dragon, after eating up women and children for several years, was slain by Deodato de Gozon and a pair of English bulldogs, which, during the encounter, had held the dragon at bay, having been specially trained for the purpose on a wooden, facsimile dragon. Generally, I'm not one to put any stock in dragons, but this particular one is pretty well documented, de Gozon's own tombstone saying, in Latin, "Skill is the conqueror of force: Deodato de Gozon, knight, slew an enormous dragon." The stone was put there by people who should have known, and we can only conclude that a terrible sort of animal was prowling about in the Middle Ages and, mercifully, has gone extinct. (Even the Bible has talk of dragons—the seventy-fourth Psalm.)

In 1444, the sultan of Egypt laid siege to the S.M.O.M.; it was lifted, but many of the knights were dead, the fortifications were out, earthquakes and a tidal wave were making them worse, and the S.M.O.M.ians were in a funk. Then, Sultan Suleiman the Magnificent, of the Ottoman Empire, laid siege again, and the people reacted in a way quite unimaginable today—by worrying about the enemy within and all but forgetting the enemy without. A lady of Spain, a pilgrim, got to be something of a celebrity by going around barefoot and putting the finger on people in high places, not naming any names, however; the first to be killed was a Turkish slave, and then a Jewish doctor, and things were far enough along for the chancellor himself to be tortured, tried, and decapitated, when Suleiman the Magnificent opened fire and conquered the S.M.O.M. "There has been nothing in the world so well lost as Rhodes," said Charles V of the Holy Roman Empire, incorrectly, and gave it Malta.

Charles V was to get a falcon every year in return, and he seems, at first, to have had the better of the deal. Malta was like a no-man's land when the S.M.O.M. got there; its castle had gone to seed, but the S.M.O.M., under the grand mastery of Jean Parisot de la Valette, worked for thirty-six years to fix it—even the women, and even la Valette, were carrying stone to the parapets—and the S.M.O.M. had its powder dry when Suleiman the Magnificent, who conquered it in Rhodes at the start of his reign, said he'd conquer it in Malta at the end. In 1565, he laid siege—one of the great sieges of history, fought a third of a year by thirty thousand Turks and only eight or nine thousand S.M.O.M.ians. And fought savagely, too: the Turks cut a Maltese cross into their prisoners and sent the bodies downstream to the S.M.O.M., and the S.M.O.M., in turn, decapitated its prisoners and fired a fusillade of human heads onto the Turks, "and from that day onwards, no quarter was given on either side," in the words of a *Short History*. They used to throw hoops and crockery pots of wildfire, like hand grenades, at one another, and there were frogman fights at sea. La Valette was told to surrender; he pointed to the trenches, saying, "There is the only ground that I will surrender, and that as a grave for the Turkish army."

The catastrophe was at hand. The S.M.O.M. was reinforced, to a degree, by a Mesquita, the governor of Notabile, who stormed the

Turkish hospitals when nobody was about, and the Turks were reinforced by Hassan, the Begler Beg of Algeria, and on Thursday, August 23, they assaulted every part of the S.M.O.M. at once. The S.M.O.M. had been forewarned—someone had shot an arrow in with THURSDAY on it—and almost every knight was out of the hospital, at the battlements. They held for a week, and then 8,500 reinforcements came from Spain, and the Turks skedaddled in panic, many of them being killed, as they did so, by their very general. Suleiman the Magnificent hit the ceiling when he heard of this, and resolved, at the age of seventy, to lead the army himself, and he sent a letter to la Valette swearing "by the god wch hath mayd heaven and yearth and by our xxvj Proffites and the foure Musaphi which fell downe out of heaven and by our chief proffit Mahomet" that nobody would be hurt if the S.M.O.M. surrendered. "But yf," Suleiman added in his second sentence—his first sentence had been 279 words long—"but yf you will not yeald yor selves as wee have said wee will roote out the foundacion of your castell upsid downe, and make you slaves and to die an evell death according to our pleasure as wee have dann to manny others and of this be you right well assured." La Valette, after reading this, sent a few men to Constantinople and blew up the Turkish navy, and that was the end of that.

Suleiman the Magnificent died in mortification the same year, and Jean Parisot de la Valette died, of sunstroke, two years later, and after that the Ottoman Empire and the S.M.O.M. took a brodie. The S.M.O.M.ians gave in to luxury and vice, and Malta, won by bravery on August 23, 1565, was lost by cowardice on Meadow 23, 6—to use the language of Napoleon's communiqué. Chiefly, the cowardice was that of the grand master, Ferdinand Joseph Anthony Herman Lewis von Hompesch, who, as Napoleon hove up with fourteen sail-of-the-line, thirty frigates, and three hundred cargo ships, did nothing at all, and the S.M.O.M. was conquered apace. ("How fortunate," said one of Napoleon's staff, "since a couple of dozen men could have held the city against us.") Von Hompesch's only worry was to keep his chinaware and jewelry safe; he didn't, and he died unable to pay for a funeral. The other S.M.O.M.ians took kit and caboodle once again and went, in a quandary, to Austria, England, and Russia, and the ones in Russia, as I have already said, elected the czar as their seventieth grand master. (That a czar should take the vows of chastity, obedience, and poverty, and still remain a czar, hadn't seemed at all irregular to the S.M.O.M. since the thirteenth century, when it took in the king of Hungary and got, in gratitude, seven hundred silver marks a year.) After a while, the S.M.O.M. was given the half acre of downtown Rome that is, still, its only territory, but as part of the bargain only three men—the grand master, the lieutenant grand master, and the chancellor—could be citizens there. The other S.M.O.M.ians were to be citizens of the country they lived in. Today there are five thousand of these in the Order of Malta, and, for them, it's very like the Order of Odd Fellows or the Benevolent and Protective Order of Elks, except if they get to be ministers; a few in the United States are Francis Cardinal Spellman, Mr. Frank Leahy, Mr. Frank Folsom, and Mr. Henry Ford II.

The two contemporary citizens of the S.M.O.M., Brother Paternó and Baron Apor, are well-behaved, exemplary men, and there isn't any need in the S.M.O.M. to have any laws or law courts, and if we wish to learn of that aspect of the S.M.O.M., we must study it when it was more heavily populated, on Malta. Those days, it was against the law to throw rocks into a window or dirt onto a door, or go to the ballet; slavery wasn't against the law (there was a big market in the capital city), but cowardice was, and a General St. Clement, who ordered a withdrawal, was found guilty of it in the sixteenth century. It was against the law to duel, but there was a narrow street, the Strada Stretta—the Narrow Street—where the S.M.O.M.ians used to get jostled, at times,' and fly extemporaneously off the handle, and it was the legal fiction that a duel fought on the Strada Stretta really wasn't, just as slander spoken in the United States Senate really isn't. Eventually, anybody who cared to duel did so on the Strada Stretta, it being closed to pedestrian traffic by the seconds. A common punishment for much of this was starvation; torture was legal, and General St. Clement, the coward, was strangled to death and thrown in a burlap bag into the Mediterranean. The S.M.O.M. gave sanctuary to the civil criminals of other countries—Caravaggio, the artist, a murderer, was one of them—and the S.M.O.M.'s hospital gave sanctuary to the civil criminals of the S.M.O.M., although, in the course of time, conspirators, traitors, murderers, perjurers, poisoners, pillagers, sodomites, arsonites, assassins, debtors, highwaymen, and thieves were barred from the hospital by one regulation or another.

Historically, the S.M.O.M.'s hospital was that of 1048—part of the caboodle taken from Jerusalem to Acre, Cyprus, Rhodes, and Malta. The hospital seems to have taken a brodie as the S.M.O.M. did; it was visited in the eighteenth century by John Howard, the philanthropist, who said it was "so dirty and offensive as to create the necessity of perfuming [the beds—of which there were 745, by the way] and yet I observed that the physician in going his rounds was obliged to keep a handkerchief to his face," while the hospital staff were "the most dirty, ragged, unfeeling and inhuman persons I ever saw. I once saw eight or nine of them highly entertained by a delirious, dying patient." He also complained that the vermicelli was dirty and the bread moldy, but, Baron Apor has assured me, this latter was on the menu for its penicillin content, the drug having been known, but not isolated, by the S.M.O.M.'s hospital in the fifteenth century. The hospital was run in every century by a high officer of the S.M.O.M., the Hospitaler, also known as the Pillar of the French Tongue. The pillar of the Italian tongue was the admiral, and the pillar of our own, English, tongue was the Turcopolier—the "son of a Turk" in the Latin tongue—who commanded the light cavalry at first, getting the coast guard afterward. That the grand commander was the pillar of the Provençal tongue, and that the Spanish tongue was pillared by the drapier till 1462, after which it was pillared partly by the drapier, in his capacity as pillar of the Aragonese tongue, and partly by the grand chancellor, as pillar of the Castilian and Portuguese tongue, is, I think, as obscure a bit of incidental intelligence as anyone could know, and might well be committed to memory by people (like me) who generally make a hobby of such things.

All of which brings us to the Sovereign and Military Order of St. John of Jerusalem, Rhodes, and Malta today—Brother Paternó and Baron Apor. The latter of these has an apartment in the Italian quarter of Rome, but the former is living on S.M.O.M.ian soil, in the

Order of Malta Palace, 68 Via Condotti, a solemn, gray, four-floored building that takes up *all* the S.M.O.M.ian soil. The palace, a minute's walk from the bottom of the Spanish Steps, may be readily identified by the letters cvcci in front, in gold, which I took at first for some sort of Roman numeral but soon realized was a sign for Signor Cucci, the haberdasher. Here at the front of the palace, Signor Cucci has rented a store, filling the windows of it with silken bathrobes and ties, and the several other stores in the palace have pearls, coral, gold tea services, and Buddhas of jade in their windows; none of the stores have extraterritoriality. Between the door to Cucci's and the door to Rapi's is the ponderous door to the S.M.O.M., indicated by a small silver plaque, SOVRANO INTERNAZIONALE MILITARE ORDINE DI MALTA, and by another, INTERNATIONAL MILI-TARY SOVEREIGN ORDER OF MALTA—two further variations on the name of the country that, according to Baron Apor, are erroneous, as is the variation on his own passport—and beyond the door is a court, smaller than a tennis court but surely large enough for the mailbox that Baron Apor envisages. The court is full of automobiles by day, some of them with S.M.O.M. plates, and is rather pretty by night: a Maltese cross, in red and white, is floodlit at the far end, and a gargoyle is spewing water into a pool of goldfish; and the whole thing can be appreciated until I A.M. from the Via Condotti, in Italy.

There is a concierge at the border of all this, but he graciously let me by, without any trouble, on the day I visited Baron Apor. The baron's office is on the palace's third floor; it is well appointed, but, unfortunately, it doesn't look into the courtyard but onto a typical scene of back-yard Italy, a *pasticcio* of dirty wood and rickety balconies, one above the other and populated, for the most part, by white, restless pieces of laundry, like mountain sheep. For five or ten minutes I sat in the anteroom and looked at this—a cat lurked, a woman in black drew the laundry in—until, presently, I was shown to the chambers of Baron Apor, who greeted me enthusiastically in English and Italian, told me the story about wine, women, and song of which I've already apprised the reader, told me several facts about the S.M.O.M. of which I've also apprised the reader, gave some hur-ried orders to a secretary standing by with a pyramid of state papers in his hands, and took me, directly, on a furious tour of the S.M.O.M. itself—a red-and-gold hall of state in which the Peruvian ambassador had presented his papers a week earlier; a red-and-gold dining room in medieval tapestries; a green-and-gold room where the delegates of the S.M.O.M.ians who don't have citizenship will meet, sometime soon, to elect a grand master; and last but not least the S.M.O.M.'s hospital, in the back rooms of the palace. All of these rooms were tidy, ship-shape, and decorated by paintings and maps of Malta, and of the seventy-six grand masters—Deodato de Gozon, who slew the dragon, looking like Man Mountain Dean, and Prince Chigi, who died in 1951, looking like a perfect old man, baldheaded and white-goateed.

The hospital was excellent, I thought. Its waiting room was lit by ultraviolet, germicidal light, and I learned that the one hundred or so patients passing through it every day are given the newest of the miracle drugs—isolated, at long last—and the best of dietary food (a far cry from the eighteenth century, when the S.M.O.M.'s hospital specified a diet of "the best soup, made of fowls, herbs, vermicelli, rice, etc., and every sort of meat . . . such as chickens, pigeons, poultry, beef, veal, game, hashes, fricassees, stews, sausages etc. in such quantities as are necessary; also fresh eggs, pomegranates, plums, and grapes, and every kind of freshment allowed to sick people; such as biscuits, apples, fruit, sugar, and all sorts of confectionery, each according to his wants"). This is the same hospital with us, inter-ruptedly, for nine centuries, but, as I learned from Baron Apor, the S.M.O.M. also has a number of hospitals on foreign soil, some of them larger than the S.M.O.M. and as far afield as London and Schles-wig-Holstein, Germany, where, at first, the flags of the S.M.O.M. were thought to be Denmark's by the Schleswig-Holsteiner, who figured the Danes weren't up to any good.

Before I left, I learned from Baron Apor of two other things the S.M.O.M. does in this twentieth century: to fly pilgrims from Italy, Ireland, and Sardinia to Lourdes, and to fly missionaries out of Africa for what in the United States Army is called R&R, a rest & recreation leave. For these purposes, the S.M.O.M. uses its air force, such as it is, which is kept on Italian soil, is flown by Italians, and, as a matter of fact, was gotten gratis from Italy at the end of World War II. The S.M.O.M. was strictly neutral in that war, as in every war since the Napoleonic ones, and its ambulances went north and south of the battle line, and even today the S.M.O.M. considers itself on friendly terms with every country on earth—except one, a country two hundred times as large and scarcely a mile away, Vatican City. The cause of the falling-out of these two Roman Catholic neighbors is that root of all evil, money: the Vatican has wanted the S.M.O.M.'s, or, at least, the right to audit it, ever since the S.M.O.M. went into the red a decade ago, when all of its navy—a rented navy—disappeared on the Atlantic Ocean with ten thousand bushels of wheat. It turned out that a Count Thun, a federal employee at the S.M.O.M., was using the S.M.O.M.'s money to play the wheat market, and it also turned out that someone else at the S.M.O.M. was playing the stock market, and that someone *else* was smuggling radios from the United States to Italy, via the S.M.O.M., in boxes that were labeled PENICILLIN. Prince Chigi, the grand master, died of a broken heart when he heard of this, and the Vatican investigated; today, though, the S.M.O.M. is in the black, and has written a secret one-hundred-page paper telling the Vatican to make itself scarce. What will come of this is hard to say, for relations between the S.M.O.M. and the Vatican have been off-again, on-again since the thirteenth century, when Pope Gregory IX threatened to excommunicate it. (Pope Gregory thought it was in cahoots with the Order of Assassins, a Moslem one, and the S.M.O.M. didn't help any by going to war, soon afterward, with the Order of the Temple, a Catholic one.) Relations between the S.M.O.M. and the nonsovereign, nonmilitary Order of the Holy Sepulcher also aren't so good; *they* have been off-again, on-again since the eleventh century, when, according to the Church of the Holy Sepulcher, the Church of the S.M.O.M. was ringing its bells too loud. Nowadays, the schism is over real estate, some profitable land at Sorrento that the S.M.O.M. and the Order of the Holy Sepulcher lay claim to. The grand commander of the Order of the Holy Sepulcher and enemy of the Order of Malta is Nicola Cardinal Canali, who was, nevertheless, named by the Vatican to investigate the Order of Malta, and who, moreover, is *in* the Order of Malta—

a pretty kettle of fish, I think, and one that I wouldn't dare to elucidate any further.

By now, I suspect that several readers who have been to Italy and the Vatican City are cursing themselves for having been only a block away and missing the chance of doing a third country, the S.M.O.M. They will be comforted to know, accordingly, that, if they saw everything in Rome expected of them as tourists, they *have* done the S.M.O.M.—unwittingly. They will recollect being taken to a shady hill by the Tiber, and being directed, by the American Express man, to peek through a keynole in a big wooden door; and what they saw was a lovely thing, a long, green avenue of trees and the dome of St. Peter's a mile beyond. The dome of St. Peter's is part of Vatican City, of course, and the keyhole is part of Italy—indeed, a national monument—but the door in which the keyhole is and the avenue of trees are part of the S.M.O.M.: it's the summer villa of the grand master, and, like the summer villa of the pope, at Castelgandolfo, it's extraterritorial.

I haven't any idea how the pope would feel about it, but, I'm pleased to report, the grand masters of the S.M.O.M. have never taken exception to the thousands of tourists who visit their summer villa and peek into the keyhole. The door itself is not opened for the tourists, though: it is opened only for the grand master, when there is a grand master, and for those people, like me, who are given what amounts to a visa by Baron Apor, and it is opened on these occasions by Signor Cesare Giacchetti, a kindly old Italian who has opened the door, closed the door, cleaned the fluff out of the national monument, pruned the avenue of trees and some persimmon trees, out of sight, and dusted the villa of the grand master since the end of World War I. Signor Giacchetti performed the first two of these functions for me, and said he uses a penknife to perform the third, the fluff being put into the national monument by a couple of young imps in the neighborhood; he also observed that, until recently, the scene to be contemplated at the end of the avenue of trees wasn't St. Peter's Cathedral but an Italian smokestack: there was an outcry in the Italian press, and the indignity was taken down. Signor Giacchetti and

I had been chatting of these matters in the garden of the grand master's villa for barely a minute, when one of those tinted, air-conditioned buses arrived, and lo! another swarm of bluebottles alighted, to peek into the keyhole; and Signor Giacchetti and I peeked back.

The bluebottles had the better peek. It encompassed not only Signor Giacchetti, me, and a national monument or two, but no fewer than three countries: Italy, the S.M.O.M., and Vatican City. It is, I think, the most extraordinary panorama of its sort to be seen anywhere on the Continent but the summit of Mt. Blanc, and I heartily commend it to the vacationist in Rome.

WILL CUPPY

Some Royal Stomachs

࿏

Cuppy was an indefatigable researcher; there's documentary proof for every word in what follows.

Royalties, naturally, do not yell and scream for their favorite foods when out in company, so it's not easy to chart their gastronomic adventures. But now and again news of the royal preferences leaked out.

Strawberries are high on the provision list of British royalty, as they should be in every well-regulated dynasty. Queen Victoria was a strawberry fan of the first order. She told somebody in 1875 that the strawberries weren't as good as they were when she was a girl. She likewise declared that the violets did not smell as sweet, and she attributed this all to the wicked gardeners, "who have no feeling for sweet scents and would sacrifice every charm of the kind to size and color." She said, also, they had spoiled the strawberries from the same causes. She may have been right at that, since old ladies still say the same thing.

Queen Victoria had no gastronomic passions, unless it was for strawberries and asparagus. It would be fair to state that during her reign of sixty-four years her intake included a little of everything. Those were the days of huge and varied collations, and she didn't starve. One scarcely pictures her as impetuous at table, yet history relates that she tucked her napkin under her chin—she was built that way. And Mr. Creevey, the diarist, who took a look at her during her early days of queendom, noted in his little book: "She eats quite as heartily as she laughs—I think I may say she gobbles."

Later on, Queen Victoria ate with more composure and was not so much amused. There is, to be sure, the story of the strictly trained little girl who, observing Victoria pick up a stalk of asparagus with her fingers and proceed to deal with it according to the sword-swallowing technique, cried: "Oh, piggy, piggy!" Whereat the queen is said to have laughed and laughed. What else could she do?

The early Georges came straight from Hanover—the natural home and cradle of sausages, you might almost say—bringing with them endless strings of *Leberwurst, Blutwurst,* and other *Würste* and *Saucischen* of many kinds and conditions including, for all I know, the original *Frankfurter* itself; not to mention *Schweinskopf, Speck-suppe,* miscellaneous pickled herrings, and assorted delicatessen.

Aside from the wursts, the first three Georges left no great claims to feeding fame. George I died of acute indigestion, however, after gorging himself on melons while en route to Hanover. He wasn't used to melons. George III's favorite meal was cold mutton and salad, plovers' eggs, stewed peas, and cherry tart.

Victoria's corpulent uncle, George IV, was one of the chicken lovers—and a sound taste that is, too, for a man with the foundations of Great Britain in his charge. He once said to his friend, Mr. Croker, who had been arguing for the pheasant as the gourmet's chief delight: "There I differ from you; nothing is as good as a fowl; if they were as scarce as pheasants and pheasants as plenty as fowls, no one would eat a pheasant."

George IV is often classed as a fancy feeder of parts, probably on the strength of his grand public entertainments. But it is worth recalling that Carême, the celebrated French chef who worked for him at Brighton in the Regency days, left him after a few months, and refused to return at double the salary and the promise of a pension. There was no conversation in England, said Carême. Privately, he more than hinted that the Prince Regent, for all his splendor, had certain bourgeois tastes in food to which he could not be a party. Can it be that the First Gentleman of Europe, as George IV was called, on somewhat flimsy grounds, harbored a secret passion for bubble-and-squeak? Let it pass, but you are probably aware that bubble-and-squeak, nine times out of ten, contains Brussels sprouts. In fact, that's what makes it squeak. And potatoes.

Long before the Hanoverian period, English rulers were busily getting their names associated with certain foods. Skipping such ancients as King Alfred, the cake man, one might start a royal banquet with the soup named dilligrout, for the compounding of which William the Conquerer bestowed the manor of Addington upon Tezelin, his cook, shortly after 1066. Nobody knows today just what this dilligrout was, though some authorities identify it with a fourteenth-century pottage made mostly of almond milk, the brawn of capons, sugar, spice, and chopped parboiled chicken. William would finish off a meal with some tasty deer, boar, and hare caught by himself, like as not, in his New Forest. If anyone else slew a hart or a hind out of turn, his eyes were put out. The Conqueror's son, William Rufus, changed the penalty to death.

William's younger son, Henry I, is the one who died of a surfeit of stewed lampreys, his favorite dish, having eaten all of this peculiar fish in sight against the advice of his doctor. Henry always said that what you like won't hurt you. King John, of Magna Charta fame, was another lamprey enthusiast, as was Edward III, but they managed to keep the hobby within reasonable bounds. The royal accounts of most of the Plantagenets, from Henry II on, especially those of the first three Edwards, show heavy expenditures for fish, particularly herrings, then considered a royal necessity in the form of herring pies.

Edward II fell into disgrace once, before he lost his throne, over cabbage, of all things. "He is accused," runs an old account, "of having made a party on the Thames in a returned fagot-barge, and of buying cabbages of the gardeners on the banks of the river to make his soup." It wasn't the cabbages so much as his frivolous and unkingly manner of obtaining them. Henry III, a little before that time, was unpopular because, after spending all his cash on clothes for his own coronation in 1236, he and his queen had to chisel their meals off their subjects, who were expected to give them rich gifts for the honor of the mealtime visits. The royal spongers ate whatever they got and liked it, presumably.

We have all heard how Henry VIII, not to be outdone by William the Conqueror, presented a manor to a cook for inventing a new pudding sauce. I prefer the version which makes it a sauce for barbecued porpoises, partly because the story makes more sense. Any sauce will do for a pudding, but a sauce for barbecued porpoises would have to be good enough to make you forget what you're eating.

Venison with sour cream may be palatable, and roast bustard has its admirers, but I can't say much for the swans, peacocks, cranes, and sea gulls served at one of Henry's banquets. Sea gulls strike me as something of an emergency ration, like muskrats. One thinks better of the orange pies, quinces, capons, strawberries, and lantony cheeses he sent to Anne Boleyn—before the beheading, of course. And I suppose he and Catherine Howard enjoyed many a plate of his favorite sweets before she in turn hit the chopping block.

It looks now as though Henry VIII never knighted that loin of beef by striking it with his sword and exclaiming, "Arise, Sir Loin!" or whatever he did, thus giving us sirloin. The tale is pinned to James I and Charles II as well, but modern experts say there's nothing in it, that sirloin is simply above-the-loin, from the French *sur,* meaning above. Anyway, Henry thought there was nothing like a good steak.

Mary Queen of Scots hated haggis. She found it so completely atrocious that she said it must never on any account, for the credit of her realm, be taken out of Scotland. For centuries thereafter the obedient Scots, when carrying haggis to English markets, would drop a pinch of the stuff into the river, thus achieving a symbolic or ceremonial destruction without actually endangering sales.

This queen, having been raised abroad, was sold on the French *cuisine,* as was Charles II, the most interesting of her descendants. No account of Stuart food, though, would be complete without a word on William of Orange, the brute who married a daughter of James II and became William III, the lesser half of William and Mary, and a sort of semi-Stuart. He it was who snatched and devoured all the green peas on the table while lunching with Princess Anne, his wife's sister, offering her not a single one. As the Duchess of Marlborough put it, William was no gentleman. His manners, another critic states, were "habitually bad."

Not long afterward Princess Anne was reigning as Queen Anne. She ate far too much of everything, including peas. She drank too much chocolate and far too much brandy.

Imagination boggles at the thought of catering to certain sovereigns who infested continental thrones in the palmy days of monarchy—one of the Looeys, for instance. An exception would be Louis XIII, who made his own griddle cakes, or *les gâteaux de flanelle,* as they were called.

One of Louis XIV's suppers, typical of the meals he downed every night just before retiring, consisted of four plates of different soups, a whole pheasant, a partridge, a large dish of salad, a thumping portion of mutton, two good slices of ham, an entire plateful of French pastry, a small mountain of other sweets, quantities of fruit, and, very likely, any odds and ends he saw lying around. He would then stagger off to his bedroom, where a cold buffet lunch had been placed in case he might be hungry. And he wondered why he had nightmares. Don't worry about all that soup, for it is probable that only a fraction of it ever reached its objective. Louis spilled things.

Glutton that he was, Louis XV possessed a streak of genius enabling him to knock the top off a boiled egg at a single stroke of his fork. Naturally, he always had boiled eggs when the public was let in to see royalty eat, for why hide a talent like that? Between times, he could be found in his kitchen, whipping up a new kind of omlette, making a fresh pot of coffee, swallowing cold *pâtés* of larks, swigging champagne (then a still wine), or taking medicine for his chronic indigestion. Those were stirring times for a gourmand and amateur cook, for the modern French *cuisine* was just getting its grip. "It is an entirely new idiom," wrote an astonished contemporary. "I have tasted viands prepared in so many ways and fashioned with such art that I could not imagine what they were."

Louis XV's wife, Marie Leszczinska, was a prodigious feeder, too. Though not so much so as Marie-Thérèse, the equally lonely mate of Louis XIV, who "ate all day long." Marie Leszczinska's father, the deposed King Stanislas of Poland, invented the rum baba and started the Parisian vogue for onion soup. May I add that Madame de Pompadour created for Louis XV a dish called *filets de volaille de la Bellevue,* which always struck me as the perfect name for whatever it may have been.

Louis XVI was worse and more of it. He has been called, rather neatly, a walking stomach. On the life-and-death flight from the Tuileries with Marie Antoinette and the Dauphin, he slowed up the works by taking along his portable kitchen, with huge hampers of food and drink, and he insisted on stopping three hours for lunch at Étoge, when safety lay only in whirlwind speed. They nabbed him at Varennes. Once home again, he ate a whole chicken and noted in his diary the meals he had polished off on his way back. If you saw anybody gnawing a roast chicken around the palace at any hour of the day or night, it would be Louis.

Nor did Louis XVI go empty in his prison, the Temple, after he had grabbed a crust of bread from a bystander on his way there, more from habit than necessity. His first light lunch in jail featured six veal cutlets, eggs in sherry, a roast chicken, game, and wine. Right up to the very guillotine his midday meal had to include at least three soups, two entrées, two roasts, four entremets, several compotes, fruit, malmsey, claret, and champagne. The night before his execution, his appetite was fine. Well, the poor man was hungry.

Not much of a Looey, as those things go, Louis XVIII was the most uppity of the lot in the matter of victuals. He wouldn't touch a chop or a cutlet unless it had been broiled between two other chops or cutlets to preserve its juices for the greater edification of his alimentary tract. His ortolans, for much the same reason, were cooked inside of partridges stuffed with truffles, so that, according to the learned Ellwanger, "he often hesitated in choosing between the delicate bird and the fragrant esculent." He seems to have been unaware that the truffles with which the partridges were stuffed should have been stuffed with ortolans, a refinement actually achieved a few years afterward.

Napoleon, who was around in those days, was not so particular. All he wanted was quick service, and his minions had to toss him a chicken, cutlets, and coffee the instant he said the word. Perhaps the shoulder of mutton with onions which is said to have lost him the battle of Leipzig was underdone, as the story goes, or maybe he bolted too much at a time, as usual. Waterloo, by the way, was no meeting of gourmets. The Duke of Wellington, who won the fight, once replied to a renowned gastronome who had asked him how he liked the Lucullan fare he had provided, "It was excellent, but to tell you the truth, I don't care much about what I eat."

If a host of today were threatened with a visit from Peter the Great of Russia via some new time wave, his best course would be to cut and run, even if he could afford the necessary barrels of brandy and the tons of provender gulped by the czar and his pals. Peter's habit of forcing all and sundry to drink huge bowls of brandy until they dropped senseless to the floor, or died, might not appeal to some constitutions.

On his visit to England in 1698, he and his entourage of twenty disposed at a single supper of five ribs of beef, one sheep, three quarters of a lamb, a shoulder and a loin of veal, eight pullets, eight rabbits, three dozen of sack, one dozen of claret, and bread and beer in proportion. Before breakfast they demanded seven dozen eggs with salad, and for breakfast proper half a sheep, nineteen pounds of lamb, twenty-two chickens, and three quarts of brandy. Not excessive for twenty-one persons, perhaps, but it all counts up.

At home in Russia, Peter was likely to take a hundred or more friends with him when he dined out. His appetite, except for drink, was nothing fabulous. His biographers speak of caviar, raw herring, sour cabbage soup, beet soup, suckling of pig stuffed with buckwheat, fish pasty, salted cucumbers, oysters, sprats, ducks feet in sour dressing, carrot pie, cherries, and Limburger cheese—a taste acquired abroad. One list of his special likings includes sharp sauces, brown and hard bread, green peas, sweet oranges, apples, pears, and aniseed water (Kümmel). Also vodka, kvass, beer, many kinds of wine, and more brandy. Many of Peter's fantastic cruelties happened when he was not, to put it mildly, quite himself.

Catherine the Great kept her own table expenses down, but footed enormous grocery bills for her lovers. Her favorite dish was boiled beef with salted cucumbers; her drinks were water with gooseberry syrup and five daily cups of coffee, brewed from a whole pound of coffee and so strong that nobody else could touch it. She took a great deal of snuff, and she pinned her napkin securely under her chin before meals. "She could not otherwise," history states, "eat an egg without dropping half of it on her collarette."

The tastes of Frederick the Great of Prussia, an elder contemporary of Catherine, were something else again. He stuffed himself with eel pies and other rich foods so highly spiced that his physicians were always in despair; and Prussian peas, which Dr. Zimmermann declared to be "certainly the hardest in the world," not to mention that he flavored his coffee with champagne and mustard. He should have stuck to bacon and greens, like his father, Frederick William I.

Eel pies, oddly enough, hastened the end of Charles V, king of Spain and emperor of the Holy Roman Empire, who passed away in 1558 after many years of the most spectacular gorging ever witnessed in Europe. A victim of gout and indigestion from early youth, he kept right on eating to the last, preferring—as did Frederick the Great—whatever was worst for his case; and this in spite of the fact that he had long since lost all sense of taste. Fish always made him ill, but that didn't stop him. Eel pies gave him colic, so he demanded another, and yet another. One day he ate his last eel pie. Where there's a will, there's a way.

JOHN BUCHAN

Space

❧

An eerie piece of "anti-science fiction."

Leithen told me this story one evening in early September as we sat beside the pony track which gropes its way from Glenavelin up the Correi na Sidhe. I had arrived that afternoon from the south, while he had been taking an off day from a week's stalking, so we had walked up the glen together after tea to get the news of the forest. A rifle was out on the Correi na Sidhe beat, and a thin spire of smoke had risen from the top of Sgurr Dearg to show that a stag had been killed at the burn head. The lumpish hill pony with its deer saddle had gone up the Correi in a gillie's charge, while we followed at leisure, picking our way among the loose granite rocks and the patches of wet bogland. The track climbed high on one of the ridges of Sgurr Dearg, till it hung over a caldron of green glen with the Alt-na-Sidhe churning in its linn a thousand feet below. It was a breathless evening, I remember, with a pale-blue sky just clearing from the haze of the day. West-wind weather may make the north, even in September, no bad imitation of the tropics, and I sincerely pitied the man who all these stifling hours had been toiling on the screes of Sgurr Dearg. By and by we sat down on a bank of heather, and idly watched the trough swimming at our feet. The clatter of the pony's hoofs grew fainter, the drone of bees had gone, even the midges seemed to have forgotten their calling. No place on earth can be so deathly still as a deer forest early in the season before the stags have begun roaring, for there are no sheep with their homely noises, and only the rare croak of a raven breaks the silence. The hillside was far from sheer—one could have walked down with a little care—but something in the shape of the hollow and the remote gleam of white water gave it an air of extraordinary depth and space. There was a shimmer left from the day's heat, which invested bracken and rock and scree with a curious airy unreality. One could almost have believed that the eye had tricked the mind, that all was mirage, that five yards from the path the solid earth fell away into nothingness. I have a bad head, and instinctively I drew farther back into the heather. Leithen's eyes were looking vacantly before him.

"Did you ever know Hollond?" he asked.

Then he laughed shortly. "I don't know why I asked that, but somehow this place reminded me of Hollond. That glimmering hollow looks as if it were the beginning of eternity. It must be eerie to live with the feeling always on one."

Leithen seemed disinclined for further exercise. He lit a pipe and smoked quietly for a little. "Odd that you didn't know Hollond. You must have heard his name. I thought you amused yourself with metaphysics."

Then I remembered. There had been an erratic genius who had written some articles in *Mind* on that dreary subject, the mathematical conception of infinity. Men had praised them to me, but I confess I never quite understood their argument. "Wasn't he some sort of mathematical professor?" I asked.

"He was, and, in his own way, a tremendous swell. He wrote a book on number which has translations in every European language. He is dead now, and the Royal Society founded a medal in his honor. But I wasn't thinking of that side of him."

It was the time and place for a story, for the pony would not be back for an hour. So I asked Leithen about the other side of Hollond which was recalled to him by Correi na Sidhe. He seemed a little unwilling to speak. . . .

"I wonder if you will understand it. You ought to, of course, better than me, for you know something of philosophy. But it took me a long time to get the hang of it, and I can't give you any kind of explanation. He was my fag at Eton, and when I began to get on at the bar I was able to advise him on one or two private matters, so that he rather fancied my legal ability. He came to me with his story because he had to tell someone, and he wouldn't trust a colleague. He said he didn't want a scientist to know, for scientists were either pledged to their own theories and wouldn't understand, or, if they understood, would get ahead of him in his researches. He wanted a lawyer, he said, who was accustomed to weighing evidence. That was good sense, for evidence must always be judged by the same laws, and I suppose in the long run the most abstruse business comes down to a fairly simple deduction from certain data. Anyhow, that was the way he used to talk, and I listened to him, for I liked the man, and had an enormous respect for his brains. At Eton he sluiced down all the mathematics they could give him, and he was an astonishing swell at Cambridge. He was a simple fellow, too, and talked no more jargon than he could help. I used to climb with him in the Alps now and then, and you would never have guessed that he had any thoughts beyond getting up steep rocks.

"It was at Chamonix, I remember, that I first got a hint of the matter that was filling his mind. We had been taking an off day, and were sitting in the hotel garden, watching the Aiguilles getting purple in the twilight. Chamonix always makes me choke a little— it is so crushed in by those great snow masses. I said something about it—said I liked open spaces like the Gornergrat or the Bel Alp better. He asked me why: if it was the difference of the air, or merely the wider horizon? I said it was the sense of not being crowded, of living in an empty world. He repeated the word 'empty' and laughed.

" 'By "empty" you mean,' he said, 'where things don't knock up against you?'

"I told him No. I meant just empty, void, nothing but blank ether.

" 'You don't knock up against things here, and the air is as good as you want. It can't be the lack of ordinary emptiness you feel.'

"I agreed that the word needed explaining. 'I suppose it is mental restlessness,' I said. 'I like to feel that for a tremendous distance there is nothing round me. Why, I don't know. Some men are built the other way and have a terror of space.'

"He said that that was better. 'It is a personal fancy, and depends on your *knowing* that there is nothing between you and the top of the Dent Blanche. And you know because your eyes tell you there is nothing. Even if you were blind, you might have a sort of sense about adjacent matter. Blind men often have it. But in any case, whether got from instinct or sight, the *knowledge* is what matters.'

"Hollond was embarking on a Socratic dialogue in which I could see little point. I told him so, and he laughed.

" 'I am not sure that I am very clear myself. But yes—there *is* a point. Supposing you knew—not by sight or by instinct, but by sheer intellectual knowledge, as I know the truth of a mathematical proposition—that what we call empty space was full, crammed. Not with lumps of what we call matter like hills and houses, but with things as real—as real to the mind. Would you still feel crowded?'

" 'No,' I said, 'I don't think so. It is only what we call matter that signifies. It would be just as well not to feel crowded by the other thing, for there would be no escape from it. But what are you getting at? Do you mean atoms or electric currents or what?'

"He said he wasn't thinking about that sort of thing, and began to talk of another subject.

"Next night, when we were pigging it at the Géant *cabane,* he started again on the same tack. He asked me how I accounted for the fact that animals could find their way back over great tracts of unknown country. I said I supposed it was the homing instinct.

" 'Rubbish, man,' he said. 'That's only another name for the puzzle, not an explanation. There must be some reason for it. They must *know* something that we cannot understand. Tie a cat in a bag and take it fifty miles by train and it will make its way home. That cat has some clue that we haven't.'

"I was tired and sleepy, and told him that I did not care a rush about the psychology of cats. But he was not to be snubbed, and went on talking.

" 'How if space is really full of things we cannot see and as yet do not know? How if all animals and some savages have a cell in their brain or a nerve which responds to the invisible world? How if all space be full of these landmarks, not material in our sense, but quite real? A dog barks at nothing, a wild beast makes an aimless circuit. Why? Perhaps because space is made up of corridors and alleys, ways to travel and things to shun? For all we know, to a greater intelligence than ours the top of Mont Blanc may be as crowded as Piccadilly Circus.'

"But at that point I fell asleep and left Hollond to repeat his questions to a guide who knew no English and a snoring porter.

"Six months later, one foggy January afternoon, Hollond rang me up at the Temple and proposed to come to see me that night after dinner. I thought he wanted to talk Alpine shop, but he turned up in Duke Street about nine with a kit-bag full of papers. He was an odd fellow to look at—a yellowish face with the skin stretched tight on the cheekbones, clean-shaven, a sharp chin which he kept poking forward, and deep-set, grayish eyes. He was a hard fellow, too, always in pretty good condition, which was remarkable considering how he slaved for nine months out of the twelve. He had a quiet, slow-spoken manner, but that night I saw that he was considerably excited.

"He said that he had come to me because we were old friends. He proposed to tell me a tremendous secret. 'I must get another mind to work on it or I'll go crazy. I don't want a scientist. I want a plain man.'

"Then he fixed me with a look like a tragic actor's. 'Do you remember that talk we had in August at Chamonix—about space? I daresay you thought I was playing the fool. So I was in a sense, but I was feeling my way toward something which has been in my mind for ten years. Now I have got it, and you must hear about it. You may take my word that it's a pretty startling discovery.'

"I lit a pipe and told him to go ahead, warning him that I knew about as much science as the dustman.

"I am bound to say that it took me a long time to understand what he meant. He began by saying that everybody thought of space as an 'empty homogeneous medium.' 'Never mind at present what the ultimate constituents of that medium are. We take it as a finished product, and we think of it as mere extension, something without any quality at all. That is the view of civilized man. You will find all the philosophers taking it for granted. Yes, but every living thing does not take that view. An animal, for instance. It feels a kind of quality in space. It can find its way over new country because it perceives certain landmarks, not necessarily material, but perceptible, or if you like, intelligible. Take an Australian savage. He has the same power, and, I believe, for the same reason. He is conscious of intelligible landmarks.'

" 'You mean what people call a sense of direction,' I put in.

" 'Yes, but what in heaven's name is a sense of direction? The phrase explains nothing. However incoherent the mind of the animal or the savage may be, it is there somewhere, working on some data. I've been all through the psychological and anthropological side of the business, and after you eliminate clues from sight and hearing and smell and half-conscious memory there remains a solid lump of the inexplicable.'

"Hollond's eye had kindled, and he sat doubled up in his chair, dominating me with a finger.

" 'Here, then, is a power which man is civilizing himself out of. Call it anything you like, but you must admit that it is a power. Don't you see that it is a perception of another kind of reality that we are leaving behind us? . . . Well, you know the way nature works. The wheel comes full circle, and what we think we have lost we regain in a higher form. So for a long time I have been wondering whether the civilized mind could not re-create for itself this lost gift, the gift of seeing the quality of space. I mean that I wondered whether the scientific modern brain could not get to the stage of realizing that space is not an empty homogeneous medium, but full of intricate differences, intelligible and real, though not with our common reality.'

"I found all this very puzzling, and he had to repeat it several times before I got a glimpse of what he was talking about.

" 'I've wondered for a long time,' he went on, 'but now, quite suddenly, I have begun to know.' He stopped and asked me abruptly if I knew much about mathematics.

" 'It's a pity,' he said, 'but the main point is not technical, though I wish you could appreciate the beauty of some of my proofs.' Then he began to tell me about his last six months' work. I should have mentioned that he was a brilliant physicist besides other things. All Hollond's tastes were on the borderlands of sciences, where mathematics fades into metaphysics and physics merges in the abstrusest kind of mathematics. Well, it seems he had been working for years at the ultimate problem of matter, and especially of that rarefied matter we call ether or space. I forget what his view was—atoms or molecules or electric waves. If he ever told me I have forgotten, but I'm not certain that I ever knew. However, the point was that these ultimate constituents were dynamic and mobile, not a mere passive medium but a medium in constant movement and change. He claimed to have discovered—by ordinary inductive experiment—that the constituents of ether possessed certain functions, and moved in certain figures obedient to certain mathematical laws. Space, I gathered, was perpetually 'forming fours' in some fancy way.

"Here he left his physics and became the mathematician. Among his mathematical discoveries had been certain curves or figures or something whose behavior involved a new dimension. I gathered that this wasn't the ordinary fourth dimension that people talk of, but that fourth-dimensional inwardness or involution was part of it. The explanation lay in the pile of manuscripts he left with me, but though I tried honestly I couldn't get the hang of it. My mathematics stopped with desperate finality just as he got into his subject.

"His point was that the constituents of space moved according to these new mathematical figures of his. They were always changing, but the principles of their change were as fixed as the law of gravitation. Therefore, if you once grasped these principles you knew the contents of the void. What do you make of that?"

I said that it seemed to me a reasonable enough argument, but that it got one very little way forward. "A man," I said, "might know the contents of space and the laws of their arrangement and yet be unable to see anything more than his fellows. It is a purely academic knowledge. His mind knows it as the result of many deductions, but his senses perceive nothing."

Leithen laughed. "Just what I said to Hollond. He asked the opinion of my legal mind. I said I could not pronounce on his argument, but that I could point out that he had established no *trait d'union* between the intellect which understood and the senses which perceived. It was like a blind man with immense knowledge but no eyes, and therefore no peg to hang his knowledge on and make it useful. He had not explained his savage or his cat. 'Hang it, man,' I said, 'before you can appreciate the existence of your spatial forms you have to go through elaborate experiments and deductions. You can't be doing that every minute. Therefore you don't get any nearer to the *use* of the sense you say that man once possessed, though you can explain it a bit.' "

"What did he say?" I asked.

"The funny thing was that he never seemed to see my difficulty. When I kept bringing him back to it he shied off with a new wild theory of perception. He argued that the mind can live in a world of realities without any sensuous stimulus to connect them with the world of our ordinary life. Of course that wasn't my point. I supposed that this world of space was real enough to him, but I wanted to know how he got there. He never answered me. He was the typical Cambridge man, you know—dogmatic about uncertainties, but curiously diffident about the obvious. He labored to get me to understand the notion of his mathematical forms, which I was quite willing to take on trust from him. Some queer things he said, too. He took our feeling about left and right as an example of our instinct for the quality of space. But when I objected that left and right varied with each object, and only existed in connection with some definite material thing, he said that that was exactly what he meant. It was an example of the mobility of the spatial forms. Do you see any sense in that?"

I shook my head. It seemed to me pure craziness.

"And then he tried to show me what he called the 'involution of space,' by taking two points on a piece of paper. The points were a foot away when the paper was flat, but they coincided when it was doubled up. He said that there were no gaps between the figures, for the medium was continuous, and he took as an illustration the loops on a cord. You are to think of a cord always looping and unlooping itself according to certain mathematical laws. Oh, I tell you, I gave up trying to follow him. And he was so desperately in earnest all the time. By his account space was a sort of mathematical pandemonium."

Leithen stopped to refill his pipe, and I mused upon the ironic fate which had compelled a mathematical genius to make his sole confidant of a philistine lawyer, and induced that lawyer to repeat it confusedly to an ignoramus at twilight on a Scotch hill. As told by Leithen it was a very halting tale.

"But there was one thing I could see very clearly," Leithen went on, "and that was Hollond's own case. This crowded world of space was perfectly real to him. How he had got to it I do not know. Perhaps his mind, dwelling constantly on the problem, had unsealed some atrophied cell and restored the old instinct. Anyhow, he was living his daily life with a foot in each world.

"He often came to see me, and after the first hectic discussions he didn't talk much. There was no noticeable change in him—a little more abstracted perhaps. He would walk in the street or come into a room with a quick look round him, and sometimes for no earthly reason he would swerve. Did you ever watch a cat crossing a room? It sidles along by the furniture and walks over an open space of carpet as if it were picking its way among obstacles. Well, Hollond behaved like that, but he had always been counted a little odd, and nobody noticed it but me.

"I knew better than to chaff him, and we had stopped argument, so there wasn't much to be said. But sometimes he would give me news about his experiences. The whole thing was perfectly clear and scientific and aboveboard, and nothing creepy about it. You know how I hate the washy supernatural stuff they give us nowadays. Hollond was well and fit, with an appetite like a hunter. But as he talked, sometimes—well, you know I haven't much in the way of nerves or imagination—but I used to get a little eerie. Used to feel the solid earth dissolving round me. It was the opposite of vertigo, if you understand me—a sense of airy realities crowding in on you—crowding the mind, that is, not the body.

"I gathered from Hollond that he was always conscious of corridors and halls and alleys in space, shifting, but shifting according to inexorable laws. I never could get quite clear as to what this consciousness was like. When I asked he used to look puzzled and worried and helpless. I made out from him that one landmark involved a sequence, and once given a bearing from an object you could keep the direction without a mistake. He told me he could easily, if he wanted, go in a dirigible from the top of Mont Blanc to the top of Snowdon in the thickest fog and without a compass, if he were given the proper angle to start from. I confess I didn't follow that myself. Material objects had nothing to do with the spatial forms, for a table or a bed in our world might be placed across a corridor of space. The forms played their game independent of our kind of reality. But the worst of it was that if you kept your mind too much in one world you were apt to forget about the other, and Hollond was always barking his shins on stones and chairs and things.

"He told me all this quite simply and frankly. Remember his mind and no other part of him lived in his new world. He said it gave him an odd sense of detachment to sit in a room among people, and to know that nothing there but himself had any relation at all to the infinite strange world of space that flowed around them. He would listen, he said, to a great man talking, with one eye on the cat on the rug, thinking to himself how much more the cat knew than the man."

"How long was it before he went mad?" I asked.

It was a foolish question and made Leithen cross. "He never went mad in your sense. My dear fellow, you're very much wrong if you think there was anything pathological about him—then. The man was brilliantly sane. His mind was as keen as a keen sword. I couldn't understand him, but I could judge of his sanity right enough."

I asked if it made him happy or miserable.

"At first I think it made him uncomfortable. He was restless because he knew too much and too little. The unknown pressed in on his mind, as bad air weighs on the lungs. Then it lightened, and he accepted the new world in the same sober practical way that he took other things. I think that the free exercise of his mind in a pure medium gave him a feeling of extraordinary power and ease. His eyes used to sparkle when he talked. And another odd thing he told me. He was a keen rock climber, but, curiously enough, he had never a very good head. Dizzy heights always worried him, though he managed to keep hold on himself. But now all that had gone. The sense of the fullness of space made him as happy—happier I believe—with his legs dangling into eternity, as sitting before his own study fire.

"I remember saying that it was all rather like the medieval wizards who made their spells by means of numbers and figures.

"He caught me up at once, 'Not numbers,' he said. 'Number has no place in nature. It is an invention of the human mind to atone for a bad memory. But figures are a different matter. All the mysteries of the world are in them, and the old magicians knew that at least, if they knew no more.'

"He had only one grievance. He complained that it was terribly lonely. 'It is the desolation,' he would quote, 'spoken of by Daniel the prophet.' He would spend hours traveling those eerie shifting corridors of space with no hint of another human soul. How could there be? It was a world of pure reason, where human personality had no place. What puzzled me was why he should feel the absence of this. One wouldn't, you know, in an intricate problem of geometry or a game of chess. I asked him, but he didn't understand the question. I puzzled over it a good deal, for it seemed to me that if Hollond felt lonely, there must be more in this world of his than we imagined. I began to wonder if there was any truth in fads like psychical research. Also, I was not so sure that he was as normal as I had thought: it looked as if his nerves might be going bad.

"Oddly enough, Hollond was getting on the same track himself. He had discovered, so he said, that in sleep everybody now and then lived in this new world of his. You know how one dreams of triangular railway platforms with trains running simultaneously down all three sides and not colliding. Well, this sort of cantrip was 'common form,' as we say at the bar, in Hollond's space, and he was very curious about the why and wherefore of sleep. He began to haunt psychological laboratories, where they experiment with the char- woman and the odd-man, and he used to go up to Cambridge for *séances*. It was a foreign atmosphere to him, and I don't think he was very happy in it. He found so many charlatans that he used to get angry and declare he would be better employed at mothers' meetings!"

From far up the glen came the sound of the pony's hoofs. The stag had been loaded up, and the gillies were returning. Leithen looked at his watch. "We'd better wait and see the beast," he said.

. . . "Well, nothing happened for more than a year. Then one evening in May he burst into my rooms in high excitement. You un- derstand quite clearly that there was no suspicion of horror or fright or anything unpleasant about this world he had discovered. It was simply a series of interesting and difficult problems. All this time Hol- lond had been rather extra well and cheery. But when he came in I thought I noticed a different look in his eyes, something puzzled and diffident and apprehensive.

"'There's a queer performance going on in the other world,' he said. 'It's unbelievable. I never dreamed of such a thing. I—I don't quite know how to put it, and I don't know how to explain it, but— but I am becoming aware that there are other beings—other minds —moving in space besides mine.'

"I suppose I ought to have realized then that things were beginning to go wrong. But it was very difficult, he was so rational and anxious to make it all clear. I asked him how he knew. There could, of course, on his own showing be no *change* in that world, for the forms of space moved and existed under inexorable laws. He said he found his own mind failing him at points. There would come over him a sense of fear—intellectual fear—and weakness, a sense of something else, quite alien to space, thwarting him. Of course he could only describe his impressions very lamely, for they were purely of the mind, and he had no material peg to hang them on, so that I could realize them. But the gist of it was that he had been gradually becoming conscious of what he called 'presences' in his world. They had no effect on space —did not leave footprints in its corridors, for instance—but they affected his mind. There was some mysterious contact established between him and them. I asked him if the affection was unpleasant, and he said 'No, not exactly.' But I could see a hint of fear in his eyes.

"Think of it. Try to realize what intellectual fear is. I can't, but it is conceivable. To you and me fear implies pain to ourselves or some other, and such pain is always in the last resort pain of the flesh. Consider it carefully and you will see that it is so. But imagine fear so sublimated and transmuted as to be the tension of pure spirit. I can't realize it, but I think it possible. I don't pretend to understand how Hollond got to know about these presences. But there was no doubt about the fact. He was positive, and he wasn't in the least mad—not in our sense. In that very month he published his book on number, and gave a German professor who attacked it a most tremendous public trouncing.

"I know what you are going to say—that the fancy was a weakening of the mind from within. I admit I should have thought of that, but he looked so confoundedly sane and able that it seemed ridiculous. He kept asking me my opinion, as a lawyer, on the facts he offered. It was the oddest case ever put before me, but I did my best for him. I dropped all my own views of sense and nonsense. I told him that, taking all that he had told me as fact, the presences might be either ordinary minds traversing space in sleep; or minds such as his which had independently captured the sense of space's quality; or, finally, the spirits of just men made perfect, behaving as psychical researchers think they do. It was a ridiculous task to set a prosaic man, and I wasn't quite serious. But Hollond was serious enough.

"He admitted that all three explanation were conceivable, but he was very doubtful about the first. The projection of the spirit into space during sleep, he thought, was a faint and feeble thing, and these were powerful presences. With the second and the third he was rather impressed. I suppose I should have seen what was happening and tried to stop it; at least, looking back that seems to have been my duty. But it was difficult to think that anything was wrong with Hollond; indeed the odd thing is that all this time the idea of madness never entered my head. I rather backed him up. Somehow the thing took my fancy, though I thought it moonshine at the bottom of my heart. I enlarged on the pioneering before him. 'Think,' I told him, 'what may be waiting for you. You may discover the meaning of 'spirit.' You may open up a new world, as rich as the old one but imperishable. You may prove to mankind their immortality and deliver them forever from the fear of death. Why, man, you are picking at the lock of all the world's mysteries.'

"But Hollond did not cheer up. He seemed strangely languid and dispirited. 'That is all true enough,' he said, 'if you are right, if your alternatives are exhaustive. But suppose they are something else, something . . .' What that 'something' might be he had apparently no idea, and very soon he went away.

"He said another thing before he left. He asked me if I ever read poetry, and I said, 'Not often.' Nor did he: but he had picked up a little book somewhere and found a man who knew about the presences. I think his name was Traherne, one of the seventeenth-century fellows. He quoted a verse which stuck to my flypaper memory. It ran something like this:

> Within the region of the air,
> Compassed about with Heavens fair,
> Great tracts of lands there may be found,
>   Where many numerous hosts,
>   In those far distant coasts,
> For other great and glorious ends
> Inhabit, my yet unknown friends.

Hollond was positive he did not mean angels or anything of the sort. I told him that Traherne evidently took a cheerful view of them. He admitted that, but added: 'He had religion, you see. He believed that everything was for the best. I am not a man of faith, and can only take comfort from what I understand. I'm in the dark, I tell you. . . .'

"Next week I was busy with the Chilean arbitration case, and saw nobody for a couple of months. Then one evening I ran against Hollond on the Embankment, and thought him looking horribly ill. He walked back with me to my rooms and hardly uttered one word all the way. I gave him a stiff whisky-and-soda, which he gulped down absentmindedly. There was that strained, hunted look in his eyes that you see in a frightened animal's. He was always lean, but now he had fallen away to skin and bone.

" 'I can't stay long,' he told me, 'for I'm off to the Alps tomorrow and I have a lot to do.' Before then he used to plunge readily into his story, but now he seemed shy about beginning. Indeed I had to ask him a question.

" 'Things are difficult,' he said hesitatingly, 'and rather distressing. Do you know, Leithen, I think you were wrong about—about what I spoke to you of. You said there must be one of three explanations. I am beginning t think that there is a fourth. . . .'

"He stopped for a second or two, then suddenly leaned forward and gripped my knee so fiercely that I cried out. 'That world is the desolation,' he said in a choking voice, 'and perhaps I am getting near the abomination of the desolation that the old prophet spoke of. I tell you, man, I am on the edge of a terror, a terror,' he almost screamed, 'that no mortal can think of and live.'

"You can imagine that I was considerably startled. It was lightning out of a clear sky. How the devil could one associate horror with mathematics? I don't see it yet. . . . At any rate, I— You may be sure I cursed my folly for ever pretending to take him seriously. The only way would have been to have laughed him out of it at the start. And yet I couldn't, you know—it was too real and reasonable. Anyhow, I tried a firm tone now, and told him the whole thing was arrant raving bosh. I bade him be a man and pull himself together. I made him dine with me, and took him home, and got him into a better state of mind before he went to bed. Next morning I saw him off at Charing Cross, very haggard still, but better. He promised to write to me pretty often. . . ."

The pony, with a great eleven-pointer lurching athwart its back, was abreast of us, and from the autumn mist came the sound of soft Highland voices. Leithen and I got up to go, when we heard that the rifle had made direct for the lodge by a short cut past the Sanctuary. In the wake of the gillies we descended the Correi road into a glen all swimming with dim purple shadows. The pony minced and boggled;

the stag's antlers stood out sharp on the rise against a patch of sky, looking like a skeleton tree. Then we dropped into a covert of birches and emerged on the white glen highway.

Leithen's story had bored and puzzled me at the start, but now it had somehow gripped my fancy. Space a domain of endless corridors, and presences moving in them! The world was not quite the same as an hour ago. It was the hour, as the French say, "between dog and wolf," when the mind is disposed to marvels. I thought of my stalking on the morrow, and was miserably conscious that I would miss my stag. Those airy forms would get in the way. Confound Leithen and his yarns!

"I want to hear the end of your story," I told him, as the lights of the lodge showed half a mile distant.

"The end was a tragedy," he said slowly. "I don't much care to talk about it. But how was I to know? I couldn't see the nerve going. You see I couldn't believe it was all nonsense. If I could I might have seen. But I still think there was something in it—up to a point. Oh, I agree he went mad in the end. It is the only explanation. Something must have snapped in that fine brain, and he saw the little bit more which we call madness. Thank God, you and I are prosaic fellows. . . .

"I was going out to Chamonix myself a week later. But before I started I got a postcard from Hollond, the only word from him. He had printed my name and address, and on the other side had scribbled six words—'*I know at last—God's mercy.—H. G. H.*' The handwriting was like a sick man of ninety. I knew that things must be pretty bad with my friend.

"I got to Chamonix in time for his funeral. An ordinary climbing accident—you probably read about it in the papers. The press talked about the toll which the Alps took from intellectuals—the usual rot. There was an inquiry, but the facts were quite simple. The body was only recognized by the clothes. He had fallen several thousand feet.

"It seems that he had climbed for a few days with one of the Kronigs and Dupont, and they had done some hair-raising things on the Aiguilles. Dupont told me that they had found a new route up the Montanvert side of the Charmoz. He said that Hollond climbed like a '*diable fou,*' and if you know Dupont's standard of madness you will see that the pace must have been pretty hot. 'But monsieur was sick,' he added; 'his eyes were not good. And I and Franz, we were grieved for him and a little afraid. We were glad when he left us.'

"He dismissed the guides two days before his death. The next day he spent in the hotel, getting his affairs straight. He left everything in perfect order, but not a line to a soul, not even to his sister. The following day he set out alone about three in the morning for the Grèpon. He took the road up the Nantillons glacier to the Col, and then he must have climbed the Mummery crack by himself. After that he left the ordinary route and tried a new traverse across the Mer de Glace face. Somewhere near the top he fell, and next day a party going to the Dent du Requin found him on the rocks thousands of feet below.

"He had slipped in attempting the most foolhardy course on earth, and there was a lot of talk about the dangers of guideless climbing. But I guessed the truth, and I am sure Dupont knew, though he held his tongue. . . ."

We were now on the gravel of the drive, and I was feeling better. The thought of dinner warmed my heart, and drove out the eeriness of the twilight glen. The hour between dog and wolf was passing. After all, there was a gross and jolly earth at hand for wise men who had a mind to comfort.

Leithen, I saw, did not share my mood. He looked glum and puzzled, as if his tale had aroused grim memories. He finished it at the lodge door.

". . . For, of course, he had gone out that day to die. He had seen the something more, the little bit too much, which plucks a man from his moorings. He had gone so far into the land of pure spirit that he must needs go further and shed the fleshly envelope that cumbered him. God send that he found rest! I believe that he chose the steepest cliff in the Alps for a purpose. He wanted to be unrecognizable. He was a brave man and a good citizen. I think he hoped that those who found him might not see the look in his eyes."

BERTON ROUECHÉ

The Steeple

𝕰

An enormous story—softly told in approved New Yorker *style.*

One early autumn afternoon, on a day of wild winds and sudden silences, I drove out to the village of Sag Harbor to make a pilgrimage to the Whalers' Presbyterian Church there. Sag Harbor is on the north shore of the southeastern fluke of Long Island and covers a secluded point on Shelter Island Sound, near the head of Gardiners Bay. It was settled around the beginning of the eighteenth century. For a few years just before the Revolution, it was a busier port than New York; it once had as rich and restless a whaling fleet as New Bedford or Nantucket; it has been almost motionless since the Civil War; and it is full of big, splendid, creaky old houses and intimations of mortality. The Whalers' Church, although little more than a hundred years old, is its noblest and most disquieting structure. It would be arresting anywhere. Except for a mean and slovenly copy in Essex, Connecticut, it is the only building of its kind in the world.

The Whalers' Church was designed by Minard Lafever, a gifted and expensive New York architect, whose more accessible works include the Church of St. James, near Chatham Square, and the Church of the Holy Trinity, in Brooklyn, and it was put together by local shipbuilders and ships' carpenters. The foundation was laid in the spring of 1843 and the church was dedicated on May 16, 1844. It cost seventeen thousand dollars. That was an immense sum in the 1840's (carpenters were paid a dollar and a half for a twelve-hour day, the finest St. Croix rum sold for three cents a glass, and clear Havana stogies were two cents each), but it was not considered excessive by Sag Harbor Presbyterians. Most of the parishioners who made substantial contributions to the building fund were whaling officers, shipyard owners, shipowners, or ship chandlers and outfitters, and several were among the wealthiest men on Long Island; practically all the members of the congregation, including farmers and shopkeepers, held rewarding shares in at least one whaler. The first Sag Harbor whaling voyage on record was made in 1775, by a brig called the *Lucy;* she returned home with some three hundred barrels of oil on that occasion. The last Sag Harbor whaler was the *Myra;* she put out in July 1871 and never returned.

In the intervening years, Sag Harbor whalers made more than five hundred successful voyages, many of which lasted three or four years, and brought back between twenty-five and thirty million dollars' worth of whale oil, sperm oil, and whalebone. The first ship to sail through the Bering Strait was the *Superior,* a Sag Harbor whaler, in 1848. The first American ship to enter a Japanese port was the *Manhattan,* in 1845, commanded by Mercator Cooper, a Sag Harbor whaling captain; Commodore Matthew C. Perry, who is commonly celebrated for this feat, turned up off Japan eight years later. Between 1820 and 1850, Sag Harbor's richest period, the local fleet brought in a total of 83,102 barrels of sperm oil, 812,595 barrels of whale oil, and 6,728,809 pounds of bone, with an aggregate value of more than $15 million. The industry began to decline in the 1850's, and it collapsed in the '60's; an abundance of petroleum, which had just been discovered in western Pennsylvania, had all but put an end to the demand for whale oil. The Whalers' Church was completed in Sag Harbor's most vigorous year; the town's fleet in 1844 numbered sixty-three vessels, and its population was 3,621. Sag Harbor no longer has even the semblance of a fleet, its harbor is deserted except for a few pleasure craft in summer, its railroad station has been boarded up since 1939, and its population is 2,373.

Sag Harbor is surrounded on the north and east by the waters of Shelter Island Sound, and a sandy cove hems it in on the west. Above it, to the south, rises a wilderness of scrub oak and jack pine that stretches almost to the ocean, seven miles away. Three or four rambling, humpbacked roads, cut through the woods, link the village to the Montauk Highway, which skirts the seacoast. On the day of my visit I turned into one of these roads at about two o'clock. After a couple of miles, I passed a woman on a wobbly bicycle. Farther on, I passed a weathered sign: GOOD LUCK AND SAFE RETURN—WELCOME TO SAG HARBOR. Just beyond it was a cemetery. Then the road curved, and I emerged abruptly into a wide, angular, downhill street of arching elms and peeling white clapboard houses. The houses sat close to the sidewalk, behind rickety picket fences; there were leaded fanlights over most of their doorways, and one had a widow's walk on the roof. An elderly man in a blue serge suit and an army sweather was puttering around in one of the yards. He was the only human being in sight. I pulled up and asked him if he could direct me to the Whalers' Church. He leaned on the fence and gazed at me.

"Want to have a look at it, eh?" he said. "Well, it's a sight. Should have come down here ten years ago, though, before the hurricane carried off the steeple. Wouldn't of been any need to ask your way then. You'd of seen it for yourself from here, downstreet, or anywhere. Far as that goes, you could see it from Montauk. That steeple was two hundred feet high, more or less, and there wasn't two parts of it alike. They were every one different. That steeple really tickled me. I enjoyed looking at it. Religion aside, of course. I run with the Methodists, when I go." The old man fished a package of chewing gum from his pocket, popped a stick into his mouth, and jerked his thumb in the direction I was headed. "Two blocks down, turn left at the blinker, and you'll see it," he said. "I guess there's enough of it left to hold you."

I thanked him and drove on down the windy, deserted street. The air smelled wet and salty. As I made the turn at the blinker, a ragged army of gulls wheeled overhead. Then I saw the church. It came hulking up through the heaving treetops—big and baleful and as white as an old clamshell. Set on a wooded knoll, well back from the street, between a row of splayed early eighteenth-century cottages and a crumbling graveyard, it looked larger than Grand Central Station, and it held me. I parked my car and got out and stared at it. It is a numbing blend of the chaste, the finical, and the stolid. Its façade is predominantly Babylonian and Theban Egyptian in style. The auditorium—of clapboard, slate-roofed, boxy, and severe—is pure meetinghouse colonial. A kind of annex, jutting out in back, is mid-Victorian. From where I stood, at one end of a semicircular walk leading up to the church, only a corner of the main body of the building was visible. The auditorium is 130 feet long, 65 feet wide, and the equivalent of three considerable stories in height, but the façade obscured it. A massive, shingle-sided, 100-foot truncated pyramidal wooden tower, some 40 feet square at the base and tapering to almost half that at the top, forms the center of the façade. It is flanked by two similar, though broader and slightly lower, wing pylons. Surmounting each of the pylons and the tower is a fragile parapet. The cornices are decorated with a complicated Corinthian frosting. A toothy row of antefixes conceals the eaves. Just below this is a banding of classic-Grecian verticals. An uncovered porch, with an iron-pipe railing, runs the width of the façade. Opening onto it are three narrow, story-high, white, paneled doors, one in the tower and one in each pylon. The antefixes are repeated on their cornices, and the center door is crowned by another parapet. Above each door, and rising almost to the roof line, is a tall window of opaque and faintly lavender small-paned glass. I stood there for a minute or two gazing up at the church, and then I started up the walk leading to the porch. It was hard to imagine a mighty steeple rearing above that vast, chalky face. The building didn't look at all incomplete. It didn't even look old. It looked like a brand-new mausoleum.

I tried all three doors and found them locked. As I turned uncertainly away from the last one, I heard voices approaching, and then a sudden shriek of laughter. I almost jumped. Then an unshaven old man in work clothes and a hunting cap came around the side of the building. With him was a somewhat younger woman. She had on a pink dress, a grass-green coat, and golden slippers, and there was a red patent-leather pocketbook under her arm. I went over to them. They were laughing and chattering, but they broke off when they saw me, and stopped dead. I said I had come out from New York to see the church and asked if the pastor was around.

"Here?" the man said, studying me closely. "Ain't he down to the manse?"

His companion giggled. "If Reverend Crawford was here," she said, "he'd have me down on my knees. He's been praying for me to find a job. I'm praying right along with him, too."

"He's down to the manse," the man said. "Either that or he's out preaching a funeral."

"Probably a funeral," the woman said cheerfully. "There's nothing likelier in this town. How many did you say he had last week, Mr. Cleveland?"

"Four," Mr. Cleveland said. "I doubt there's one today, though."

The woman turned to me. "Mr. Cleveland, here, is sexton of the church," she said. "He knows everything that's going on. That's why I come by and see him—to learn the news."

"Sexton, janitor, superintendent, and a little bit of everything else," Mr. Cleveland said. "You might say I've got more jobs here than there is congregation. We had eighty turn up last Sunday. There's room in there for a thousand, spread out just four to the pew. I guess they used to fill her up—sides, center, and gallery—but not in my time. Nor in my dad's, neither. In the old days, most everybody in town was Presbyterian. The R.C.s got the edge now."

"I wonder why that is," the woman said. "Unless it's those Poles and Italians at the watch factory."

"Times change," Mr. Cleveland said. "I remember when there was steamboats running down to New York from here and over to New London, and Sag Harbor was the end of the main line of the Long Island Railroad. That was in the nineties, before they built on out to Montauk and stuck us off on a branch. Now we ain't even on that. You must of drove out here—you don't look like you walked. Well, I've got the time and the right to open her up and let you in—done it before for visitors. But maybe you'd better get Crawford to take you through. Since you come all the way out from New York, he'd be sorry to miss you. You see that gray house with a fence around it down there at the end of the block—where that old dog is laying in the drive? That's the manse. I'll show you one thing, though. You've heard about the famous steeple we had, I guess, and how it went down in the hurricane. September 21, 1938, at three-thirty in the afternoon, was the date. Well, see that patch of new-looking concrete in the walk there, alongside the burying-ground wall? That's where the butt of the steeple hit. I live just the other side of the burying ground, and I was looking out the window and I saw it go. I couldn't hardly believe my eyes. Why, that steeple had been there all my life. What happened was the wind caught under the louvers in the Sir Christopher Wren section. It lifted the whole shebang straight up in the air—the whole hundred and fifty-or-more feet of it—swung it clear of the building, and dropped it on the walk there. Then it toppled over into the burying ground and smashed to smithereens. All except the bell. That didn't get a scratch on it. We've got it set up inside now, in the lobby. I won't say I heard the bell ring because I didn't. I was inside, and the wind was too loud. But I know people that did. It rang once, hanging up there in midair, just before it hit. And that patch there is the exact spot where the steeple come down."

"I've got a piece of it at home for a souvenir," the woman said. "I guess everybody in town has. Mine's part of the Chinese part."

I left Mr. Cleveland and his friend on the church steps and walked down to the manse. The sidewalk tilted every which way, and there were tree roots as big as my arm pushing up through the cracks. Most of the houses in the block were so old that moss was growing on their roofs. The dog in the driveway made a halfhearted attempt to rise as I pushed through the front gate, and then slumped somnolently back. Before I could knock at the door, it swung open and a sleek, bald, broad-shouldered man of about forty looked out. He wore metal-rimmed glasses and had on a red flannel shirt, faded dungarees, and dirty white sneakers, and he was eating an apple. "Heard you at the gate," he said, a bit indistinctly. Then he swallowed, grinned, and added, "It's as good as a bell." I introduced myself and explained why I was there. "That's fine," he said. "I'm Donald Crawford. Excuse me." He tossed the core of his apple over my head, out into the street. "Come right in. You picked a good days for your visit. For me, anyway. This is my day off—hence these clothes. I've been burning some trash." I stepped into a dim hall. From upstairs came the sound of running water and an occasional wail. "That's my little helper," Mr. Crawford remarked. "Douglas, aged four. He's enduring a bath. Our other treasure is at school. Mary Alice is seven. Let's go in the parlor." I followed him into a small, high-ceilinged room gently ravaged by time and children. A tall, lanky, whitehaired man in a somber suit and a high collar was leaning against the mantel of a handsome white marble fireplace. In an ash tray at his elbow lay an elaborate spiral of apple peel. "This is Dr. Charles H. Tillinghast," Mr. Crawford said to me. "He hasn't got a care in the world. He's just retired after forty-nine years of dentistry, and he recently ended a long term as president of our church board of trustees. You're not interrupting anything. He just dopped by for a chat. How about it, Doctor? Would you like to go up to the church with us?"

Dr. Tillinghast extended me a bony hand. "My boy," he said, "it would be a privilege to show you through. Historic Sag Harbor and its proudest monument, the Whalers' Church, are the chief interests of my declining years. As you may know, we have here the second largest number of authentic colonial buildings of any community in the United States. We are exceeded only by Nantucket. But even Nantucket, if I may say so, has no such church as ours. My one regret is that our glorious steeple is gone. You've read of it, I'm sure. Perhaps you have seen pictures of it. A work of art." He shook his head. "It was the crowning glory of Minard Lafever's ecclesiastical masterpiece. I miss it as I would an old and cherished friend."

"I'll go get my coat," Mr. Crawford said.

Dr. Tillinghast nodded, cleared his throat, and continued, "It was a loss that everyone felt deeply. One of our local poetesses, the late Annie Cooper Boyd, wrote very movingly about it. I believe I have a copy of her poem here. You might care to glance at it." He drew a wallet from his pocket, extracted a tousled clipping, and handed it to me. The poem, eleven stanzas long, was entitled "The Steeple." It began:

> The Steeple—what!—the Steeple—
> Don't say that *it* has gone!"
> Thus spoke the village people
> With voice and face forlorn.

Another stanza read:

> Oh, lovely, lofty steeple,
> We loved thee from the heart—
> Thy curious construction,
> Thy myriad types of art!

"Of course," said Dr. Tillinghast as I returned the clipping, "we must be thankful that the church itself was spared."

Mr. Crawford, wearing an elegant covert-cloth topcoat, appeared in the hall doorway. I helped Dr. Tillinghast into his coat, he placed a floppy hat on his head, and we filed out to the street. Just outside the gate, Dr. Tillinghast halted. "Perhaps," he said, "we should call our young friend's attention to some of the historic points of interest adjacent to this particular corner. The magnificent Greek Revival edifice that you have undoubtedly noticed directly across the street is the old Benjamin Huntting place. Its architect was none other than Minard Lafever. I see that surprises you. I'll admit that the resemblance between Sag Harbor's two examples of the great Lafever's art is not pronounced. The answer lies in the fact that he was a man of great versatility. Captain Huntting was one of our whaling princes and, I'm proud to say, a prominent member of our church. In fact, like myself, he served as president of our board of trustees. His home was built in 1846. It was later purchased by Mrs. Russell Sage, whom we claim as a fellow citizen and esteem as a generous civic benefactor."

"She put a new coat of paint on the church once," Mr. Crawford said.

"At least once," Dr. Tillinghast said. "Including the steeple. The old Huntting place is now our whaling museum. That large white clapboard structure over there on the right is the old Hannibal French mansion, built around 1800. And behind those trees in the distance is the old customs house, built in 1790. In its yard is a boxwood bush that there is every reason to believe was grown from a slip presented to our first collector of port by Martha Washington herself. Our port, unfortunately, was discontinued in 1905, but the old customs house, quite properly, has been preserved."

"Don't forget the manse, Doctor," Mr. Crawford said. He grinned at me and began to move on up the street. "Built in eighteen-twenty-something and never restored. It's a good thing I'm handy."

"I know, Donald," Dr. Tillinghast said mildly. "As I recall, Mr. Barrett often said the same."

"My predecessor," Mr. Crawford explained. "I'm number nine-

teen in the line. The ministry here goes back to 1794. It gives me a
funny feeling sometimes to realize that this church had already gone
through four generations of ministers before my home town was even
founded."

"You're not from around here?" I asked.

"Hardly," Mr. Crawford said. "I'm from Chicago—Winnetka, to
be exact. If you'll forgive me, Doctor, I'm not sure that I'd ever even
heard of Sag Harbor until I received my call. That was only back in
1940. I must say it seems like a lifetime ago, though. Time sags along
pretty slowly in Sag Harbor."

Dr. Tillinghast smiled a thin smile. "The name of Sag Harbor, as
Donald knows, does not refer to that, however," he said. "It derives
from a Shinnecock Indian word, *sagaponack,* which means 'place of
the groundnuts.' Groundnuts are an edible root, something like a
potato."

"Actually," Mr. Crawford said, "my call to Sag Harbor wasn't
much more unexpected than my call to the ministry. My mother has
never really got over that. Selling stocks and bonds was more the
custom in our family. I may not look it, but I used to be a bond sales-
man. As soon as I got out of Yale—I was class of '28—I went right
into a brokerage house back home. Sold bonds all day and danced all
night. Then the market crashed. That did something to me. It wasn't
simply a matter of economics. I can't explain it—I walked around in
a daze. Then, one Sunday night in November 1929, I wandered into
the old Moody Church, on North LaSalle Street. That evening
changed my entire life. I came out converted. I went on selling bonds,
of course. I had to. But I spent my nights at the Moody Bible Institute, studying the Bible and making up for lost time. When I was
ready—in 1936—I quit my job and came East and started all over
again, at Princeton Theological Seminary. My family—well, one of
my aunts—helped put me through. I was ordained in 1940. That was
an eventful year for me. I was ordained, I got married, and I got this
call. My wife is a Philadelphian. We were on our honeymoon when
the call came, and she cried for hours." He shrugged. "She likes it
here now—we both do. Sag Harbor's a little off the beaten trail, but
there's a tremendous spiritual challenge here. When a whole town

lives in the past . . . I mean there are some extraordinary problems."

"Youth is always restless," Dr. Tillinghast said comfortably. He turned to me. "It might interest you to know that the *Long Island Herald,* founded in Sag Harbor in 1791, was the first newspaper published on Long Island. No one would have called this off the beaten path a hundred years ago. One of America's greatest preachers, Edward Hopper, served our church from 1852 to 1863, and it was the daring seamen of Sag Harbor who inspired him to write his immortal hymn 'Jesus, Saviour, Pilot Me.' James Fenimore Cooper lived here for some years, before he established himself as a writer. *The Pioneers* and *The Sea Lions* are both full of Sag Harbor. Why, this very street has known the tread of half the races of mankind. It was nothing in the old days to see Fiji Islanders, Malayans, Kanakas, Chinamen, Portuguese, Shinnecocks, and Montauks, and heaven only knows what else, roaming all over town. I imagine you've read *Moby Dick.* Old Melville knew what he was doing when he had his pagan harpooner Queequeg brought to America on a Sag Harbor whaler."

"Well," Mr. Crawford said, with a wave of his hand, "there she blows—the church that whale oil built. I sometimes think that God placed me in Sag Harbor to humble me, but He certainly gave me a beautiful church."

The sight of the church was momentarily silencing. Familiarity didn't seem to diminish it. Even Dr. Tillinghast gazed at it without comment. There was no sign of Mr. Cleveland or his friend. Nobody spoke until we were halfway up the walk. Then Dr. Tillinghast gave a short puzzled laugh. "In all fairness," he said, "I should point out that our church has attracted a few—a very few—unfavorable criticisms. We had an architect visiting here one summer who called it a hodgepodge. The unconventionality of its parts apparently blinded him to the beauty of the whole. He was from one of the newer settlements in the Middle West."

I remarked that Lafever must have been an extremely imaginative man.

"Lafever scorned the commonplace," Dr. Tillinghast said. "The old Benjamin Huntting place, though traditional, has many unusual touches. But I'm not sure that the style of our church was entirely Lafever's idea. His was the guiding hand, of course, but it must be remembered that he was dealing here with men who sailed the seven seas and had absorbed the flavor of foreign lands. They had their own ideas. What Lafever did was combine their impressions with his own. I think he was also inspired to suggest something of their courageous way of life. Look at the curious design of the railings up there on the tower and pylons and over the center door. One of our less appreciative visitors said they looked like a row of lollipops." A trace of pain crossed Dr. Tillinghast's face. "Of course," he went on, "that motif is a stylized version, in what I take to be the Gothic manner, of the whaler's blubber spade. That would be obvious to anyone who had examined the fine collection of old Sag Harbor whaling implements at the museum. Ridicule comes easy to some people. It may surprise you to hear that even our steeple was not completely immune to criticism. The *Sag Harbor Corrector*, now defunct, once called it 'fantastic' and Lafever 'bewildered.' If you could only have seen that glorious steeple! Perhaps I can describe it to you. It rose, naturally, from the top of the tower, and the height of it was truly majestic— 187 feet. Its height was another seafaring note. Our mariners wanted their church spire to serve as a landmark, visible to the returning ship as it rounded Montauk Point. For many years, a whale-oil beacon lamp at the pinnacle was lighted every night."

"I've read somewhere that it used to be noted on the U.S. Coast and Geodetic Survey maps," Mr. Crawford said.

"Very likely," Dr. Tillinghast said. "Our steeple was composed in three tapering sections, each smaller in diameter than the one beneath it. I don't think it was accidental that it resembled somewhat the sea captain's spyglass in use at that time. I doubt, too, if anyone but a shipwright could have raised it. It was raised by ox power, each section pulled up through the inside of the preceding one. The lowest section, in which the bell was installed, was in the seventeenth-century English style of Sir Christopher Wren, and extremely decorative. The main feature of it was an octagonal colonnade. In its pediment were four beautiful clocks. The derivation of the second section is uncertain. It was probably either Greek or, as some experts have suggested, Phoenician. Its chief ornamentation, at any rate, was a series of long panels, in which were cut the ancient Phoenican swastika. That was a symbol, I understand, of good luck. The topmost section was a replica of a Chinese pagoda. Needless to say, the entire structure was made of the finest Suffolk County white pine, chosen and seasoned by our own shipbuilders, and every inch of it was hand-carved." Dr. Tillinghast shook his head. "No," he said, "I hardly think that you or any person with a feeling for beauty would have called our steeple 'fantastic.' "

"Is there any prospect of restoring it?" I asked.

"We talk about it," Mr. Crawford said. "A year or two ago, we even had an architect out from New York to look into it. He said it could be done. There are plenty of good photographs of the old steeple around that an expert could go by. There hasn't been so much talk of it since we got his estimate, though. It was a little over seventy-five thousand dollars." Mr. Crawford unlocked the center door, pushed it open, and waved us in. "That's just about five times the original cost of the whole church."

We entered the lobby, big and square and gloomy. Opening off it were three paneled oak doors leading to the auditorium and the flanking pylons. The walls were dark and hung with marble memorial plaques, one of which read:

REV. SAMUEL KING,
A Native of England,
who departed this life Nov. 29th 1833;
after having ministered to this
congregation
one year and three months,
in the 42 year of his life.

THIS TABLET
as a token of respect
is devoted to the memory of a stranger and
a good man.
"The memory of the just is blessed."

Mounted on a low wooden frame in the middle of the lobby was a mighty bell. Dr. Tillinghast caught up a knotted end of rope attached to it as we passed. "Listen to this tone," he said, and struck the bell a savage whack. It gave an exhausted moan. "Sound as a dollar," he said. "I venture to say not many bells could survive such a fall."

"God spared what He deemed essential," Mr. Crawford said. "If you like, I'll take you up on the bell deck—what used to be the bell deck—before we leave. But right now . . ." He opened the auditorium door and took me by the arm. The three of us stepped into a silent immensity of whiteness. At the foot of a long center aisle, carpeted in faded green and lined with boxed pews, was a high rostrum. It was set in a *trompe-l'œil* circular arcade, flanked on either side by a door, and framed by a pair of round, fluted Corinthian columns and two square pilasters that rose, well over fifty feet, to a coffered ceiling. Two steeply inclined overhanging galleries, faced with an intricate frieze of carved volutes and rosettes, ran the length of the side walls. Behind each of them was a row of tall, tinted windows, ablaze with frosty lavender light. Except for the carpet, three tortuous black chairs on the rostrum, and a narrow trimming of rich, red mahogany along the sides and backs of the pews, the entire chamber was salt-white, and they made it look even whiter. For an instant, it was as dazzling as sun on snow.

Mr. Crawford dropped his hand from my arm. "It's beautiful, isn't it?" he said. "I don't mean to seem proud." I said, quite truthfully, that I'd never seen a more handsome room. "No," he said. "Of course, it's a few sizes too big for us now. I guess it always was. The sad thing is that it was built for the future. A hundred years ago, you know, there was a tremendous religious revival sweeping the country, and at the same time Sag Harbor was getting more prosperous every year. We had the main floor pretty well filled for our centennial celebration. Maybe someday . . ." He sighed and smiled. "Those doors on either side of the platform go into the Sunday school. That's a good, big room, too."

"The Sunday-school annex is a later addition," Dr. Tillinghast said, without interest. Moving briskly down the aisle, he continued, "Let me call your attention to the fine Cuban-mahogany trimming on these pews—a very unusual touch. One of our whaling captains selected the wood himself in Cuba and brought it home in his own ship. The workmanship is that of shipwrights. You may have seen some photographs of old ships' railings that resembled it. And notice the little silver nameplates and numerals on the pew doors. That's another pretty touch. Up to about the Civil War, I understand, every pew was also furnished with a fine brass spittoon. Those old Sag Harbor whalers were a rough lot." He shook his head with a kind of admiration and pointed up at the wall. "I mentioned the Phoenician-swastika motif," he went on. "Well, there it is again, in that frieze just under the ceiling. Also, the columns supporting the galleries are exactly like those that formed the colonnade in the Sir Christopher Wren section of the steeple. You see how perfectly Lafever tied everything together?"

"There's another example of it, up there in the choir loft," Mr. Crawford said, turning back toward the lobby. He nodded in the direction of a third, and smaller, gallery, which linked the two side ones just above the door to the lobby. In a niche in the wall behind it stood what appeared to be a replica in miniature of the church's towering façade. I could even make out a row of tiny blubber spades around the parapets. "Our organ," he said. "You can see the pipes through those vents in the casing." He glanced at his watch. "If we're going up on the bell deck, we'd better get started. It's a good climb. How about you, Doctor?"

"You flatter me, Donald," Dr. Tillinghast said. "I'll try to content myself here below. I think, in fact, I'll sit down."

We left Dr. Tillinghast, looking wistfully after us, among the melancholy plaques in the vestibule. A circular staircase in the pylon to the right led us up to a bare anteroom on the gallery level. We went through a door into the choir loft, where there was another door, about the size of a transom, leading into the base of the tower. Mr. Crawford squirmed through this one. "I don't know who designed this," he said, "but he must have been thinking of a porthole." I followed him into a cobwebby cubicle behind the organ niche. It was not quite pitch-dark. "Watch yourself, now," he said. "These steps are steep." We went up two angular flights to a twilit landing, where Mr. Crawford directed my hand to the rail of an almost perpendicular step-ladder. Then he disappeared overhead, breathing hard. I felt my way slowly after him to another landing and another ladder. We were well up in the tower now, and I could hear the sound of the wind outside. Light appeared above, and broadened into a tinted window, extending a foot or two above the level of a third landing, where we found ourselves in a forest of bare joists, beams, and up-rights. On one of the uprights was painstakingly carved "J.M.F., Sept. 27, 1862." Mr. Crawford leaned limply against a foot-square, hand-hewn pillar. It was anchored, like a mast, in a thick, cast-iron shoe bolted to a wooden girder. "This was one of the steeple supports," he said, giving it an indifferent pat. "The only one that held. It snapped off higher up. The others sailed away with the steeple. Listen to that wind up there. They tell me the steeple used to shake like a tree on a day like this. One more climb and we'll be in the middle of that gale." He moved off along a catwalk of teetering planks. It ended at the foot of a runged ladder, which rose some twenty feet to a trapdoor in the ceiling. The ladder was as unsteady as a rope as I followed him up. "Hold your hat," he said, and heaved back the trap. We stepped out, coattails flying and trousers flapping, onto a creaking tin roof. It seemed like the top of the world.

We gazed down, over roofs and treetops and the spires of three humbler churches at the deserted harbor. Beyond it lay the gray-green plain of the sea and the hazy gray sand bluffs of faraway points and islands. "That's Shelter Island, straight ahead," Mr. Crawford said, hunching deeper into his coat. "Over there to the left of it is Noyack Bay. The smudge in the distance is the north fluke of Long Island—we're about on a line here with Greenport. That's another old whaling ruin. Off to the right, there, you can see the Rhode Island shore on a good, bright day."

I said it was quite a view. "It must have been magnificent from the top of the old steeple," I added.

"I suppose so," Mr. Crawford said. He turned and looked at me. "I suppose," he went on, "you noticed that our organ casing hasn't got a steeple. It was made that way. Prophetic, wasn't it?" There was an odd expression on his face. "I'll tell you what I think," he said. "Our steeple wasn't blown down by accident. These people here had got so they were worshiping the steeple more than they did God. So He took it away."

ANTON CHEKHOV

The Student

&✽

Supposedly this was Chekhov's own favorite among all his stories. Read it and you'll understand why.

At first the weather was fine and it was very quiet. Blackbirds sang, and from the neighboring marshes something living could be heard making a pathetic moaning sound like air being blown in an empty bottle. A solitary woodcock flew up, and someone aimed, and a shot rang out vividly and joyfully on the spring air. Then as the woods grew dark a cold and penetrating wind rose unreasonably from the east, and everything was silent. Needles of ice stretched over the pools; darkness, misery, and loneliness hung over the woods. It smelled of winter.

Ivan Velikopolsky, a student in the theological seminary and the son of a sacristan, was making his way home from hunting, barefoot, taking the path through the waterlogged meadows. His fingers were numbed, and his face burned by the wind. It seemed to him that the sudden fall of temperature had somehow destroyed the order and harmony of the universe, and the earth herself was in agony, and that was why the evening shadows fell more rapidly than usual. All around him there was only emptiness and a peculiar obscurity. The only light shone from the widows' gardens near the river; elsewhere, far into the distance and close to him, everything was plunged in the cold evening fog, and the village three miles away was also hidden in the fog. The student remembered that when he left home his mother was sitting on the floor in the doorway cleaning the samovar, while his father lay coughing on the stove; and because it was Good Friday, no cooking had been done in the house and the student was ferociously hungry. Oppressed by the cold, he fell to thinking that just such a wind as this had blown in the time of Rurik and in the days of Ivan the Terrible and Peter the Great, and in those days men suffered from the same terrible poverty and hunger; they had the same thatched roofs filled with holes; there was the same wretchedness, ignorance, and desolation everywhere, the same darkness, the same sense of being oppressed—all these dreadful things had existed, did exist, and would continue to exist, and in a thousand years' time life would be no better. He did not want to go home.

The widows' gardens were so called because they were kept by two widows, a mother and daughter. There a wood fire was crackling and blazing, throwing a great circle of light over the plowed earth. The widow Vasilissa, a huge, bloated old woman, was wearing a man's coat. She stood gazing dreamily at the flames while her daughter Lukerya, a little pockmarked woman with a stupid expression, sat on the ground washing a kettle and some spoons. Apparently they had just finished supper. Men's voices could be heard; they were the local farm workers watering their horses at the river.

"Well, winter's back again," the student said, going up to the fire. "Good day to you!"

Vasilissa gave a start, but she recognized him and smiled at him warmly.

"I did not recognize you at first," she said. "God bless you! You'll be rich one day!"

They went on talking. Vasilissa was a woman of experience; she had served the gentry first as a wet nurse and then as a children's nurse, and she expressed herself with refinement. A grave and gentle smile never left her lips. Her daughter Lukerya was a peasant; the life had been crushed out of her by her husband. She screwed up her eyes at the student and said nothing. She had a strange expression, like that of a deaf-mute.

"On just such a cold night as this St. Peter warmed himself by a fire," the student said, stretching his hands over the flames. "So it must have been very cold! What a terrible night, eh? Yes, it was an extraordinarily long, sad night!"

Saying this, he gazed at the encircling shadows, gave a little convulsive shake of his head, and went on: "Tell me, have you ever attended a reading of the Twelve Gospels?"

"Yes, I have," Vasilissa answered.

"Then you'll remember that at the Last Supper, Peter said to Jesus: 'I am ready to go with thee down into darkness and death,' and the Lord answered: 'I tell thee, Peter, the cock, the bird of dawning, shall not crow this day, before that thou shalt thrice deny that thou knowest me.' After the supper Jesus suffered the agony in the garden, and prayed, but poor Peter was faint and weary of spirit, and his eyelids were heavy, and he could no longer fight against sleep. So he slept. Then, as you know, Judas came that same night and kissed Jesus and betrayed him to his tormentors. They bound him and took him to the high priest and beat him, while Peter, worn out with fear and anxiety, utterly exhausted, you understand, not yet fully awake, feeling that something terrible was about to happen on earth, followed after him. For he loved Jesus passionately and with all his soul, and he saw from afar off how they were beating him. . . ."

Lukerya dropped the spoons and looked fixedly in the direction of the student.

"They came to the house of the high priest," he went on, "and they began to interrogate Jesus, while the workmen lit a fire in the courtyard because it was cold, and they warmed themselves around the fire, and Peter stood close by the fire, and he too warmed himself, just as I am doing now. There was a woman who recognized him and said: 'This man also was with Jesus,' meaning that he too should be taken for interrogation. And all the workmen who were standing round the fire must have looked at him searchingly and suspiciously, for he was troubled and said: 'I do not know him.' After a while someone recognized him as one of the disciples of Jesus, and said: 'You were one of them.' And again Peter denied it. And then for the third time someone turned toward him and said: 'Did I not see thee with him in the garden?' And again Peter denied it, and at that very moment the cock crew, and Peter gazing from afar off at Jesus remembered the words spoken to him earlier in the evening. . . . He remembered and suddenly recovered his senses and went out from the courtyard and wept bitterly. The Gospels say: 'He went out and wept bitterly.' And so I imagine it—the garden was deathly still and very dark, and in the silence there came the sound of muffled sobbing. . . .'"

The student sighed and fell into deep thought. Though her lips still formed a smile, Vasilissa suddenly gave way to weeping, and the heavy tears rolled down her cheeks, and she hid her face in her sleeve as though ashamed of her tears, while Lukerya, still gazing motionlessly at the student, flushed scarlet, and her expression became strained and heavy as though she were suffering great pain.

The farm workers returned from the river, and one who was on horseback came near them, and the light from the fire glittered on him. The student bade good night to the widows and went on his way. Once again the shadows crowded close around him, and his hands froze. A cruel wind was blowing, winter had settled in, and it was hard to believe that Easter was only the day after tomorrow.

The student fell to thinking about Vasilissa. It occurred to him that because she had been weeping, everything that happened to Peter on the night of the Last Supper must have a special meaning for her. . . .

He looked around him. He could see the solitary fire gleaming peacefully in the dark, but there was no longer anyone near it. Once more the student thought that if Vasilissa gave way to weeping, and her daughter was moved by his words, then it was clear that the story he had been telling them, though it happened nineteen centuries ago, still possessed a meaning for the present time—to both these women, to the desolate village, to himself, and to all people. The old woman wept, not because he was able to tell the story touchingly, but because Peter was close to her and because her whole being was deeply affected by what happened in Peter's soul.

And suddenly his soul was filled with joy, and for a moment he had to pause to recover his breath. "The past," he thought, "is linked to the present by an unbroken chain of events all flowing from one to the other." And it seemed to him that he had just seen both ends of the chain, and when he touched one end the other trembled.

When he took the raft across the river, and afterward when he was climbing the hill and looking back in the direction of his native village and toward the west, where the cold purple sunset was no more than a thin streak of light, it occurred to him that the same truth and the same beauty which reigned over humankind in the garden and in the courtyard of the high priest had endured uninterruptedly until the present time, and always they were the most important influences working on human life and everything on the earth; and the feeling of youth, health, and vigor—he was only twenty-two—and the inexpressible sweet expectation of happiness, of an unknown and secret happiness, took possession of him little by little, and life suddenly seemed to him ravishing, marvelous, and full of deep meaning.

IVAN BUNIN

Sunstroke

&»

Bunin got the Nobel prize for his famous story The Gentleman from San Francisco. *This is one of his finest "other" stories.*

After dinner they came up on deck and stood close by the rail, leaving the bright, hot lights of the dining room behind them. She closed her eyes, pressed the back of her hand to her cheek, and laughed a frank, charming laugh—everything was charming about that small woman—and said:

"I'm quite drunk. . . . And anyway, I've gone quite mad. Where did you come from? Three hours ago I didn't even know you existed. I don't even know when you came on board. Was it in Samara? But

it doesn't matter. . . . Am I dizzy or are we turning around somewhere?"

Ahead lay darkness and lights. A soft steady breeze blew into
their faces from the darkness, and the lights rushed away from them
in an arc. With the dash of a Volga craft, the boat swung in a wide
curve as it ran up to a small pier.

The lieutenant took her hand and raised it to his lips. The hand,
small and strong, smelled of sunburn. And his heart came to a blissful and frightening standstill when he thought how strong and tanned
her whole body must be under that light linen dress, after lying on
the hot sand beneath a southern sky for a whole month (she told him
she was on her way from Anapa).

"Let's get off." he muttered.

"Where?" she asked, surprised.

"At this stop."

"What for?"

He said nothing. She pressed the back of her hand to her hot cheek
again.

"You're mad. . . ."

"Let's get off," he repeated dully. "Please."

"All right, as you wish," she said, turning away.

Coming on at full speed, the ship thudded softly against a dimly
lit pier, and they almost fell on top of one another. A cable flew over
their heads, the ship was driven back, water churned noisily and
gangplanks rumbled. . . . The lieutenant rushed for their luggage.

A minute later they passed the sleepy little office, came out on
the beach, sinking ankle-deep in the sand, and silently got into a dusty
carriage. The drive up the long slope, soft with dust and marked by
infrequent crooked lampposts, seemed endless to them. But now they
topped the rise and the wheels clattered on the cobblestones: here
was a market square or something, now came the government buildings, the fire tower, and the warmth and scents of a provincial town
on a summer night. The driver stopped before a lighted doorway
beyond which they could see a steep old wooden staircase and an old,
unshaven porter in a pink shirt and a frock coat, who took their suitcases with a disagreeable air and led the way upstairs on his shambling

feet. He brought them to a large but dreadfully stuffy room, searingly heated by the day's sun, with white curtains at the windows and a couple of new candles on the dressing table. And the minute they walked in and the porter had left them, closing the door behind him, the lieutenant rushed to her so impetuously, and desire so vehement smothered them both when they kissed, that this moment was to remain in their memories for many years to come: neither he nor she had ever experienced anything like it in all their lives.

At ten o'clock in the morning—a sunny, hot, and joyous morning with church bells pealing, with the noise and bustle of the market in front of the hotel, with the smells of hay, tar, and again all those strong mixed scents of a Russian provincial town—she, that small nameless woman who had not told him her name after all, but, laughing, had called herself a fair stranger, went away. They had not had much sleep, but in the morning, when she left the bed and came around the screen, washed and put on her clothes in five minutes, she looked as fresh as a girl of seventeen. Was she feeling embarrassed? Only very slightly. She was as simple and cheerful as ever, and her common sense was already asserting itself.

"No, no, dearest," she said in answer to his plea that they continue their voyage together. "No, you must stay behind until the next boat. If we go on together everything will be spoiled. It would be very unpleasant for me. I give you my word of honor that I'm not at all what you might have thought me to be. Nothing even remotely like this has ever happened to me before, nor will it ever happen again. I must have lost my senses. Or, rather, we both had something like a sunstroke. . . ."

And the lieutenant agreed with her with a certain lightheartedness. He took her as far as the pier with a light and happy heart, arriving there just as the pink *Samolyot* was ready to sail. He kissed her in front of everyone on deck and barely managed to jump down the gangplank before it was hauled up.

He got back to the hotel feeling as lighthearted and carefree as before. However, he found that some change had already occurred there. Without her the room somehow looked quite different. It was still filled with her presence, but empty! That was odd! The room still smelled of her good English *eau-de-Cologne,* her unfinished cup of tea was still standing on the tray, and yet she was no longer there. . . . And the lieutenant's heart was suddenly wrung with such tenderness that he hastened to light a cigarette and began pacing up and down the room.

"What a strange adventure!" he said aloud with a laugh, conscious of the tears welling up in his eyes. " 'I give you my word of honor I'm not at all what you might have thought me to be.' And now she's gone. . . ."

The screen had been moved back, the bed not yet made. And he felt he simply could not bear to look at that bed now. He put the screen back to hide it, closed the windows to shut out the noise of the market crowd and the squealing of wheels, he let down the white, puffed-up curtains, and sat down on the sofa. Well, that was the end of his "shipboard adventure"! She was gone and by now she was far away, probably sitting in the white glass lounge or lying back in a deck chair, gazing at the vast river gleaming in the sun, at the timber rafts moving downstream, at the yellow shoals, at the bright vista of water and sky, at all this infinite expanse of the Volga. . . . And good-by now, forever. . . . For where could they ever meet again? "After all," he thought, "how could I, for no reason at all, suddenly appear in the town where she lives with her husband, her three-year-old daughter, all the rest of her family and her whole everyday world!" And this town seemed to him different somehow, a sacred town, and the thought that she would just go on living her lonely life there, perhaps thinking of him often, remembering their chance meeting and those fleeting hours, while he would never see her again—this thought staggered him. No, that could not be! It would be too mad, too unnatural and incredible! And he felt a pain so poignant, such futility in all the life that stretched before him without her, that terror and despair gripped him.

"What the hell!" he thought, getting up and starting to pace the room again, trying not to look at the bed behind the screen. "What's come over me? After all, this isn't the first time. . . . And what's so wonderful about her? What did happen? It's really like a sunstroke!

But the main thing is how on earth am I going to get through the rest of the day without her in this miserable town?"

He still remembered everything about her, all the slightest details that singled her out. He remembered the smell of her sunburn and her linen dress, her strong body, and the lilting, frank and cheerful sound of her voice. He still felt with extraordinary vividness the ecstasy he had experienced from all her feminine charm, and yet this other, this quite novel feeling was the more important now, this peculiar, strange feeling which he did not have at all when they were together, of which he had never suspected himself capable when he began the affair the night before, thinking it would be an amusing experience, this feeling which he could tell to no one, no one now! "And the worst of it is, I'll never be able to tell her!" he thought. "What am I to do? How can I live through this endless day with these memories, this agony that cannot be appeased, in this God-forsaken little town on the same gleaming Volga that has carried her away in the pink ship?"

He had to seek salvation, to find something to distract his mind, to go somewhere. He resolutely put on his cap, picked up his cane, briskly walked down the empty corridor with a jingle of spurs, and ran down the steep staircase to the front door. Yes, but where was he to go? A cab stood by the entrance, and the driver, a young chap, smartly dressed, sat calmly smoking a cigarette, evidently waiting for someone. The lieutenant threw a perplexed and amazed look at him: how could he sit on his coach box so calmly, smoke a cigarette and altogether be so ordinary, carefree, and indifferent? "I expect I'm the only one in this whole town who's so dreadfully unhappy," he thought as he started out toward the market place.

The market was already thinning. He walked aimlessly between carts loaded with cucumbers, stepping on the fresh manure, and strolled among new pots and bowls, while the women sitting on the ground vied with one another to offer him their wares. They picked up their pots and tapped them with their fingers, making them ring to show their quality, while the men deafened him with their shouts: "Here, the best cucumbers ever, your honor!" It was all so stupid and preposterous that he fled from the market. He dropped into the cathedral toward the end of the service, where the singing of the choir was already loud, joyful, and deliberate, with the consciousness of duty done; and after that he walked for a long time, around and around the little neglected garden perched on the cliff above the boundless, steel-gray expanse of the river. . . . The shoulder straps and buttons on his tunic were too hot to touch. The band inside his cap was sticky with sweat, his face was flaming. When he got back to the hotel he was delighted and relieved to walk into the large, empty, cool dining room on the ground floor, to take off his cap and sit down at a table close to an open window which let in hot air, but it was air anyway, and to order iced beetroot soup.

Everything was fine, everything held immeasurable happiness and great joy; even in this very heat, in the market smells, in all of the strange, wretched little town and in this old provincial hotel, there was joy, and yet his heart was breaking. He drank several glasses of vodka and while he ate his dill pickles he was thinking he would be willing to die on the morrow, without a moment's hesitation, if only she could be brought back by some miracle, if only he could spend one more day with her—spend it with her just so that he could tell her, convince her, prove to her somehow that he loved her desperately and rapturously. . . . But why prove it? Why convince her? He did not know why, but it was more necessary than living.

"My nerves are all shot to blazes!" he muttered, pouring out his fifth glass of vodka.

He pushed his soup away, ordered some black coffee, and sat smoking and thinking hard: what was he to do now, how to shake off this sudden and unexpected love? But to shake it off was impossible. All at once he quickly got up again, took his cap and cane, and, having asked where the post office was, hurried off toward it, already framing the wording of his telegram in his mind: "From now and forever my life is in your power until death." But when he got to the old, thick-walled building of the post office and telegraph, he stopped, horrified: he knew the town where she lived, he knew that she had a husband and a three-year-old daughter, but he did not know her name! He had kept asking her to tell him at dinner the night before and afterward at the hotel, but every time she merely laughed and said:

"But why do you want to know my name? I'm Marya Marevna the fairy-tale princess. Isn't that good enough for you?"

There was a photographer's window on the corner, next to the post office. He stood staring for a long time at a large photograph of an officer with thickly fringed epaulets, protuberant eyes, a low fore-head, amazingly sumptuous sideburns and the broadest of chests completely covered with decorations. . . . How mad, how absurd and horrible was all that was ordinary and trivial when your heart was smitten—yes, it was smitten, he knew it now—with that frightening "sunstroke," with a love that is too strong, with happiness that is too great! He looked at a wedding group—the young bridegroom in a long frock coat and white tie, with cropped hair, standing rigidly at attention, arm in arm with a girl in a bridal veil—he brought his eyes to rest on a picture of a pretty and saucy-looking girl wearing a student's cap at a rakish angle. . . . And then, tormented by distressing envy for all these people he did not know, people who were not suffering, he looked with strained attention down the street.

"Where shall I go? What shall I do?"

The street was quite empty. The houses were all alike, white, two-storied, middle-class homes with large gardens, and there did not seem to be a soul in any of them; the street was carpeted with thick white dust, and all of it blinded one, all of it was flooded with sunlight, passionate and joyous, but somehow out of place. In the distance the street humped uphill and butted into the cloudless, grayish, and shimmering sky. There was a hint of the south in this, reminding him of Sevastopol, Kerch . . . Anapa. . . . This was particularly unbearable. And with drooping head, squinting in the glare, his eyes fastened anxiously on the ground before him, staggering and stumbling, getting tangled in his spurs, the lieutenant made his way back.

He felt so shattered with weariness when he got to the hotel that he might have traversed great spaces somewhere in the Sahara Desert or in Turkestan. Mustering his remaining strength, he entered his large and empty room. It had already been tidied, deprived of all trace of her, and only a hairpin she had dropped lay on the bedside table. He took off his tunic and looked at himself in the mirror: his face—an ordinary officer's face, dark-gray with sunburn, with a colorless mustache bleached in the sun and bluish eyeballs which looked whiter still against his tan—now held an agitated, frenzied expression. There was something youthful and profoundly unhappy in his thin white shirt with its starched turned-up collar. He went to the bed and lay down on his back, putting his feet in their dusty top boots on the rail at its foot. The windows were open, the curtains down, and a gentle breeze puffed them out now and again, bringing into the room the heat of the sweltering iron roofs and all that brilliant and now utterly desolate and soundless world. He lay with his hands behind his head, staring fixedly before him. Then he clenched his teeth and closed his eyes, feeling the tears rolling down his cheeks, and at last he fell asleep. When he opened his eyes, the reddish-yellow sunset was already aglow behind the curtains. The breeze had died down, the room was stuffy and as hot as an oven. And he recalled the previous day and that morning as if they had been ten years ago.

Unhurriedly he got up, unhurriedly he washed, drew the curtains, rang, asked for a samovar and his bill, and then he leisurely drank his lemon tea. After this he ordered a cab, had his suitcases taken down, and as he got into the carriage and settled on its seat of faded, rusty brown, he tipped the porter a whole five-ruble note.

"Looks to me, your honor, it was I who brought you here last night," the driver said cheerfully as he picked up his reins.

When they came down to the pier, the blue summer night had already spread over the Volga, and many little lights of different colors were already scattered down the river, and lanterns hung suspended from the masts of the ship as it swung up to the pier.

"Got you here on time!" the driver said ingratiatingly.

The lieutenant tipped him with a five-ruble note too, bought his ticket, and went down to the pier. . . . Just like the night before, there was the soft thud against the mooring block, a slight dizziness because of the heaving floor, and then a flying cable, the noise of water churning and rushing forward beneath the wheels of the boat which was driven back somewhat. And this crowded ship, already fully lighted and smelling of the kitchen, gave him a feeling of extraordinary friendliness and contentment.

A minute later they were on their way, upriver, the same way that she had gone off earlier that morning.

The dark glow of the summer sunset died away far ahead casting its gloomy, drowsy, and varicolored reflection upon the water that still quivered and glimmered here and there with ripples far below the glow, and the lights, scattered in the darkness about them, floated far, far away. . . .

The lieutenant sat on deck under an awning feeling as though he had aged ten years.

GEORGE W. HERALD
and EDWARD D. RADIN

Systems and Superstitions in Monte Carlo

&~

About the man who broke the bank of Monte Carlo—by sheer luck.

One of the tourist sights in Monte Carlo is the equestrian statue of Louis XIV in the entrance to the Hôtel de Paris. Visitors always smile at the way the horse's knee has been worn almost smooth by the caresses of countless superstitious gamblers on their way to the casino. And more than a few of the laughing sightseers will run their fingers across it in the guise of testing its smoothness, and then quickly enter the casino themselves, while considerate hotel attendants hold their smiles.

Gambling and superstition are more than closely allied; they have been hand-holding partners since man shifted his challenge from wielding a skull-cracking weight to placing a bet, and the casino even caters to this. A gypsy fortuneteller is allowed to ply her trade within the building, but she cannot predict winning or lucky numbers, only general information as to whether the inquirer will be lucky or unlucky that night. It is a most happy situation for the soothsayer; all she has to do is be gloomy and seldom be wrong.

The paint was hardly dry on the walls of the newly opened casino when players began to bring their endless variety of charms, talismans, mystic motions, maneuvers, and sitting positions, all designed to foil the immutable laws of mathematics.

One of the earliest visitors who caused an uproar was an Italian countess who mixed reverent piety with irreverent greed. In preparation for her visit to the casino she went to the Vatican, where she induced an official she knew to place a gold louis among the rosaries, medals, and other items to be blessed by the pope, pretending she wanted it for a charitable purpose. Convinced that this coin now would ward off the evil of too many losing numbers, she journeyed to Monte Carlo and used it to make her bets, always removing it and substituting another coin when the spin of the roulette wheel went against her.

Her lucky coin seemingly worked for two days, and she was ahead. On the third day her attention was distracted at the moment the ball dropped into a slot, and the croupier promptly raked in the bets of the losers, her coin among them. Her shrieks stopped further play as she frantically searched through the pile, but she had neglected to place any identifying mark on her particular lucky piece, and one gold louis looked very much like another.

The determined countess returned home prepared to get another coin blessed, but news of her impious act already had reached Rome, and she received such a tongue lashing from the high-placed churchman she had duped that she is said to have entered a convent. At least she did not return to the casino.

Author Adolphe Smith encountered an unusual form of good-luck charm, unusual even for Monte Carlo. He was seated next to a vivacious widow who was having a winning streak, and he congratulated her on her lucky run. The woman opened her purse and told him to look inside for the answer. The handbag contained some silver coins, similar to those the woman was using in placing her bets, and on the bottom he noticed a slimy gray mass, about the size of a ten-cent piece. Unable to identify it, he asked her what it was.

"It's the heart of a bat," was her unexpected reply. She explained that she had paid a porter to catch and kill one of the bats that roosted in the railroad freight yards, then had taken it to her hotel room and removed the heart herself. She gaily informed Smith that she had had to pay the porter only ten francs for the flying mammal because he had not known its true value; she would have been willing to pay much more. All the coins in her purse that rubbed against the bat's heart were lucky ones.

Keeping a straight face, Smith asked the widow if she would allow him to drop one of his gold coins on the bat's heart to see if some of its magic might rub off for him. He never knew whether his voice betrayed him, or if he really had selected the wrong coin. The woman glanced at him sharply and then said, "It is my mistake, of course. I had the impression that you were a brother, a fellow initiate. The bat is a creature of the moon, she corresponds to the feminine in nature. Her metal is silver, so how can you expect a bat to influence gold, the metal of the sun?"

Gamblers look for signs everywhere, as the Reverend Taylor, pastor of the Anglican church in Monte Carlo, found out. There was a sudden upsurge in Sunday attendance, so much so that he began to think of the need for constructing a larger building. But the pastor also knew his Monte Carlo. He telephoned the director of the casino and asked him if he had heard anything that could account for the increased popularity of his sermons. Camille Blanc was equally puzzled, but said he would have his men investigate. The answer was soon supplied. Several weeks earlier the minister had selected Hymn No. 36 for his congregation to sing. A visitor from South Africa, present at the services, looked upon the number as a signal from heaven. Immediately after he left church he went to the casino, staked 2,000 francs on 36, and won. He could not resist talking about it; and as word spread among the gamblers, they joined the faithful flock each Sunday, waiting for the number of the hymn. Even though the pastor's selections had not been that lucky in the next two weeks, the gamblers still came hopefully. With this information, Reverend Taylor promptly made it a rule that no hymn under No. 37 would be selected, and since the highest number on the roulette wheel is 36, attendance at Sunday services quickly returned to normal.

Many men prefer a more lively talisman, like a pretty blonde, brunette, or redhead of the evening. These girls always fervently wish for their escorts to have a winning night the first time they go out with him. They know from experience that if he does win, he will regard them as a good-luck charm and will insist upon their company any time he goes to the casino after that. Not only are they able to raise their fees, but they also can wheedle a handful of chips at a time when these stack high in front of him. One pretty blonde wound up with $25,000 when her companion had a good run of luck for several days. By the end of the week he had lost all his money; the girl wisely had banked her nest egg.

Superstitions are individual whims and seldom affect the amount of money a player will gamble, but it is the system player who brings an anticipatory gleam to the eyes of casino officials. Once a person thinks he has an infallible system, he will bet far more heavily than the others.

In the days when fabulous fortunes were won and lost at its tables, the casino dreaded just one kind of publicity, stories about suicides. Not only did they stir up agitation against gambling, but they had a depressing effect on players, and many stayed away.

A young Italian girl started just such a chain reaction. Eleonora Duse, the great actress, was appearing nightly in the theater and after her performance, would go to the gaming rooms, where she would lose the salary being paid her—in itself, one reason why Monte Carlo did not mind paying stars high salaries, as Las Vegas hotels have since learned. On this night Duse was seated next to a pretty young girl who became increasingly agitated as her pile of chips dwindled. The actress, noticing the girl's distress, told her to take it easy, but the girl brushed her aside, placed something in her mouth, and a short time later slumped over in her chair. She had taken a quick-acting poison and was dead.

Deeply shaken by what she had just witnessed, La Duse stood up, announced in her ringing voice that she would never gamble again, and walked out of the casino. And she kept her word. Other celebrities soon followed. Isadora Duncan, who always made Monte Carlo one of her stops on her world dancing tours, also vowed to stay away from the gaming tables.

The worst blow for the casino was yet to come. Sarah Bernhardt was then the great public idol. Few people knew that she was a compulsive gambler. She lost huge amounts at the Monte Carlo Casino, but because she earned large sums, no one paid any attention. Actually her losses were outstripping her tremendous earnings, and she was in debt.

The casino was still unsettled by the bad publicity it had been receiving, when the Divine Sarah entered one night. In her purse was the last of her remaining capital, 100,000 francs. She was determined to stake it all that night in an attempt to recoup her losses. Three hours later the entire sum had been lost.

Sarah returned to her room in the Hôtel de Paris and took an overdose of sleeping powder. Fortunately, a short time later, one of her friends, the Vicomte de Rohan, called at her suite, discovered what had happened, and quickly summoned medical aid. When she recovered, he lent her 300,000 francs, and Sarah Bernhardt joined the ranks of those who stayed away from the casino. American Princess Alice, wife of Prince Albert of Monaco, was a friend of Sarah Bernhardt's, and her banker father, Michael Heine, took charge of the actress' finances. Within six months she was able to repay the loan, and the financier made shrewd investments of her earnings, so that when she finally retired from the stage, she was a wealthy woman.

The suicide attempt of Sarah Bernhardt was too important a story for Blanc to hush up completely, and as a result some of the heavy losers became more cautious, and casino revenues began to drop.

It was at this low ebb that Charles Wells, a short, paunchy cockney, came to the casino in July 1891 and won fame as the man who broke the bank of Monte Carlo. He gave the casino a much-needed shot in the arm. He said he was an inventor and had patented a musical rope that had been a fad in London. The total capital he had brought with him was 10,000 francs; many of the titled and wealthy regulars at the casino risked more than that on one spin of the wheel.

Wells started out cautiously, but in the parlance of the gambling fraternity, he was "hot." No matter what he played, black or red, or the full numbers, he was winning with almost monotonous regularity. He increased his betting to 2,000 francs at a time, doubling his stakes each time he lost, until they reached the maximum.

Excitement swelled in the casino when he broke the bank. Actually it was not the casino bank, but the bank at the table where he was playing. Each table started the day with a cash reserve of 100,000 francs. If a player succeeded in winning this money, the wily Blanc had devised a ceremony to call attention to this feat and give a psychological lift to the losing players. A black cloth was draped over the table, and it was momentarily out of play until guards marched up in ostentatious display with a fresh bankroll.

Pandemonium broke out when, for the second time in one day, Wells again broke the bank. Members of nobility clawed at each other as they fought to get close to the table and make the same bets Wells was placing.

The *chef de parti* Bertollini, who supervised the play at Wells's table, said later of this conduct, "The worst thing was the greed that his success aroused in the other guests. They crowded around his table eight ranks deep, and all wanted to play the same numbers he did. They would shout at my croupiers in English, German, French, Italian, Indian, and Kurdish. In the end, I could do nothing else but limit the number of players at the table. That led to new violent clashes with persons who thought I was afraid they might win too much."

Wells seemed to be operating with a purposeful system. All the full numbers he bet on were under 10, and he made most of his bets on 1 and 2. He would let his winnings stand for three consecutive runs. Notetakers were standing on chairs, scribbling on charts like mad, and these were being sold to those on the fringes who could not get close to follow the play.

His stamina equaled his luck. He remained at the table for eleven straight hours until he finally called it a day. Croupiers stared with disbelief the next morning when Wells turned up at the opening hour. Although the casino opened at ten o'clock, this usually was for the small bettors; the wealthy did not consider it fashionable to appear until after dinner and the theater. By 3 P.M. the unfashionable Englishman in a hurry had broken the bank for the third time. By now the Russian grand dukes and a king or two had rushed to watch what was going on, and newspaper reporters were sending the story all over the world. The bad publicity the casino had been receiving faded out in the excitement.

The run of luck continued on the third day, and by that night Wells had won one million francs. He stopped playing roulette at that point and made for the door to cash in his chips. As he passed a baccarat table, he couldn't resist making a few more bets. In the next half-hour he accumulated another 150,000 francs.

Wells returned to England, where he was greeted as a national hero. He gave lavish parties, patronized the best supper clubs, and tipped heavily.

Although some casino officials were alarmed when they saw Wells depart with all that money, Camille Blanc was not worried. He predicted that Wells would be back. "We'll get our money back," he assured them.

Part of his prediction came true in November when Wells again returned to Monte Carlo, but the Englishman picked up where he had left off. He started out by placing 1,200 francs on number 5, and let it ride for five successive spins. Five came up five times in a row and Wells, in a matter of minutes, had won 98,000 francs.

Even Blanc was staggered at the news. He began to suspect collusion and that night called the croupiers into his office and questioned them thoroughly. He finally assigned ten of his best detectives to watch Wells every moment and to keep a sharp eye on the wheel and the croupiers at the table. They were to report to him twice a day. History repeated itself, and again in three days Wells won another million francs and left the casino. The detectives had absolutely nothing to report; there had been no signals exchanged, no tampering with the wheel. Wells's winnings had been legitimate.

By now the most phenomenal run of luck in the casino's history was a page-one story wherever newspapers were published. That winter Charles Coburn introduced the song "The Man Who Broke the Bank at Monte Carlo" in a London revue, and the song became a hit in England, spread throughout the Continent, and soon was being sung, hummed, and whistled in the United States.

People everywhere talked of the nobody who had won a fortune at Monte Carlo, and debated his system. They could make little sense of the published charts of some of his plays; only he had the key, and he refused to discuss it. The loss that the casino had suffered was really a windfall since it made Monte Carlo a household name.

Once again Wells went on a wild spree when he returned to London. He was picked up by society, wore tails and a top hat; and wherever he made his entrance, the band was certain to play "The Man Who Broke the Bank at Monte Carlo."

Wells made his third appearance at the casino during the 1892 winter season, arriving in a style suitable for a man of his importance, aboard the yacht *Palais Royal* and accompanied by his mistress Joan Burns, an artist's model from Chelsea. When he seated himself at his favorite roulette table, Camille Blanc served personally as *chef de parti*, the man who supervises the play at the table. The bubble burst for the little Englishman—and he lost steadily. He cabled to London for fresh funds, which he also lost.

But Charlie Wells was not gambling his own money. He had squandered his winnings in riotous living. The little cockney was a small-time crook and confidence man, and had talked his newly found rich friends into backing an invention he claimed to be perfecting, a fuel-saving device for steamships. Among his dupes were the son of Lord Ashton and a sister of Lord Phillimore. The yacht he was using had been chartered by his backers, supposedly for test trials of his nonexistent device. When he lost at Monte Carlo, he had taken the precaution of wiring his backers for more money from neighboring Ventimiglia, rather than Monaco, stating that his machine was out of order and he needed the money rushed for repairs. It was after Wells sailed from Monte Carlo that his victims learned that he had been gambling. He was arrested aboard the yacht at Le Havre and extradited to England. After being convicted on a charge of obtaining some $150,000 under false pretenses, the man who broke the bank of Monte Carlo was sentenced to eight years in prison.

One person remained faithful to him, his mistress Joan Burns.

When he had served his sentence, she met him at the prison gates, and they went to Paris. Here he developed a scheme Ponzi later was to use with great success in the United States. He advertised that he would pay 1 per cent interest per day on funds left with him. The few lucky persons who were among the first investors were promptly paid their daily interest; this started the bandwagon rush, and some 60,000 Frenchmen had been fleeced when Wells was finally arrested, once again aboard a yacht. He later died in poverty in Paris.

If it was Edward VII, while he was the Prince of Wales, who made Monte Carlo fashionable with royalty and the millionaires; it was the little trickster, with his fabulous run of luck, who made the casino popular with the well-to-do middle classes. Visitors began swarming in from everywhere, all hoping to duplicate the feat of the man who broke the bank, many of them looking for systems.

Years later Wells admitted that he had had no system, that it had been blind luck; but by then hundreds of books had been published, all containing sure-fire systems and with such intriguing titles as *Life Made Pleasant by Roulette* and *One Hundred Infallible Systems to Win at Monte Carlo*. Noblemen and millionaires were being jostled by shabby figures who became known as "the writers" or "the thinkers." They hovered about the tables, busy jotting down all the winning numbers and deducing from these new infallible methods of winning.

The circulation of a morning newspaper published in Nice began to boom when it started listing the numbers that had come up the previous day in the Monte Carlo Casino. And when the numbers failed to arrive in time, the editors did not want to disappoint their faithful readers, and so they made up lists of winning numbers for the system players to peruse.

Business boomed at the casino; but, in fairness to Camille Blanc, it must be said that he publicly scoffed at players who believed in systems, and even offered a prize of two million francs to anybody who could present an infallible one. The prize was never claimed.

Theoretically, there is one system with which a player can always come out even in the long run, provided that he has enough money. This is the mother of all systems, the martingale. It requires that each time a player loses, he continue to double his bet until he wins. Since there are men wealthy enough to do that, the casino, from the very first, installed a maximum betting limit, which would prevent anybody from doubling a small stake more than twelve times. With this edge, and a zero which sweeps the board, it is impossible for any system to be infallible. J. P. Morgan once stalked angrily out of the casino because he wanted the limits raised. The casino would have been most happy to make an exception and win his money, but they knew that once they did so, they could be opening the door to future difficulties.

Excitement was so intense after Wells's exploits that Sir Hiram Maxim, the American-born inventor of the one-man machine gun, made a special trip to Monte Carlo to study the possibilities of a system. At his first session at the roulette table, black came out twenty times in a row. Two men next to him were so certain that it was impossible for black to win again that they started betting heavily on red. The wheel spun six more times to black, and the system players next to Maxim lost 72,000 francs.

He also watched a Dutch planter named Kilian, who did not play himself but hired men to gamble for him. He gave each of them 2,000 francs with instructions that they were not to worry if they lost the money. The puzzled inventor asked the reason for it. Kilian replied, "In order to win, you must dare. Someone who plays with other people's money is much less afraid to run the kind of risks that have to be run if one wants to land a major coup."

Though many of his hired gamblers did lose their stakes, now and then one of them would hit a lucky streak; and Maxim observed such a man turn over 45,000 francs to Kilian. The planter, though, refused to tell whether he was ahead or behind in his strange system.

Maxim finally wrote his conclusions in a letter to the Paris edition of the *New York Herald* in which he said:

All roulette systems are worthless. If red comes out 20 times, there is no reason why the ball should not fall on red 40 or 70 times. The laws of probability are not valid for this game. Each round offers a 50/50 chance—neither more nor less.

The ball follows its own law, and this is different every time. Where the ball falls depends on how it has been thrown, how often it turns around the wheel, and which metal pieces it hits on its way. All this is pure hazard and cannot be influenced by anything that happened before or may happen afterward.

The inventor was jeered and denounced by system players, and the gamblers merrily went on inventing new systems, even though Blanc said bluntly, "The only way of earning money with systems is to sell them to fools."

One of his favorite stories concerned a syndicate of four Parisians who came to Monte Carlo with a substantial fund of 500,000 francs and an ardent belief in their sure-fire system. They were so certain of success that they hired a bookkeeper to keep their accounts.

The malicious goddess of fate was kind to them for three weeks, and their bankroll grew to 1,200,000 francs. They did not want to keep the money in a bank, and so they bought a safe, moved it into their bookkeeper's room, and hired a watchman to sit there on the alert with a cocked pistol. The next morning they returned to the room to see how things were going, and the watchman assured them that everything was fine—no strangers had dared come near the safe. But when they opened it, they found it empty. The bookkeeper, who had access to the safe, had rifled it before the watchman came on the job, and had lost all the money gambling while using their system. Blanc paid their carfare home.

A Scottish engineer, William Jaggers, did develop a system that was a nightmare for casino officials until they discovered his secret. He had made a careful study of the construction of the roulette wheel, probing for weak points. Each wheel rested on a steel cylinder whose upper end was hollow. A small metal pin under the wheel fitted into this socket. Jaggers realized that if this pin got worn, a slight deviation would favor certain numbers.

He stationed men at every table to record the winning numbers. This went on for five weeks, and then he noticed that at one table certain numbers came up more frequently than others. He now was ready to play and within four days amassed more than Wells ever won, 2,400,000 francs. The loss to the casino was even greater, since many other players were following his lead.

The casino now began an investigation of its own, and made a record of the numbers Jaggers was playing. That night, after closing time, an unusual game went on in the salon. Blanc and the other directors played the wheel against the house, using Jaggers' list of numbers. They came out 50,000 francs ahead. Blanc promptly ordered the wheels switched on the different tables, and Jaggers began losing when he returned to his particular table the next day. As his losses climbed, the canny Scotsman realized that the wheels must have been switched. He stopped playing and made a leisurely tour of the casino, stopping at each table. With an engineer's eye for detail, he had noticed that his particular wheel had a tiny, barely noticeable scratch on the brass handle. Within an hour he had located his wheel of fortune and resumed winning. Since there was nothing illegal in what Jaggers was doing, the casino was helpless.

At that time the roulette wheels used at Monte Carlo were manufactured in Strasbourg. A casino official hurried there for advice and was told that if the partitions around the little slots in the wheel were changed daily, these would make up for any slight irregularities in the balance of the wheel. The corrective measure worked; and when Jaggers discovered he no longer could predict the numbers the wheel would favor, he lost interest in gambling and left Monte Carlo with a neat profit of 1,200,000 francs.

One of the most unusual system players was the Irish-born Count of Hammond, who became interested in astrology when he lived in India. Using the professional name of Cheiro, he became a famous astrologer-chiromancist, and his clients included Edward VII, Gladstone, Lord Kitchener, and a young reporter of that time named Winston Churchill.

The invention of the roulette wheel has been attributed to Pascal, but Hammond claimed that it existed long before in the Far East as an instrument of occult calculations to determine the rhythm in which figures appear and reappear. He pointed out that the astrologer's zodiac contains 360 degrees while the roulette wheel has 36 cases and a zero. In addition, the cylinder of the roulette has four arms dividing the wheel, and the zodiac is divided into four sectors of the year and four cardinal points.

Like all astrologers, he believed that the stars emit radiations that affect the world, and he felt that certain conjunctions or configurations of planets within certain signs could affect the series of figures coming out on the roulette wheel. Hammond would play only one hour at a time after he had established the planetary aspects for that given hour and deduced which numbers and colors would appear during that sixty minutes. He claimed that the numbers 2, 11, 20, and 29 were under the influence of the moon and were therefore feminine, and that was why they were painted black on the wheel, while numbers 9, 18, 21, and 36 were under the influence of Mars, and therefore masculine and so were painted red.

Listeners struggled hard trying to figure out Hammond's system but were completely baffled by it. Nevertheless, each season he appeared in Monte Carlo, gambled only on certain dates and at certain hours, and usually emerged a winner.

The casino was not alone in profiting from system players. Sam Lewis, a London moneylender, was a familiar figure for years at Monte Carlo, but he did not come to play. He was there to help finance, at a good rate of interest, the titled Englishmen who had run short of funds while backing their latest scheme for beating the wheel. Sam was a snob at heart and liked nothing better than to be invited to the homes of his august clients. One season he was accosted in the lobby of the Hôtel de Paris by an English lord who had had a phenomenal run of bad luck, and was so deeply in debt to the money broker that Lewis refused to advance any further funds.

When the rebuffed nobleman later complained to a friend, the latter told him to invite Lewis to his castle, which was always good for a loan.

The bankrupt player shook his head. "Not much point to inviting a man to a home he already owns," he replied.

The system players are still at Monte Carlo, but the center of their activities is not the inner fashionable *salons privés* but the large outer room, known locally as "The Kitchen," which opens every morning and is patronized mainly by elderly retired men and women, living on pensions or small annuities, who rarely gamble more than a handful of francs a day. Many of them sit with notebooks in their hands, making mysterious jottings now and then, and a run of luck that brings in a few hundred francs is cause for wild elation. The casino provides a focal point and serves as a social center for them, and the working out of a system provides them with a pleasant way to pass their time. The casino does not mind; it finds that the steady accumulation of these small wagers makes pleasant reading in the annual financial statement, and treats them with the same deft service and courtesy that would be extended to a millionaire plunger.

It was an American girl named Susan who came up with the best system ever seen at Monte Carlo, one which croupiers still talk about with admiration.

Susan had fallen in love with a Polish count she had met at a party, and she was determined that he would marry her. The count's great love, though, was the roulette wheel. Although she dogged his heels, she could not woo him away from the green baize of the gaming tables. His luck was bad, and he not only lost the money he had inherited, but also began dipping into funds that had been left to him in trust.

When Susan learned this, she rushed to the casino and stood watching from a distance. As she suspected, he was having no better luck this night. She moved closer, and he was so absorbed in his play that he did not notice her standing behind one of the seated players. He was concentrating on color, and Susan quickly pulled money from her purse and began to bet the opposite. He placed 3,000 francs on red, and she made a similar bet on black. Red lost, black won. On the next round, he distributed 6,000 francs over the first and second columns, and Susan placed 3,000 francs on the third column. He lost and she won 6,000 francs.

Her winnings continued to pile up while his chips dwindled. Susan also made bets of her own and hit a winning streak, meanwhile continuing to bet directly opposite the count. The count finally left the table stony broke and started pacing the terrace. When Susan came up to him, he confessed that he had taken the funds from the trust fund and advised her to forget him, since he faced jail.

Susan then told him how she had bet opposite him, thrust the bankroll into his hand and told him, "It's yours. I was winning it back for you."

Although croupiers say that her system is dangerous because a loser can suddenly start winning, they know of no finer system for getting a husband. Susan and the count were married.

W. SOMERSET MAUGHAM

The Taipan

❧

I found this story embedded in one of Somerset Maugham's less known travel books. ("Taipan" was a title given to foreign merchants in pre-Communist China.)

No one knew better than he that he was an important person. He was number one in not the least important branch of the most important English firm in China. He had worked his way up through solid ability and he looked back with a faint smile at the callow clerk who had come out to China thirty years before. When he remembered the modest home he had come from, a little red house in a long row of little red houses, in Barnes, a suburb which, aiming desperately at the genteel, achieves only a sordid melancholy, and compared it with the magnificent stone mansion, with its wide verandas and spacious rooms, which was at once the office of the company and his own residence, he chuckled with satisfaction. He had come a long way since then. He thought of the high tea to which he sat down when he came home from school (he was at St. Paul's), with his father and mother and his two sisters, a slice of cold meat, a great deal of bread and butter and plenty of milk in his tea, everybody helping himself, and then he thought of the state in which now he ate his evening meal. He always dressed and whether he was alone or not he expected the three boys to wait at table. His number one boy knew exactly what he liked and he never had to bother himself with the details of housekeeping; but he always had a set dinner with soup and fish, entrée, roast, sweet and savory, so that if he wanted to ask anyone in at the last moment he could. He liked his food and he did not see why when he was alone he should have less good a dinner than when he had a guest.

He had indeed gone far. That was why he did not care to go home now; he had not been to England for ten years, and he took his leave in Japan or Vancouver where he was sure of meeting old friends from the China coast. He knew no one at home. His sisters had married in their own station; their husbands were clerks and their sons were clerks; there was nothing between him and them; they bored him. He satisfied the claims of relationship by sending them every Christmas a piece of fine silk, some elaborate embroidery, or a case of tea. He was not a mean man and as long as his mother lived he had made her an allowance. But when the time came for him to retire he had no intention of going back to England, he had seen too many men do that and he knew how often it was a failure; he meant to take a house near the race course in Shanghai: what with bridge and his ponies and golf he expected to get through the rest of his life very comfortably. But he had a good many years before he need think of retiring. In another five or six Higgins would be going home and then he would take charge of the head office in Shanghai. Meanwhile he was very happy where he was, he could save money, which you couldn't do in Shanghai, and have a good time into the bargain. This place had another advantage over Shanghai: he was the most prominent man in the community and what he said went. Even the consul took care to keep on the right side of him. Once a consul and he had been at loggerheads and it was not he who had gone to the wall. The taipan thrust out his jaw pugnaciously as he thought of the incident.

But he smiled, for he felt in an excellent humor. He was walking back to his office from a capital luncheon at the Hong Kong and Shanghai Bank. They did you very well there. The food was first rate and there was plenty of liquor. He had started with a couple of cocktails, then he had some excellent sauterne and he had finished up with two glasses of port and some fine old brandy. He felt good. And when he left he did a thing that was rare with him; he walked. His bearers with his chair kept a few paces behind him in case he felt inclined to slip into it, but he enjoyed stretching his legs. He did not get enough exercise these days. Now that he was too heavy to ride it was difficult to get exercise. But if he was too heavy to ride he could still keep ponies, and as he strolled along in the balmy air he thought of the spring meeting. He had a couple of griffins that he had hopes of and one of the lads in his office had turned out a fine jockey (he must see they didn't sneak him away; old Higgins in Shanghai would give a pot of money to get him over there) and he ought to pull off two or three races. He flattered himself that he had the finest stable in the city. He pouted his broad chest like a pigeon. It was a beautiful day, and it was good to be alive.

He paused as he came to the cemetery. It stood there, neat and orderly, as an evident sign of the community's opulence. He never passed the cemetery without a little glow of pride. He was pleased to be an Englishman. For the cemetery stood in a place, valueless when it was chosen, which with the increase of the city's affluence was now worth a great deal of money. It had been suggested that the graves should be moved to another spot and the land sold for building, but the feeling of the community was against it. It gave the taipan a sense of satisfaction to think that their dead rested on the most valuable site on the island. It showed that there were things they cared for more than money. Money be blowed! When it came to "the things that mattered" (this was a favorite phrase with the taipan), well, one remembered that money wasn't everything.

And now he thought he would take a stroll through. He looked at the graves. They were neatly kept and the pathways were free from weeds. There was a look of prosperity. And as he sauntered along he read the names on the tombstones. Here were three side by side; the captain, the first mate, and the second mate of the barque *Mary Baxter,* who had all perished together in the typhoon of 1908. He remembered it well. There was a little group of two missionaries, their wives, and children, who had been massacred during the Boxer troubles. Shocking thing that had been! Not that he took much stock in missionaries; but, hang it all, one couldn't have these damned Chinese massacring them. Then he came to a cross with a name on it he knew. Good chap, Edward Mulock, but he couldn't stand his liquor, drank himself to death, poor devil, at twenty-five: the taipan had known a lot of them do that; there were several more neat crosses with a man's name on them and the age, twenty-five, twenty-six, or twenty-seven; it was always the same story; they had come out to China: they had never seen so much money before, they were good fellows and they wanted to drink with the rest: they couldn't stand it, and there they were in the cemetery. You had to have a strong head and a fine constitution to drink drink for drink on the China coast. Of course it was very sad, but the taipan could hardly help a smile when he thought how many of those young fellows he had drunk underground. And there was a death that had been useful, a fellow in his own firm, senior to him and a clever chap too: if that fellow had lived he might not have been taipan now. Truly the ways of fate were inscrutable. Ah, and here was little Mrs. Turner, Violet Turner, she had been a pretty little thing, he had had quite an affair with her; he had been devilish cut up when she died. He looked at her age on the tombstone. She'd be no chicken if she were alive now. And as he thought of all those dead people a sense of satisfaction spread through him. He had beaten them all. They were dead and he was alive, and by George he'd scored them off. His eyes collected in one picture all those crowded graves and he smiled scornfully. He very nearly rubbed his hands.

"No one ever thought I was a fool," he muttered.

He had a feeling of good-natured contempt for the gibbering dead. Then, as he strolled along, he came suddenly upon two coolies digging a grave. He was astonished, for he had not heard that anyone in the community was dead.

"Who the devil's that for?" he said aloud.

The coolies did not even look at him, they went on with their work, standing in the grave, deep down, and they shoveled up heavy clods of earth. Though he had been so long in China he knew no Chinese, in his day it was not thought necessary to learn the damned language, and he asked the coolies in English whose grave they were digging. They did not understand. They answered him in Chinese and he cursed them for ignorant fools. He knew that Mrs. Broome's child was ailing and it might have died, but he would certainly have heard of it, and besides that wasn't a child's grave, it was a man's and a big man's too. It was uncanny. He wished he hadn't gone into that cemetery; he hurried out and stepped into his chair. His good humor had all gone and there was an uneasy frown on his face. The moment he got back to his office he called to his number two:

"I say, Peters, who's dead, d'you know?"

But Peters knew nothing. The taipan was puzzled. He called one of the native clerks and sent him to the cemetery to ask the coolies. He began to sign his letters. The clerk came back and said the coolies had gone and there was no one to ask. The taipan began to feel vaguely annoyed: he did not like things to happen of which he knew nothing. His own boy would know, his boy always knew everything, and he sent for him; but the boy had heard of no death in the community.

"I knew no one was dead," said the taipan irritably. "But what's the grave for?"

He told the boy to go to the overseer of the cemetery and find out what the devil he had dug a grave for when no one was dead.

"Let me have a whiskey and soda before you go," he added as the boy was leaving the room.

He did not know why the sight of the grave had made him uncomfortable. But he tried to put it out of his mind. He felt better when he had drunk the whiskey, and he finished his work. He went upstairs and turned over the pages of *Punch*. In a few minutes he would go to the club and play a rubber or two of bridge before dinner. But it would ease his mind to hear what his boy had to say and he waited for his return. In a little while the boy came back and he brought the overseer with him.

"What are you having a grave dug for?" he asked the overseer point blank. "Nobody's dead."

"I no dig glave," said the man.

"What the devil do you mean by that? There were two coolies digging a grave this afternoon."

The two Chinese looked at one another. Then the boy said they had been to the cemetery together. There was no new grave there.

The taipan only just stopped himself from speaking.

"But damn it all, I saw it myself," were the words on the tip of his tongue.

But he did not say them. He grew very red as he choked them down. The two Chinese looked at him with their steady eyes. For a moment his breath failed him.

"All right. Get out," he gasped.

But as soon as they were gone he shouted for the boy again, and when he came, maddeningly impassive, he told him to bring some whiskey. He rubbed his sweating face with a handkerchief. His hand trembled when he lifted the glass to his lips. They could say what they liked, but he had seen the grave. Why, he could still hear the dull thud as the coolies threw the spadefuls of earth on the ground above them. What did it mean? He could feel his heart beating. He felt strangely ill at ease. But he pulled himself together. It was all nonsense. If there was no grave there it must have been an hallucination. The best thing he could do was to go to the club, and if he ran across the doctor he would ask him to give him a look over.

Everyone in the club looked just the same as ever. He did not know why he should have expected them to look different. It was a comfort. These men, living for many years with one another lives that were methodically regulated, had acquired a number of little idiosyncrasies—one of them hummed incessantly while he played bridge, another insisted on drinking beer through a straw—and these tricks which had so often irritated the taipan now gave him a sense of security. He needed it, for he could not get out of his head that strange sight he had seen; he played bridge very badly; his partner was censorious, and the taipan lost his temper. He thought the men were looking at him oddly. He wondered what they saw in him that was unaccustomed.

Suddenly he felt he could not bear to stay in the club any longer. As he went out he saw the doctor reading *The Times* in the reading room, but he could not bring himself to speak to him. He wanted to see for himself whether that grave was really there and stepping into his chair he told his bearers to take him to the cemetery. You couldn't have an hallucination twice, could you? And besides, he would take the overseer in with him and if the grave was not there he wouldn't see it, and if it was he'd give the overseer the soundest thrashing he'd ever had. But the overseer was nowhere to be found. He had gone out and taken the keys with him. When the taipan found he could not get into the cemetery he felt suddenly exhausted. He got back into his chair and told his bearers to take him home. He would lie down for half an hour before dinner. He was tired out. That was it. He had heard that people had hallucinations when they were tired. When his boy came in to put out his clothes for dinner it was only by an effort of will that he got up. He had a strong inclination not to dress that evening, but he resisted it: he made it a rule to dress, he had dressed every evening for twenty years and it would never do to break his rule. But he ordered a bottle of champagne with his dinner and that made him feel more comfortable. Afterward he told the boy to bring him the best brandy. When he had drunk a couple of glasses of this he felt himself again. Hallucinations be damned! He went to the billiard room and practiced a few difficult shots. There could not be much the matter with him when his eye was so sure. When he went to bed he sank immediately into a sound sleep.

But suddenly he awoke. He had dreamed of that open grave and the coolies digging leisurely. He was sure he had seen them. It was absurd to say it was an hallucination when he had seen them with his own eyes. Then he heard the rattle of the night watchman going his rounds. It broke upon the stillness of the night so harshly that it made him jump out of his skin. And then terror seized him. He felt a horror of the winding multitudinous streets of the Chinese city, and there was something ghastly and terrible in the convoluted roofs of the temples with their devils grimacing and tortured. He loathed the smells that assaulted his nostrils. And the people. Those myriads of blue-clad coolies, and the beggars in their filthy rags, and the merchants and the magistrates, sleek, smiling, and inscrutable, in their long black gowns. They seemed to press upon him with menace. He hated the country. China. Why had he ever come? He was panic-stricken now. He must get out. He would not stay another year, another month. What did he care about Shanghai?

"Oh, my God," he cried, "if I were only safely back in England."

He wanted to go home. If he had to die he wanted to die in England. He could not bear to be buried among all these yellow men, with their slanting eyes and their grinning faces. He wanted to be buried at home, not in that grave he had seen that day. He could never rest there. Never. What did it matter what people thought? Let them think what they liked. The only thing that mattered was to get away while he had the chance.

He got out of bed and wrote to the head of the firm and said he had discovered he was dangerously ill. He must be replaced. He could not stay longer than was absolutely necessary. He must go home at once.

They found the letter in the morning clenched in the taipan's hand. He had slipped down between the desk and the chair. He was stone dead.

RICHARDSON WRIGHT

Two Sweet Little Demons

ॐ

So that's *how spiritualism started!*

The forties and fifties of the past century were a paradise of pitch-men. Towns and cities and the countryside as well became a vast and constant carnival at which vendors of all manner of good, medium and cheap-jack amusements, half-baked religions, strange sects, diluted science, and novelties in philosophy hawked their wares. The cultured and the misleading, the true and the false, mingled with easy grace. From the sublime heights of singing by Jenny Lind and

Kate Hayes, dancing by Effie Ellsler and acting by the elder Forrest, it ranged down through the circus under the aegis of Barnum and others, and the itinerant theater under the cheapest types of barn-stormers, to ludicrous but nevertheless solemnly delivered lectures on mesmerism, phrenology, animal magnetism, and spiritualism. And America accepted them with the undivided credulity of the neophyte. It was an era of fads.

The sects that arose to grip popular imagination and gain follow-ing were legion. The hydropaths set great store by water in unlimited quantities, and the vegetarians, eschewing all flesh, hoped to gain heaven and health by following Nebuchadnezzar's taste for green vegetables. There were those who gravely trailed after Graham and ate only rough whole-wheat bread. The name Graham applied to the bread still reminds us of those days.

Meantime, the followers of Fourier, that innocuous little French traveling-salesman preacher of utopia, went off into rural colonies to save the world and themselves by communistic living, high think-ing, and rustic endeavors. "Professors" displayed charts whereon the human cranium was subdivided, like a real estate development, into the bumps of amativeness, caution, combativeness, self-esteem, and such, and the wondering populace held that phrenology had become a demonstrable science. Mountebanks armed with galvanic batteries were making decorous ladies tingle beneath their ample hoopskirts. Men and women sat around in circles gravely holding a rope wound with wire, and felt the thrill of animal magnetism. The followers of Mesmer demonstrated their skill on their confederates and whoso-ever from the audience was bold enough to present himself as a subject. Physicians solemnly proclaimed that even serious opera-tions could be performed without pain on persons who had been mesmerized.

Most of these "professors" and lecturers were charlatans of the worst kidney, cheap showmen with a gift of gab that impressed the credulous. Many of them were not above petty theft and even worse crimes. Yet America enjoyed them, for the country had reached that age when it lusted after novelties and was willing to throw away its pennies, its time, and its good sense on cheap attractions. It demanded strange gods—and the charlatans saw to it that the gods were furnished them aplenty.

Out of all these amusing phenomena the one that survived many generations and comes down to the palpitating and incredulous present was spiritualism. Like the mighty oaks that grow from little acorns, it had a humble and obscure beginning, one that involved two equally humble and obscure young women—the Fox sisters. In the Valhalla of spiritualism, in the burning heart of the celestial Seventh Circle of the spirit world, these two little country girls may still sit enthroned as goddesses of superior quality. Between that heavenly beatification and their beginnings in life lay the picturesque path of their careers.

Sometime in December 1847, John D. Fox moved his family from Rochester into a house in Hydesville, a section of Arcadia, Wayne County, New York. Besides himself and his wife were his two daughters, Margaret, aged seven, a mild, gentle child, with no especial cunning in her face, and Katherine, six. Two miles away lived a son, David, and in Rochester a married daughter, Ann Leah Fish.

It was an ordinary humble dwelling, but it had gained a strange reputation under its previous owner. Michael Weekman, who lived in it from 1846 to 1847 had been annoyed with rappings on the outside door about nine o'clock one night. When he investigated the source of the noises, he could find no one around the house, and though the raps continued and he persistently trailed them, he never found out where they came from. So it was really a haunted house that John Fox elected to live in. Of course the neighbors had heard all about it and John and the girls were soon told its reputation. Being a good Methodist, the father paid no attention to these silly rumors, whereas his wife, a weaker mortal, kept all these things in her heart.

December passed, and after it most of the winter. The Foxes lived the normal, hard-working life of a small country settlement. The neighbors forgot those stories about the rappings the previous tenant had heard, but in the impressionable minds of the two young daughters they remained vivid and unforgettable. One night toward the end of March 1848, after they had gone to bed, the girls said they heard rappings. It was as though someone was knocking on the floor and moving chairs. These sounds varied from a light, clear, metallic ting to a dull, muffled thud like the rapping of knuckles on a cloth-covered partition. The girls called their parents, and the house was searched. No one was found. The next night the same noises were heard and equally unsuccessful was the second investigation. By the thirty-first, things had gotten to such a pass and the family was so worked up, that neighbors were called in.

The noises invariably issued from where the two girls stood. Growing suspicious, a neighbor began cross-questioning them: were they positive that they hadn't been making those noises? To this one of the girls replied in a way that must go down to fame as among our sublime utterances: "We are innocent," she vowed ecstatically. "How good it is to have a clear conscience!"

This assurance from the lips of an eight-year-old set at peace all rumors of deception. Verily upon the Fox girls had descended a strange, psychic power. Immediately they were considered to be children set apart from all the other children of the place. The world began making a beaten path to their door. A committee came to investigate—and went away mystified.

It was evident to those who looked into this mystery that the knockings were the efforts of disembodied spirits to communicate with mortals. Before the messages could be decoded an alphabet must be evolved. After a time the mother, the elder sister, and brother David, assisted by the neighbors, decided that one rap meant *No,* two *I don't know,* three *Yes,* and so on through a long alphabet and code that could spell out intricate answers to questions. Neighbors and a host of visitors sat around with the Fox family both at night and by day and listened for messages from the spirits that the two little girls delivered. Thus from this Nazarean Hydesville came the wonder of the spiritualistic séance.

Fame having descended upon them, Margaret was taken to Rochester where she lived with her eldest sister, Mrs. Fish. This worthy matron of thirty-three had been abandoned by her dissolute husband and was obliged to give music lessons to make ends meet. Here the noises were heard again, clearly demonstrating that Margaret was psychic. Katherine, the younger, was taken to Auburn, and here also noises were heard in her vicinity, thus establishing her claim.

On November 14, 1849, in Corinthian Hall at Rochester the two girls gave a public demonstration. An investigating committee from the audience watched them carefully. The noises came as usual. There could be no doubt that they were media for spirits struggling to convey messages.

Naturally the news of these strange occurrences soon spread beyond central New York. From Stratford and Norwalk, Connecticut, Newark, New Jersey, Syracuse, New York, Cincinnati, Ohio, and scores of other places came reports of persons hearing spiritualistic raps. The minister at Stratford attributed them to the devil, and in Syracuse a house fairly thundered with evil sounds. With such competition arising on all sides, it was evident that if the Fox sisters were to keep their pristine reputation as psychics they must go on the road and demonstrate their gifts to the entire country. So they were taken on tour by Mrs. Fish.

At Buffalo where a great crowd of the credulous and curious gathered on February 17, 1851, a committee of physicians from the university was asked to investigate them. Some of these doctors were assigned the task of watching the girls' faces. The others placed the sisters in chairs with their feet resting on cushions on chairs in front of them so that the toes were elevated and the feet separated, a position that made the ligaments of the joints tense and gave no chance to make pressure with the foot or to displace or snap the foot bones. Result? No raps. Then the doctors placed the girls' hands on their knees and stood aside to see the result. Again no raps. But immediately their knees were not held or their feet were taken down from their tense positions on the chairs, raps were audible. From the expressions on their faces it was evident that the making of these noises involved an effort even though the girls strove to conceal every indication of voluntary effort. Also they seemed completely exhausted after the demonstration.

Nothing to it! The committee handed down a learned report that amounted to the following:

The raps are produced by snapping certain tendons at the knee and ankle joints. The girls merely snap the tendon of the *posterior tibia* over one of the ankle bones. If this is done near a table it causes a slight concussion. Also when they lay their hands on the edge of a table they make raps by pressing against the ledge of the table the *os pisciforum*, a bone at the outer angle of that portion of the palm adjoining the wrist. By slightly contracting the contiguous muscles the bone is displaced and a rap results. This trick of the hands can be done without a perceptible movement.

Having rendered their decision, the physicians stepped down from the stage. When they reached Boston a committee of professors from Harvard investigated them, and with equally pronounced reports on their fraudulent methods. However, audiences and the country at large were not to be taken in by professional long words. No amount of scientific explanation could convince these good people that the Fox sisters were not media for messages from the spirit world. What if they did make those raps by snapping their *os pisciforum;* indeed these very bones were spiritualistic media!

So the Fox sisters went on their way, gathering adherents wherever they traveled. And their tours took them to all parts of the country, and brought them a tidy and comfortable living. Mrs. Fish ceased mourning for her departed Fish and became Mrs. Brown. She and Margaret gave demonstrations in New York, first in a house at Eighth Avenue and Nineteenth Street and later at Barnum's Hotel, where crowds gathered to see them. At this time Margaret was only eleven and Katherine nine. They acquired enough through séances to take a house on Twenty-sixth Street, then a thoroughfare of fine residences. In the metropolis they were patronized by such leaders of the time as Fenimore Cooper, George Bancroft, the historian, William Cullen Bryant, Drs. Hawker, Frances, and Griswold, John Bigelow, Theodore Parker, Alice Carey, Bayard Taylor, and others of like standing. Horace Greeley entertained the sisters in his house at Turtle Bay, now East 48th Street, and became their devoted follower. It was he who saw to it that the younger sister Katherine was given an education.

The success of the Fox sisters soon brought to light a host of rival media who laid claim to their fame and fortune. Many strove to prove that their venture into the spirit world antedated the Rochester knocking. Countless numbers improved on their style. Spiritualistic mediums became highly specialized and highly diversified callings.

Among the earliest rivals were those two picturesque sisters: Tennie C. Claflin and Victoria Claflin Woodhull. Natives of Homer, Ohio, they claimed to have received spirit messages long before the Fox sisters trembled in their sheets at Hydesville. At the tender age of fourteen, Victoria fell into the clutches of a gay young rake by the name of Dr. Canning Woodhull, who treated her abominably. Finally she drifted out to California where, with the assistance of Anna Cogswell, the actress, she was given a part in *New York by Gas Light,* a roaring comedy of the times. While playing here, she claimed, she had a spirit summons from her sister Tennie C., and she flew back to Ohio where, in Cincinnati, she and her sister put on séances. In a short time Victoria gained a wide reputation as a spiritualistic healer, and the halt and the lame and the sick came to her from all parts of the surrounding country. They lavished their gifts on her and she waxed rich. In one year her income was said to have reached $100,000 and up to 1869, she claimed to have made $700,000.

Victoria Woodhull's reach for fame started early. As a child she was aware of her guardian angel—a glistening person in a Greek tunic. Verily "a majestic guardian," for he later turned out to be none other than Demosthenes himself. Now a person who had Demosthenes for guardian angel, Victoria argued, was intended by the Divine Wisdom to become an orator. And it was as an orator for many causes that she won fame and attracted a following.

The spirit urged her to go to New York; in the metropolis alone would she find a field worthy of her talents. With Demosthenes guiding their every move, she and her sister descended upon the city and, to the astonishment of conservative businessmen, invaded their field by opening a brokerage office at 44 Broadway. In this case Demosthenes assumed the human form of Commodore Vanderbilt, their patron and angel. Having attained this foothold, Victoria began issuing learned opinions on finance, national affairs, scientific matters, and the condition of the market. Powerful magnetic currents flowing around her, she said, supplied the information for these statements.

Would that some of our captains of industry and giants of finance were equally humble! Victoria attributed her information and right to speak on such profound and diverse subjects to an influence other than herself; these contemporary issuers of solemn *obiter dicta* are not so self-effacing. They really believe that they know something about the subjects on which they speak. Their opinions, save where they impinge on their immediate world, are as valueless, of course, as were the opinions of the Claflin girls.

Their later history is entwined with several movements of national interest. Victoria was elected president of the National Association of Spiritualists. She and her sister Tennie C. started, under the guidance of the great Demosthenes, a paper called *Woodhull and Claflin's Weekly* in which women's rights, among other things, were championed. And Victoria was founder of the picturesque Cosmo-Political Party which in 1872 nominated her for President of the United States. As an advocate of free love, she managed to split the feminist ranks. Her name also came into the Henry Ward Beecher–Tilton wrangle.

Much lower in the scale of psychic cherubim was Henry C. Gordon. In 1835 Bridgeport, Connecticut, saw his birth, and invisible hands rocked his cradle. Even when young, mysterious noises gyrated about him and he would fall into trances. Like the boy in *Slovenly Peter,* who so misbehaved himself at meals that he upset the table, young Henry would come to supper and immediately his spiritualistic powers would move the table until it came perilously near spilling the food. This must have been very distressing to his parents. As he entered adolescence he began hearing raps, and in Hartford in the year of grace 1851, his eyes were astonished to see the form of a beautiful young woman arise through the leaves of a table at which he was seated. Strange things, indeed, may happen in Hartford, but this occurrence deserves a place at the head of the list.

Mr. Gordon's claim to the remembrance of posterity lies in the fact that whereas the Fox sisters were the first American female mediums, he was the first male to follow that calling. And follow it he did, through a stormy and bellicose career. For six years, from 1852 to 1858, he traveled about the country doing levitation, ringing spirit bells, and performing the miracle of "full form materialization."

He had "demonstration rooms" for a number of years in New York at Fourth Avenue near Twenty-seventh Street, to which both the curious and the believing flocked.

But the way of the medium is hard. In 1873 a female patron of his séances lured him into marriage. Having accomplished this, she turned his "circle" against him, and gave him poison to drink. However, the stupor from the poison was only temporary, but in the meantime she had managed to depart with his furniture and his paraphernalia and saw to it that he was bundled off to an insane asylum. Released three months later, he came back, like Enoch Arden, to find her posing as a widow and engaging the attentions of an ardent lover. Gordon punched the lover's nose and then started on the wife's, whereupon she had him arrested. On another occasion in Philadelphia, one of his patrons at a séance, dissatisfied with what the spirits told him, started to wreak vengeance on Mr. Gordon's anatomy. The police had to be called, and the judge sentenced them both to sufficient time in Moyamensing Prison to soothe their injured feelings.

Though Gordon advertised himself as "medium for personification, transformation and materialization," and though he and his works have been immortalized in a biography, we must bow before the unrelenting fact that he belonged to the rowdy charlatan class. And that—to cite him as a type—is the sole excuse we have for including him in these pages.

A third type is represented by the Davenport Brothers, the playboys, the vaudeville artists of the spiritualistic world.

So many of these mediums were frank imitators of the Fox sisters that it is amusing to see just how the influence of those two girls worked. Thus the Claflins were quite emphatic, indeed, snobbish, in their claim to antedating the Daughters of Hydesville. From the obscurity of Dixboro, Washington County, Michigan, arose a bold soul who saw ghosts nine times and three angels as early as 1843. These angelic and ghostly visitations antedated the Foxes by three years. The Davenport brothers, on the other hand, made no claim to priority; they were satisfied to elaborate the simple creed and ritual of the Hydesville demon-stalkers.

The senior Davenport was a painter by trade, resident in Buffalo. He had gone to lectures on animal magnetism, phrenology, and mesmerism, he had drunk abundant water with the hydrophants and gnawed raw carrots with the vegetarians and munched rough bread with the Grahamites. He had seen and heard the Foxes. In fact, he had run the gamut of extraordinary religions, beliefs, sciences, and experiences; and he saw no reason why he should not capitalize it. So he went home and experimented with tipping tables. Sure enough, he could make tables move. Then he turned out the lights and by projecting his spiritualistic powers, he could make a violin float around the air like a bird and strum its strings. A man with such capacities should not hide his light under a bushel. Mr. Davenport was highly gratified when the public began coming to his séances.

There were two sons in the family—Ira E., the elder, and William. Both followed in their father's spiritualistic footsteps. In trances William would speak a strange tongue. These two burst upon the credulous world as full-fledged mediums in 1855, at the respective ages of sixteen and fourteen—small statured, heavily built, exuberant lads. A sister, Mrs. E. Davenport Colie, joined the troupe and together they began touring the country, giving demonstrations and constantly running up against the authorities because they lacked the license of showmen.

Their act, for it was a vaudeville act, added luster to the fast-growing diversion of *diablerie*. It consisted of the following: The curtain rose revealing a cabinet about six feet high, six feet wide, and two and one-half feet deep with three doors on the front that opened out toward the audience. In the upper part of the middle door was a diamond-shaped opening covered with a black cloth. The middle door could be bolted from the inside. On each side were two seats and holes on each side wall gave room for ropes to be passed through by which the boys were tied. A table stood between these seats, on which were various stringed instruments.

The boys appeared on the stage and entered the cabinet. There came a sound of ropes rattling. From the audience was summoned a committee of investigation who attested that the boys were tied so close to the side walls that they couldn't move, and their hands were closely bound together. Then a member of the committee bolted the middle door by reaching through the opening. The lights were lowered. A moment of suspense came, followed by a loud noise from the cabinet. This brought the audience to the edge of its seats. Everyone listened intently and peered onto the darkened stage. Gradually there drifted out over the audience the sound of a guitar, a violin, a zither, and the tinkle of bells. Now strumming furiously, now gently, the music kept up for a long time. The lights went on. The committee stepped on the stage. The boys were still bound as they had been. They were unleashed and stepped out before the footlights, amid gasps and applause.

Sometimes the committee did the tying, which certainly carried conviction, but usually, so the brothers attested, it was done by spirit power. Spirits, of course, strummed the instruments.

What actually happened was this: the ropes were so arranged that even if the most skeptical investigator did the tying the boys could slip out of the knots. They usually tied themselves in and the knots were made to appear solid.

They also could make the spirits play instruments without the aid of the cabinet. Here a confederate was usually employed, although even an innocent bystander could be dragged on to the stage and mystified. A table was placed on the stage to hold the instruments. One of the boys sat with his right side to the table, the other took a seat across, at the left. The investigator sat in front of them and placed a hand on the head of each. Then, reaching up, each boy put his hands close together on the investigator's arm. The audience saw them posed: both their hands were placed and their heads were held. Lights down. Without moving their heads or showing any movement of the body, each boy took from the investigator's arm the hand farthest from the audience, strummed an instrument, and then put his hand back just before the lights went on.

Both these stunts they did in New York at Cooper Union and at Union Hall on the Bowery. Committees of the clergy and eminent citizens sat on the stage and pretended to investigate them. James Gordon Bennett was so fascinated by these musical spirits that he invited them to his house for private séances. Of course time and again they were proven to be frauds, but there was always enough of the audience which believed them. This is the phase of mob psychology on which all conjurers depend for their support and reputation. Barnum, of course, was on to their trick in a minute. "Well, boys," he said, "you are greater humbugs than I am. You may take my hat!"

Although the Davenport brothers traveled the Atlantic coastal towns and cities, the business was too productive for the family to part with. So the western towns were assigned to the sister, Mrs. E. Davenport Colie, who was assisted by a Mrs. M. A. C. Lamb in the old cabinet trick. Meantime Papa Davenport toured with the boys and gave lectures on spiritualism.

By no means do the three kinds of mediums cited in the previous section represent all types that flourished, gulled the public and took their money in those years.

As spiritualism developed it evolved six distinct types of mediums, viz: rapping, tipping, speaking, singing, writing, and impressible, *i.e.,* mediums whom the spirits impressed to think as they, the spirits, wished. The number of people who claimed to be either one or another of these was amazing. In 1852 it was estimated that there were over two thousand writing mediums in the United States. In that year Boston—the hub of spiritualism—held a convention of rappers, and quite a noisy convention it must have been. Over a million followers in this country were the figures the *Spiritualist* gave. In New York City alone it is said that fully forty thousand people, many of them otherwise intelligent specimens of humanity, solemnly believed in messages sent by spirit rapping. One New York cabinet-maker did a tidy trade in constructing special rapping tables, with concealed machinery for producing the raps for those who, lacking the agility of the Fox sisters, couldn't snap their *ossa pisciforums.* At one time the medium business proved so profitable that the *New York Telegraph* carried an advertisement offering work to those endowed with psychic power and, of course, practically all newspapers printed advertisements of séances, at which the admission ranged from twenty-five cents to two dollars.

Had this credulity been limited to the lower classes, it would have caused no surprise, but men and women in the highest walks of life gathered at séances night after night in a state of spiritual elevation, awaiting messages from the departed.

Robert Hare, professor of chemistry in William and Mary College, and a man of high standing in his line, strove to prove the reality of spiritualistic communication by science. He wrote a learned book on the subject, in which his theories are demonstrated by charts. Robert Dale Owen, who helped his father and Fanny Wright found the Fourier Colony at New Harmony, Indiana, and was an active leader in the feminist cause and in abolition, wrote two dreary books on the subject of spiritualism. Robert S. Shaw, one of the prominent Boston Shaws, proclaimed himself to be the especially adopted medium of Daniel Webster.

Harriet Beecher Stowe, certainly a favorite among the female geniuses of the time, took to spiritualism as a duck to water after she lost her second son by drowning. She went about from séance to séance, frantically listening for messages from the boy, and she insisted on her husband's—who didn't believe a word of them—being dragged to these performances. On one occasion the poor dear's faith wavered. She doubted if it was her son Henry who twanged the guitar. Perhaps it was her husband's first wife, Harriet! She counseled him to keep a guitar in his bedroom so that he might have it handy for her spirit when she wanted to communicate with him!

The experiences of Judge Edmonds, Dr. Dexter, and Governor Tallmage were even more incredible. John W. Edmonds was a New York state judge of unquestioned repute, who was initiated into spiritualism by rapping, then took to consulting clairvoyants and for three years studied spiritualism in all its phases until he was thoroughly convinced of its verity and worth. Dr. Dexter was converted at a séance in 1851, where he claimed he heard an illiterate mechanic speak Latin, Greek, and Chaldaic—this man was a speaking medium. Governor N. P. Tallmage of Wisconsin was also an easy convert. These three men kept careful notes of their experiences and corresponded constantly on them. Their letters are ludicrously like the letters of small boys and other radio fans today who correspond on the stations they are able to reach. Dr. Dexter would solemnly report that he "got" Swedenborg and Francis Bacon, whereupon Tallmage would counter with Tom Paine, Calvin, and John C. Calhoun, and Edmonds would finally take the trick with Henry Clay and Elias Hicks, the Quaker who caused the modernist split in the Society of Friends.

These three men wrote books together on spiritualism, books that are still standard for believers in occult religion. But more than once they had their legs pulled. The Ewer case was a notable example.

John F. Ewer, editor of a California magazine called *The Pioneer,* published an article of his own composition entitled "The Eventful Nights of August 20 and 21, 1854" in which he claimed that he had had spiritualistic communication with a John J. Lane. Ewer saw that this article came into the hands of Judge Edmonds and the judge gave it his mediumistic *imprimatur* in the *Sacred Circle,* a spiritualistic magazine he was editing at the time. Then Ewer exposed the whole hoax in the *New York Herald,* much to the discomfort of the judge and his followers, and the delight of the public.

From such social and intellectual heights belief in spiritualism percolated downward through all classes and orders of intelligence. Ministers who felt it luring their congregations away thundered against it as the "infidelity of the times." The press ridiculed it in every issue. Nevertheless it captivated public imagination to an amazing extent, and with good reason. The spirit of the age was materialistic, so its apologists said; it needed religion; spiritualism was created to satisfy this need. Well, all ages are materialistic in the minds of those who oppose them. Andrew Jackson Davis, one of the high priests of the new sect, attributed its rise to the fact that the age was one of unparalleled mental activity.

The flood of books, tracts, and letters that early spiritualism produced and the publicity it was accorded make one of the strangest phenomena in American history.

It supported its own newspapers and magazines. There was Edmonds' *Sacred Circle; The Spiritual Telegraph* had a large subscription list; *The Anthropologist* was published in Milwaukee to further the interests of mesmerism; *The Banner of Light,* a weekly, was read by a huge following; *The New England Spiritualist* and *Tiffany's*

Monthly also found support. In these journals all manner of spiritual-istic experience and discussion filled the pages, ranging from spirit messages of intriguing interest to grave arguments on the toe bones of the Fox sisters.

It would require many more pages than are available here to set down all the books and articles that were written under the guidance of the spirits in those years. Harriet Beecher Stowe claimed that some of her literary output was directly traceable to psychic influence. The Reverend C. Hammond, a medium of twenty-two years' standing and author of two books, wrote a fascinating series of experiences around Tom Paine in heaven in which Tom is converted from his infidel ways and pals around the celestial courts with such worthies as Emanuel Swedenborg, Benjamin Franklin, and William Penn.

Fed on such pabulum, the credulous flocked to séances day and night. People who had lost dear ones rushed from table to table frantically hoping for messages. Businessmen submitted their prob-lems. Lovers their troubles. Married people their spats. Politicians their platforms. Families and businesses were neglected and even runs on banks were started by spiritualistic prophecy.

Out of this welter of strange experiences were evolved the tenets of the spiritualist religion. The belief amounted to this: that on death the spirit enters into a state of progress in a world of seven spheres, each sphere of which is comprised of seven circles. In this material world where we reside there are likewise spheres and circles. At death a soul goes to that sphere of the spirit world which corresponds to the one he has attained in this life.

The spirit world, therefore, is a congenial place filled with all sorts of spirits—good, bad, indifferent, superior and inconsequential, meager and rich—all advancing, learning, progressing through the various concentric rings until they attain the seventh. There they pause. Beyond the Seventh Circle the progress of the spirit is not known. Through this material world of ours the disembodied spirits wander at will. Consequently the believer can communicate not only with friends and relatives whom he knew, but with any spirit he chooses. Hence the experiences of Judge Edmonds and others with great religious and political leaders who were deceased. On the other hand, some spirits, being not far advanced, will lie to, abuse, and trifle with those of this world.

Communication with spirits was possible only through a medium to whom the spirits took a fancy. The messages were delivered sometimes in rapping, sometimes by the tipping of the table, and sometimes in writing. Often this writing was illiterate, illegible, and wholly undecipherable, but the medium, under the guidance of the spirits, could readily interpret it.

This body of beliefs soon became organized. "Circles" were formed. To form a circle, Andrew Jackson Davis said, the believers must have "a childlike simple-heartedness, a manly, open, and free mindedness, combined with an honest love for truth." They should not meet more than once a week, the séances should be accompanied by music, held in a private room free from outside noises and disturbances, and those who attend the services should dress simply for the occasion. This was to be a thoroughly democratic and catholic religion.

New York City became a bedlam of spiritualists. One writer describes it vividly:

> Could New York be unroofed, either in the day or at night, a spectacle of spirit rapping would be exhibited which would astound the public by the magnitude of its extent and almost ceaseless continuance. From morning till noon, from noon till night, and from night until morning again, in parlors where flashing mirrors reflect rosewood and velvet and silver and gold; in humble rooms where the floors and walls are bare, the tables are placed, and around them men and women with their hands spread out, and eyes fixed as if on vacancy, are seated, waiting for communications from the spirit world.

But it had its darker side. An investigator of the mediums of New York calculated that of the nineteen "she-prophets" practicing in that city in 1858, selected out of several score, each was visited at the rate of a dozen customers a day; that of these visitors probably two-thirds placed implicit confidence in what they heard and paid for. Many of the clients were ignorant servant girls, unfortunate girls of the town, and uneducated and overgrown boys, as well as respectable men and women. Most of the sorceresses were prostitutes or had been prostitutes. Their darkened rooms were, in reality, places of assignation and stations for the white slave traffic of the times. Some of the mediums were professed abortionists.

Facilis descensus Averno!

Evil reports soon began to spread regarding the effects of spiritualism. Wardens of insane asylums and physicians were alarmed by the numbers of people whose reason was unhinged by these séances. In 1852 alone no less than ninety patients were admitted to asylums in various parts of the country for these reasons, and it was estimated that over a period of five years fully five hundred persons had gone mad or committed suicide due to attending séances and reading books on spiritualism.

It may seem incredible that from the mischievous snapping of their toe bones and their childish fibs two obscure country girls could start on its way a body of strange belief that was destined to engulf a nation and send its ripples to England and the Continent. And yet they—the Fox sisters—were the progenitors of this vast movement. So long as they practiced at their séances, they remained the high priestesses of the religion, but the time came when it got beyond them and when both of them renounced it altogether. In the inevitable contest between romance and spiritualism, romance won. The death blow to spiritualism was dealt by a love affair. The story is as tender a page of sentiment as one could wish.

Among the men who fired the imagination of these times was Elisha Kent Kane, arctic explorer, who had gone to the relief of Sir John Franklin and who headed a famous expedition to Grinnell Land in 1853. A native of Philadelphia, his reputation was jealously held by all citizens of that city.

In the autumn of 1852 Mrs. Fox and Margaret happened to be at a hotel in Philadelphia for a course of spiritual manifestations. They were the object of much patronage. One day Dr. Kane entered their parlor for a sitting. He had never seen Margaret Fox, and he was astonished to find her a girl of twelve who, at the moment he entered, happened to be deep in her study of French. Her extreme youth and innocence arrested him. "This is no life for you, my child," he said, "you ought to go to school." From that moment an intimacy sprang up between them, an intimacy which eventually flowered into full-blown romance. Kane became a daily visitor. He took her driving. He was seen walking constantly with her. He showered gifts on her. Their names soon were coupled by the gossips of the city, although it could have meant nothing since she was twelve and he thirty-two.

At the time he was preparing for his second expedition to the arctic and amid all the exacting preparations he found time to write her constantly. When she went to Washington he followed there and took a room in the same boardinghouse; when she settled in New York and the Foxes took the house on Twenty-sixth Street, he managed to slip over to see her. There was a third-story room that they reserved for their meetings. Here they would sit when she was not busy with clients. And this gallant young explorer used to champ at the bit when their tête-à-tête was interrupted by people who came for sittings. Margaret would rush down, snap her bones, deliver the messages, and rush upstairs again. No, it was no life for a child.

Finally he prevailed on her to go to school, and he placed her in charge of his sister, Mrs. Leiper. Margaret went to Crookville School, which is near Ridley Park, eighteen miles from Philadelphia. While she was here a constant stream of letters and presents passed between them—playful letters from an older man to a child. Among the many touching sentiments, he counseled her to remember, "as a sort of dream, that Dr. Kane of the arctic seas, loved Maggie Fox of the spirit rappings." To the little sister Katherine, then in school in New York and under Horace Greeley's eye, he wrote adorable letters, addressing them to his "Incomprehensible Kate." Mrs. Fox beamed upon the growing friendliness of the great man, but her elder daughter, the erstwhile Mrs. Fish, opposed Kane strenuously since his insistence on Margaret's education and his persuading her to give up spiritualism were threatening the income that the séances produced.

Gradually these two strange companions came nearer the day of their separation: Kane's expedition was ready. He must sail very soon. He prevails on Margaret to sit for her portrait, and when it is finished, the picture is safely stowed away in his gear for the expedition. It was this painting of Margaret Fox which Kane carried strapped to his back through his entire wanderings in the arctic. Nor did he permit it out of his sight night or day. Such was the devotion he offered this girl who intrigued him—this "strange mixture of child and woman, of simplicity and cunning, of passionate impulse and extreme self-control."

On his return he was acclaimed by the nation. He had become a public figure. He was hedged about with all manner of restrictions and ceremonies. His family and many of his friends, knowing of his attachment to Margaret Fox, did everything in their power to break it up and to prevent his seeing her. Ann Leah Brown enthusiastically aided them. Nevertheless he managed to overcome their guard and the romance started once more. They had their lovers' quarrels, their separations and reconciliations, but the affection of the girl for him and his for her cannot be doubted. He was constantly with her and she constantly in his mind. The newspapers printed rumors of their impending marriage. Denials and affirmations came fast and thick.

Due to his arduous work in the arctic, Kane's health began to fail. His doctor ordered him to England for a rest, thence he was to go to Havana. Before he left, according to Margaret Fox's statement, she and he stood together in the presence of her mother, a servant, and a young woman who was calling at the time and plighted their troth in a Quaker marriage ceremony. This ceremony was undertaken at the suggestion and express wish of Dr. Kane. His letters to her thereafter were addressed to his "wife." They planned to meet in Havana.

After a short stay in England, where he was again acclaimed, Kane went to Havana to await her, but a few days before Margaret and her mother were to sail, he died. The date was the sixteenth of February, 1857. He was aged thirty-seven. Margaret at the time was seventeen.

His death caused a profound change in the girl. She put on mourning and wore it for the subsequent fourteen years. Everyone seemed to accept her story of the marriage; she signed herself with Kane's name and was addressed by all as Mrs. Kane. Following his urgent request, she gave up spiritualism and, a year after his death, was converted to Roman Catholicism, being baptized in old St. Peter's Church in Barclay Street.

In his will Dr. Kane left a trust for Margaret, putting it not in her name but in the name of his brother, with instructions for him to pay it to her. So bitter was the family feeling against her that the brother refused to pay over the money, although he did allow her interest from it for a time. Knowing that she possessed letters and many other evidences of his famous brother's attachment, he offered to pay over the trust if she would surrender the letters. This she refused to do, and the case was eventually thrashed out in the Philadelphia courts. To establish her claim, Margaret permitted the whole story and the letters to be published in a book called *The Love Life of Dr. Kane,* a volume that appeared in 1865 and caused a furore. It is one of the rare and beautiful curiosities of the literature of American romance.

After the Civil War, the fortunes of the Fox sisters were cast in diverse lines.

Margaret's good resolution to eschew spiritualism soon encountered the stern reality of bread and butter and she went back to it again. Her oldest sister Ann Leah Brown, who directed the séances, came up in the world and was espoused to Mr. Underhill, a prosperous insurance broker, but she still gave séances and as late as 1888 stated her belief in them by writing a book, *The Missing Link of Spiritualism.* Katherine married a Mr. Jencken and bore him two healthy sons, the first of whom, "Ferdie," at the tender age of six months demonstrated psychic powers, although he never manifested them in later life.

Obliged to continue with the séances, Margaret accepted a position in Philadelphia with Henry Seybert, who planned to found a spiritual mansion. She was hired, at a satisfactory honorarium, to be high priestess. This was in 1870, after she had left off her mourning for Elisha Kane. In this esoteric job she managed to evoke spirits that hitherto had been silent. Doubtless her experience in being converted to Catholicism furnished her with new spirit fields to wander in. She became on speaking terms with saints and church fathers, and even received communications from St. Paul, St. Peter, Elijah, and the angel Gabriel!

When Seybert died he left a fund to found a chair at the University of Pennsylvania and stipulated that part of it should be expended for psychic research. This gave birth to the Seybert Commission which functioned for a time in Philadelphia. At the head was the eminent Shakespearian scholar, Dr. Horace Howard Furness. His first subject of investigation was Margaret Fox (whom, by the way, he entertained at his house and always addressed as "Mrs. Kane"). The report of the committee, delivered in November 1884, pronounced her to be unquestionably a fraud.

Thereafter both Margaret and Katherine dropped out of sight for a time. Both of them took to drinking heavily and Katherine managed to incur the displeasure of the New York Society for the Prevention of Cruelty to Children.

The next we hear of them, Margaret is returning from England. Scarcely had she arrived when she announced in the press that she was about to expose spiritualism. This threat from its very progenitor struck terror into the hearts of believers. Shortly afterward Katherine also appeared from England and set about to aid Margaret in her revelations. On October 21, 1888, in the Academy of Music at New York, Margaret Fox Kane exposed all her tricks. An investigating committee was on hand to check her up and she made no effort to deceive them—she took off her shoes and showed how the raps were produced.

In the next few weeks the whole sordid story was revealed.

The original noises that their mother had heard in the little house in Hydesville were begun as a lark by these two children. They each tied an apple to a string and after everyone was in bed, they would bounce them on the floor. When their mother came to investigate the noises, they pulled the apples into the sheets and looked innocent. Soon Katherine, the younger, discovered that she could simulate these noises by snapping her toe bones. Margaret could do it too. It was lots of fun. They even let into the secret their little niece, Mrs. Fish's daughter, who lived with them.

Being a superstitious person, and remembering the legends about the house, Mrs. Fox was easily fooled by the children, and it became their own secret game they played on her. When she asked questions of the spirits, they would answer. By and by the neighbors heard of it and they too were mystified. Soon the oldest sister, Ann Leah Fish, got wind of the noises and came down to investigate them. By this time the girls had gotten proficient in rapping.

Now Ann Leah was thirty-three. She had been deserted by a drunken husband whose association had lowered her scruples considerably. When she came to Hydesville, saw the mystification of the neighbors and heard the raps, she was not above taking advantage of the situation. The first thing she did was to talk to the children in private and find out how the noises were made. Then she insisted on their being allowed to live with her in Rochester. She herself began to develop mediumistic powers, although she was not able to make such distinct raps with her toes because her bones, being older, had set. Meantime she impressed on the children the idea that they had supernatural powers and were founders of a new religion. With the aid of her brother David, she worked out the rapping code which was taught the two girls and which became the basis for all mediumistic communications.

When they were eleven and nine respectively Mrs. Fish displayed them in Corinthian Hall in Rochester in their first big public demonstration and she took care to dress them in long gowns lest the investigating committee should see the children's toes wriggle. She also worked out a tariff of prices for séances.

From this point on, the story is as we have told it. These two poor little girls were dragged about the country by their ignorant mother and scheming elder sister, forced to go through séances, forced to snap and rap when they wanted to play, forced to work so that the money would keep coming in. Even though they knew that they were the sources of the noises, even though they could well remember the larks that started them, so fiendishly had their minds been warped that not for a moment did it occur to them to reveal their secret. They were carried away by the awe in which they were held. Only when a man of such caliber as Elisha Kent Kane opened Margaret's eyes to the folly and evil of her life did the children begin to have a glimmer of what they were doing. Nor were they aware of the extent to which their naughty, hoyden tricks had swept the country.

Here was a vast religion built up on the slim and ridiculous fabric of two little girls thumping apples on a bedroom floor! Considering how much trouble Eve is supposed to have caused with an apple and what these two Fox sisters, in their time, managed to do with that particular fruit, one is almost tempted to believe that apples should be kept out of the hands of women.

R. B. CUNNINGHAME GRAHAM

War to the Knife

ੳ✒

How the mayor of a small town in Spain declared war on Napoleon—and won.

In the year 1808 Napoleon was at the height of his renown. All Europe lay beneath his feet. England and Russia alone were still unconquered; but in due course he hoped to deal with them. Austria, Prussia, Holland, and Italy were provinces of France. Spain, that had for centuries been inaccessible to conquerors, was beaten to her knees. King Joseph, known to the Spaniards by the name of Pepe Botellas, held his court in Madrid, surrounded by a few sycophants and renegades. All patriotism seemed dead. Murat and his Mamelukes kept down the city with an iron hand. Goya was taking notes of everything, crystallizing the odious tyranny of the French, in his immortal *Horrors of War*—horrors that have never been surpassed, either in reality or paint.

The country, delivered over to the mercies of the invading troops, was seething with revolt, but wanted someone to stand out and lead. Only the partisan El Empecinado was in arms in Navarre and the Basque provinces. For all that, no Frenchman's life was worth ten minutes' purchase outside cantonments or the camp. The country people cut their throats like sheep with their long knives, and often threw their bodies into their wine vats to get rid of them. In after days, to say a wine had a French tang was long a jest among the peasantry. Still they went on, stabling their horses in the churches, violating nuns, and stealing priceless ornaments from the cathedrals and the monasteries. Spain stirred convulsively under the heel of the detested Gabacho, as the people liked to call the French. That which was to prove her strength, and had done so in ages past, was now her weakness, for the intensely local patriotism had formed each town and village into a community apart, slow to combine with one another. *Mi tierra* meant for them not Spain but every separate village and a few miles around.

At last the turbulent populace of Madrid, irritated past bearing by the Mamelukes who represented to them not the French only, but their hereditary enemies, the Moors, rose in revolt. Armed with their knives alone, they fell upon the Mamelukes in a narrow street, stabbing their horses and butchering the riders when they fell. Two heroic officers of artillery, Velarde and Daoiz, opened fire with a piece of cannon on the French. Their heroism was wasted—that is, if sacrifice is ever wasted—and the revolt was crushed that very afternoon, in what Murat referred to as a "bath of blood." The two young officers were shot, and by their death secured their immortality in Spain. Madrid was stunned, but the news soon was carried to the neighboring little towns by men escaping from the massacre.

Out on the Castilian steppes, fifteen or sixteen miles from Madrid, there lies a little town called Móstoles. It lies, almost as one might say, *à fleur d'eau* on the great brown plain. The high road to Portugal passes down its long main street. Even today it has but thirteen hundred citizens. In summer the houses, built of sun-dried bricks covered with plaster, are calcined by the sun. The winter winds, sweeping down from La Sierra de Guadarrama, scourge it pitilessly. For nine months of the year dust covers everything, falling on man and beast, on the few moribund acacias in the plaza, turning all to the color of a rabbit's back. During the other three it is a slough of mud that wheel-borne traffic and the long strings of donkeys and mules struggle through painfully. Far off the Sierra of Guadalupe and the

Gredos are just visible as faint blue lines hardly to be picked out from the clouds, except in certain states of atmosphere. In the short, fierce summer the mirage spreads illusory pools over the surface of the plain, and in the winter mornings, after a sharp frost, the woods along the foothills of the Guadarrama hang upside down upon the sky. Along the road are dotted many other little dusty towns, all with their little plaza, great church, large enough for larger congregations than they ever hold, their apothecaries with leeches in a glass jar at the door, and flyblown patent medicines in the window, and barber's shop, that serves as news exchange.

Upon the second of May of the year 1808 news filtered through to Móstoles that there had been a massacre in the capital. The seventeen kilometers of high road could easily be covered on a good horse within two hours, and it is not to be supposed the rider spared the spur.

As it was written, one Andrés Torrejon happened to be alcalde of the place. An honest countryman of six-and-sixty years of age, in all his life he had never had occasion to show what he was worth. What he was like to the outward visible eye is but a matter of conjecture. Most probably a square-built, round-faced Castilian farmer, his cheeks stubbly with a week's growth of beard—the village barber sheared but on a Sunday morning—sparing of speech, yet full of sayings fitted to every accident of life. His dress, that has but little varied, even today, kneebreeches of dark cloth, his jacket short, showing a double-breasted flowered waistcoat of a sprigged pattern, his linen dazzlingly white, 'a black silk handkerchief bound like a turban round his head, the whole surmounted by a hard-brimmed black felt hat, kept in place underneath his chin by a broad band of silk. His interior grace, his honesty, tenacity of purpose, and his enthusiasm, slow to be excited, but when once moved as irresistible as a landslide after rain, he has left stamped upon Castile. It will endure as long as her vast plains wave green with corn in spring, turn leather-colored under the fierce sun of summer, and in the winter when the keen frosts burn up all vegetation, stretch out desolate, with but the withered stalks of thistles standing up ghostlike in the waste.

The nerves of all true patriots were on edge. Never since the days of the Saracens had the invader's foot trodden Castilian soil. The news of the last outrage brought all the people out into the plaza before the parish church of the Ascension, a mosque, tradition says, in the days Spanish peasants always refer to as "the time of the Moors." All over Spain the people's nerves were twitching, but yet the heavy hand of Murat had deprived them of all spirit of revolt.

It happened, luckily for Andrés Torrejon, that the ex-secretary of the admiralty under Charles IV, Juan Perez Vilamil, was living in the town, having refused to recognize King Joseph and his usurping court. Long did the alcalde and Vilamil talk over what was the best course to pursue. Then, after praying in the church, the alcalde called a meeting of his rustic senators. The people thronged outside the council room, the very room in which today is set into the wall the tablet that commemorates what was resolved on that eventful afternoon in May. The peasant councillors sat around the council board, with their alcalde in the chair. Perez and Gomez, Camacho, Lopez and Galvan, all peasants, their hands furrowed with toil and weather, their shoulders rounded with the plough, their faces tanned to a deep brown by the hard climate of Castile, and their eyes twinkling deeply in their sockets, like the eyes of mariners, of Arabs, and of all those who pass their lives upon illimitable plains, scorched by the wind and sun, all waited for what "Uncle Andrés" had to say.

Rising with due deliberation from his seat, after having taken off his hat and placed it carefully beside him on the table, the alcalde told of what had happened in Madrid. His actual words are not recorded, only the substance of his speech. As he spoke of the massacre, the shooting down of women and of children in the streets, the execution of the prisoners drawn up opposite a wall, and of the people who had died trampled beneath the horses of the Mameluke infidel, his hearers' hands stole to their sashes, and muttering "Death to the Gabacho," they spat upon the floor. Sitting impassively like figures carved in walnut wood, the peasant council suffered under Napoleon's heel. Now and again one of them would assent in a half grunt, and anyone who did not know them might have thought they were unmoved. As they sat with their heads a little sideways, their mouths half open, and their breath coming in short gusts that heaved their chests under their heavy rustic clothes, just as a barge heaves on a canal after a steamer passes, they seemed like animals about to spring upon their prey. The alcalde recapitulated all their country's wrongs. The cuckold Charles IV a prisoner in France, the queen, a harlot left under the dominion of her lover of the day, the troops unpaid and led by officers who did not know their duty, and worst of all the miserable French puppet king, lording it on the throne of Charles V. "Spain wants a leader, someone to show the way, to gather up the scattered bands of guerrilleros and above all a straight and downright declaration that the country is at war. No one has yet stepped out to lead us, although they slaughter us like flies, scorn us and spit on us; on us Castilians, whose forefathers furnished the famous Spanish infantry that swept through France and Italy like fire. Who would think we were the heirs of those who fought at San Quentin?"

The people of the town pressed round the iron-grated windows of the council chamber, silent, but gazing on their rustic councillors, strung up with fury, cursing their impotence. At last the speaker, tightening up his sash, wiping the foam and moisture from his lips, took a long breath, and after looking round to Vilamil, who nodded at him, said: "Friends and neighbors, I have served you faithfully for years. The time has come that I must now serve Spain. Therefore I, Andrés Torrejon, duly elected the alcalde of this town of Móstoles, do declare war against the French."

For a brief moment there was silence, silence so absolute that the breath of the people peering through the gratings of the windows sounded as loudly as when a horse upon a frosty morning pants up an incline. Then, rising to their feet, the conscript peasants surrounded the alcalde, grasping him by the hand and shouting: "War, war to the knife; death to the assassins of Madrid." The people in the little plaza caught up the cry of "War, war to the knife. Uncle Andrés has declared war upon the French!"

In the closing darkness of that night of May Andrés Torrejon sat down and penned his memorable pronouncement, the first and last that he was fated to indite, but one that made his name immortal throughout the Spanish-speaking world. "Our country is in peril,

Madrid is perishing, the victim of the perfidy of the French. Span-iards, hasten to save her. May 2nd, 1808. El Alcalde de Móstoles." Nothing could have been more simple and direct, with just the touch of the ridiculous that gives sublimity. His next act was to send the son of his old colleague on the council, Simon Hernandez, on a good horse to take his proclamation to the alcaldes of the neighboring towns. At once he mounted, and first reaching Navalcarnero, left the fiery cross. Alcorcón, Navalmorál, and Escalona all received the message, and all of them at once declared war on the French. The messenger crossed the Alberche and pushed on westward, riding without a stop across the plains all through that fateful night in May. In two days' riding he reached Badajoz, his horse still fresh, after having covered nearly two hundred miles. The city rose at once, and sent on word to Cáceres. Cáceres passed on the signal and by the end of May all Spain had risen, not like an ordinary country rises in such circumstances, but town by town, village by village, each declared war upon the French.

The rest is history, the coming of the great "Lor Vilanton" as he was called in the Spain of those days, with the English troops, and the long war of the Peninsula. The hour had struck, and from that moment Napoleon's star began to pale. Moscow completed that which Móstoles began, and when the French recrossed the swift Borysthenes, slaughtered like sheep by the pursuing Cossacks, their ruin (after God) they owed to the alcalde of the little town, sun-dried and wind-scorched, in the Castilian plains.

O. O. McINTYRE

What My Dog Taught Me

ૐ

Junior was a most remarkable dog. But so of course is yours.

> Brothers and sisters, I bid you beware
> Of giving your hearts to a dog to tear!

So wrote Kipling in an excellent elegiac. I happen to be a dog lover who does not believe in that warning. Eight of the happiest years of my life were spent in the almost constant companionship of a devoted dog.

When he was taken from me, cruelly but with merciful swiftness, it was a terrific heart wrench. For two days I grieved inconsolably. For weeks I walked the streets at night, trying to get hold of myself.

Yet now, when time has dulled the pain, I can truthfully say that the joy and understanding my dog brought into my life more than compensated for the sorrow of his passing. For my dog taught me many things as enduring as the ages. Outside of the divine relationship and the human, I knew of no influence so ennobling as our relationship with a dog.

My dog's name was Junior. He was a Boston bulldog, weighing twenty-four pounds, with a blazed muzzle, white collar, and feet tipped with white. His coat was the glossy brown of an autumn leaf. He had a lovable lop ear that perked with quizzical abandon. He was full of joyous life and never outgrew his prankishness.

I picked him up in a Fifth Avenue dog shop in much the same manner that one buys a trinket. I thought he was "cute-looking." He was then four weeks old and trotted sideways with mock seriousness. I took him home in my overcoat pocket.

From that day on, for eight years, he played a big part in my life. He came to understand me better than most of my human associates did. He knew his time for play and my time for work. He did not trespass.

For six years he never varied five minutes, at the stroke of five o'clock in the evening, in coming to me with his rubber ball in his mouth, squatting at my feet, tail wagging, and whining softly. That was his hour for a romp. He demanded his hour.

One of my great faults had always been a lack of punctuality. I was distressingly derelict in keeping appointments, and this had strained many of my friendships—but I was always on the dot to keep the romping appointment with Junior! One day I got to thinking about this, and the result was that I became more careful when it came to punctuality. Surely I should show humans as much consideration as I showed my dog.

During the war I taught Junior a rather simple trick that always elicited wonder. He would sit in a chair and I would break off bits of bread, which I handed to him. I would say, "This is from King Albert!" He would gulp it down. "This is from President Wilson!" And so I would go on, perhaps naming those who were watching him at the time. He would gulp down every morsel. But when I said in exactly the same tone, "This is from the Kaiser!" he would turn his head away and refuse to eat it. The explanation was that I had taught him to interpret the word "Kaiser" as having the same meaning as "Don't."

There was a German waiter at my hotel who, having heard of this trick, resented it very much. And one day, as I was going out of the hotel, Junior being quite a bit ahead of me, this waiter kicked at him. I rushed up with vigorous remonstrance. To my surprise Junior growled his disapproval of *me!* He could not bear enmity. He loved every man, woman, and child.

The waiter offered an abject apology and became one of the dog's best friends. He even wrote me a letter of sympathy when Junior passed on.

For several years Junior and his mistress and I used to walk around the gravel path of the Central Park reservoir in New York at dusk, after his romp. At such times I would permit him to frolic and roll in the grass, unleashed and unmuzzled. He loved to scamper after pigeons and other birds, but would come back when I called him.

One evening, however, he disappeared in a clump of bushes and refused to come out at my call and whistles. I followed him, and found him squatting beside a stray dog that had been injured by a passing automobile. We called the Bide-a-Wee Home, and the hurt creature was removed to it. Here he at length recovered and later a good home was found for him.

As we continued our walk that evening Junior soon forgot the incident, but as for me I had some moments of serious introspection. How often, I asked myself, had *I* stopped along the roadside to comfort the stricken and forlorn?

We did not continue the walk home just then. Instead, we left the perfumed purlieus of Millionaires' Row, wandered over to the squalid section of New York's East Side, and mounted the rickety stairs of a crowded tenement. There we sat at the bedside of an old cobbler who had lived in our neighborhood, but who had been stricken with a fatal illness. We paid his small rent, had some food sent to him, and were occasional visitors until the end.

I can honestly say that the visit we made that night helped me to find a new meaning in existence. It is true that it came from a twinge of conscience at a rather selfish life, and was inspired by a dog. But I rejoice, just the same. I do not do so much of that sort of thing as I should, but the credit for what little I have done is due to Junior.

With one exception, this dog of mine had perfect manners; no matter who came to our door, he would rush at them and bark. It was the only thing for which he was ever given a whipping or a scolding. Yet he would not quit it.

There was much annoyance about this, for some strangers were badly frightened. The truth is that it was Junior's way of expressing his pleasure, his happy greeting and welcome. He refused, no matter what the odds, to curb his enthusiasm over the prospect of making a new friend. And no one ever left him without being his friend.

He was a remarkably healthy dog. He had none of the sicknesses of puppyhood—distemper and the like. I believed this was due to our care of him. He was fed twice a day, at noon and at midnight. We always kept him just a little bit hungry. Most of his food consisted of prepared puppy biscuits, with now and then a variation of chopped vegetables. Potatoes and sweets were denied him. He was exercised regularly and often.

His only illness displayed the heroic courage that characterized him until his death. One evening his mistress and I came home after the theater, and when we opened the door we missed his welcoming rush and bark.

We found him lying on the floor of the bathroom in a pool of blood. When I bent over him there was a feeble thump of his tail, as much as to say, "Don't worry!" His eyes were glazing and I knew he was in a desperate state. We worked over him several hours, and finally, in a wobbly manner, he stood up, walked unsteadily to the bedroom and picked up his play ball, as if to say, "See, I'm all right!" In a half hour he had another hemorrhage. With uncanny instinct, he rushed into the tile bathroom, so as not to injure the carpet! Fortunately he recovered quickly from his attack, and in two days seemed as well as ever.

Dogs are unerring in reflecting the characters of their master and mistress. To Junior I represented the play spirit—the romp and flapdoodle. He was somewhat of a roughneck in his relations with me. But with his mistress he was always gentle and careful.

One of the important lessons Junior taught me was to have more faith in my fellow beings. I had for years knocked about as a newspaper reporter and had acquired that veneer of cynicism that is typical of the craft. I had a rather smart-alecky attitude of "having to be shown."

Now, I am the average human being—as likely to err as the rest. But I found that with Junior, *because of his implicit faith in me,* I never attempted trickery! I could not bear to abuse that rare confidence. And this set me to thinking that if we humans displayed the same faith in our fellows we should be less likely to have that confidence abused.

It was along about this time that a rather important matter came up in my business life. I had a decided distrust of a certain man who was associated with me in this deal. So I determined to adopt Junior's attitude of implicit faith. I carried out the determination and, although I have heard many stories of that man's unfair dealings with others, he played absolutely square with *me* in every way.

Here is one incident which I hesitate to tell. More than likely it was the merest coincidence—but it is set down here just as is happened: Junior accompanied me one summer to my little home town in Missouri, and together we went one afternoon to the cemetery to visit the grave of my mother.

It had been a number of years since I had been there, and the place had become so strange to me that I wandered around for a half-hour or so in an effort to find the grave. Finally I gave it up as hopeless. Looking around for Junior, I saw him lying down about one hundred yards away. He didn't seem inclined to come to me, so I went to him. And I found that he was resting at the side of my mother's grave!

I told this to a Frenchman one day in Paris after the war.

"My friend," he said, "that is not unusual. When my boy went to war, a neighbor's son—who was also leaving for the front—left his dog with us, as his parents were moving to another village. My son was killed, was buried hastily near Ypres. The dog did not know him except as a passing neighbor. After the war was ended, I went to Ypres to look for my son's grave, and the dog went with me. I searched for a long time—in vain. Meanwhile the dog had disappeared. When I found him again, he was standing beside the cross that marked my son's grave."

Junior was quite a traveler for a dog. He enjoyed traveling in the baggage car, for he always made friends with mail clerks and baggagemen. He loved new acquaintances. Returning one time from California, he happened to fall in with a Santa Fe baggageman with whom, on another occasion, he had made a trip from Chicago to Kansas City. He recognized the man at once and barked his joyous greeting. At first, he had plenty of room in the car, but at Albuquerque they took on two coffins, and Junior was forced to occupy a small space high up on a trunk.

Before the coffins were put on that train, he had welcomed everyone to the baggage coach. But late that night, after we had passed

Albuquerque, the Pullman conductor roused me and said that the dog was showing signs of viciousness. He would not let the baggage-men or other trainmen pass the grilled compartment where the baggage was kept. He even growled at me when I went to see what the trouble was. At the time, I didn't even pretend to understand it, nor do I now. Possibly his uncomfortable position had irritated him beyond endurance, but an old engineer, who had strolled back to see about the delay in moving the baggage, said:

"He's guardin' them bodies. Dogs will do that!"

This may have been a mere conjecture, but the coffins were removed in Kansas, and after that the dog was frisky as ever all the way to Chicago.

During Junior's puppy days I was living at a family hotel on Central Park West, New York City. A jovial policeman, known as "Big John," was the traffic guard at the Seventy-second Street entrance to Central Park. He and Junior became fast friends, and often, at John's solicitation, the dog would sit beside him as he guided the flow of traffic.

After we moved to another part of the town there was a lapse of five years in which Junior did not see Big John. Then one night I happened to be calling on a friend on Riverside Drive, and upon leaving his place I had to walk several blocks to find a taxicab. As I was passing a corner, Junior began tugging at the leash and whining his pleasure over something. It was dark, and I though perhaps he had scented a dog on the opposite side of the drive. I pulled him along and scolded him, but he kept looking back and pulling at his leash.

Finally I decided to find out what the matter was, so I permitted him to guide me. He went straight to the center of the street and began jumping up on a man who was standing there. It was his old friend Big John, the policeman.

It is through Junior's teaching that I make it a point to keep in touch with old and valued friends. In a big city like New York we are likely to lose track of them, even though it isn't much trouble to give them a ring on the telephone now and then or to drop them a line of greeting.

I have said that Junior liked everyone. That is not strictly true.

But in his many years of meeting hundreds of people there was only one exception.

In the neighborhood of Grand Central Station I used to go to one of those rather gaudy shops filled with nuts, bonbons, bright-jacketed books, magazines, and souvenirs. The proprietor was a Turk. He wore a fez while on duty, and I never entered the store that the hair did not rise on Junior's back. Several times the Turk would attempt to pat him, but Junior would utter a low, menacing growl. I assumed that it was because of the man's foreign appearance, or perhaps it was the red cap he wore. It finally caused me so much embarrassment that I stopped going to that store.

This all happened several years ago. Then about three months before Junior went where good dogs go, I picked up a New York newspaper. On an inside page was an article headed thus: S.P.C.A. CAUSES ARREST OF TURK FOR CRUELTY TO DOGS.

The article went on to relate that the proprietor of this same souvenir shop that I had visited, and where Junior showed such displeasure, had been arrested at his home in Grand Street for whipping a dog with a whip that had a leaden slug as a tip!

It is indeed a typical dog trait to sense the ignoble. Dogs have an uncanny instinct about such things. They scent character.

There was a pretty little girl cousin of mine whom Junior loved with that unswerving fidelity that was his. She helped to take care of him, and together they had many happy walks. She came to see him at a certain hour every day. And it mattered not who was in the house or what attraction was offered, when the time came for his little friend to arrive, Junior was at the front door, his head pillowed between his paws—watching and waiting for Josephine.

I know it would be ridiculous to say that dogs know time, but I do know they sense it. I am a late sleeper. So was Junior, all his life. But at eleven o'clock each morning he was up on my bed, gently licking my hand. I have been awakened by him scores of times in this fashion and almost invariably have found it to be just eleven o'clock.

After he had awakened me, he would lie down at the foot of the bed, waiting for my slightest move, so that he could jump up and get his rubber ball—for Junior had a romp both morning and evening.

I can recall only once that Junior did not insist upon his romp. It had been for me a particularly trying day. I had been notified of a money loss through my mistaken trust in a friend, and on top of that had come one of the most grievous disappointments I had ever suffered. There appeared to me to be no silver lining to the cloud. I groped about all day in a fog of mental miasma. At four o'clock came the news of the death of a close friend.

That was the final straw. I went into my bedroom, lay down on the bed, and wept. About half an hour later I went to my typewriter to do some work that had to be done.

When it came five o'clock, the usual hour for Junior to rub his nose against my hand as the signal to romp, he remained quietly at my feet. Now and then, he looked up at me with a quizzical expression, but he did not move from his place. Finally, feeling a bit guilty, I got his ball and started to toss it for him. Junior made a few half-hearted starts—then he came back and lay down at my feet. He knew I was in no mood for play.

If that was not a supreme lesson in consideration for others I don't know what is.

I come to the final chapter of Junior's life with tears that are shed unashamed. As I have said, he was my constant companion for eight happy years. My longest absence from him was when I was in Europe, where the quarantine regulations are so strict that it is quite unfair and selfish to take a dog there.

Junior, like all good dogs, was faithful to the end. He died obeying my command—which made his loss all the more tragic to me.

I left him after his evening romp and was away until shortly after midnight. Upon my return his greeting was, it seemed to me, especially joyous. It was so joyous, in fact, that it indirectly led to his death. Shortly before I arrived, a servant had taken him out for a walk. But he was so glad to see me and he loved so to go out late at night without a muzzle or a leash on, that I humored him, and we went out again, together. At that hour there was very little traffic on Fifth Avenue, and Junior ran far ahead of me. He had been trained to wait at curbings when unleashed until he received the command "Go," then he would race across the street like a flash.

At the corner of Forty-fourth Street and Fifth Avenue I stepped to the curb, looked both ways for signs of traffic and, seeing none, shouted *"Go!"*

Junior was off at a bound. At that instant, a party of reckless joy-riders in a heavy touring car swung madly around the corner, and both wheels on one side passed over his body. There was a jeer of derision as the car shot northward—the tail lights gleaming red in the night.

Junior staggered to his feet, and as I lifted him in my arms he looked up with his soft pleading eyes, begging for the help I could not give. Hailing a taxicab, I hurried to my hotel, a few blocks away. But before I reached there, he had died—without even a whimper of pain.

He lies buried today in the picturesque little dog cemetery on the sloping hills of Hartsdale, New York.

Above him are the green grass, the whispering trees, and a stone carved with this inscription:

Junior—Faithful to the end!